Basic Concepts of ECOLOGY

CLIFFORD B. KNIGHT

Professor of Biology
East Carolina College
Greenville, North Carolina

The Macmillan Company, New York
Collier–Macmillan Limited, London

Basic Concepts of
ECOLOGY

First Printing

Library of Congress catalog card number: 65-16558

THE MACMILLAN COMPANY, NEW YORK
COLLIER-MACMILLAN CANADA, LTD., TORONTO, ONTARIO

Printed in the United States of America

To my wife, MARGARET, *and* KIM

"Curiously, by an accident of the organization of science, community structure is studied by people who call themselves ecologists and behavior by people who call themselves comparative psychologists, physiologists or, most recently, ethologists. These labels represent different points of view—but the organisms remain the same."

MARSTON BATES

PREFACE

Though this book is designed as a college text for introductory ecology courses, it may be useful to other persons in diverse occupations such as wildlife management, forestry, and agriculture. The entire text is concerned with the basic principles of modern ecology, and therefore is suitable for heterogeneous groups of students. One will elect the course in order to fulfill academic requirements in biology. This group's interests will center about the main ecological principles with little or scant concern for all of the specialized ramifications of subject matter. Another portion of the class will be the potential ecologists, an often small but important segment of any ecology class. In order to pursue their interests in ecology, they must "begin at the beginning" with a complete understanding of the foundations upon which the entire discipline is based. After mastery of the basic fundamentals, the young ecologist may follow up any line of ecological interest with the comfortable feeling that he is familiar with the generalizations of the discipline.

Topics included in this text, which seldom receive adequate attention in other ecological works, are the historical aspects of ecology and some basic statistical methods utilized by the ecologist; greater emphasis has been given to succession and microecology. No attempt has been made to render exhaustive accounts of any specific subject, as this lies beyond the scope of any general textbook. Complex graphs, complicated statistical data, and verbose accounts of advanced studies have been avoided so that the basic fundamentals and generalities may be presented and emphasized.

CLIFFORD B. KNIGHT

CONTENTS

I. Introduction

At a very early age you became aware of the surrounding environment, even before your vocabulary included such terms as *temperature, humidity,* and *wind.* When the temperature increased, you felt warm and wanted less clothing; with a decrease in temperature the reverse was so. In infancy and early childhood, you were aware of other living things and quickly responded by learning to recognize your parents. Perhaps you later acquired a pet, such as a dog or cat. The living and nonliving components of your environment governed and will continue to govern many of your reactions. But there is a reciprocal reaction; we (and many other living organisms) can change the environment. Thus we would find that a fallen log on the forest floor, if devoid of all life, would possess an internal environment quite different from a log of the same size, shape, and species of tree if infested with fungi, bacteria, beetles, termites, and a countless array of other organisms. Man can drastically alter the environment by cultivating the soil of a prairie or by exploding an atomic device over the Pacific Ocean and filling the atmosphere and surface waters with radioactive debris. Since we are capable of altering our environment and yet are at the mercy of many of these changes, a more thorough understanding and appreciation of basic ecological concepts could alleviate possible future environmental problems.

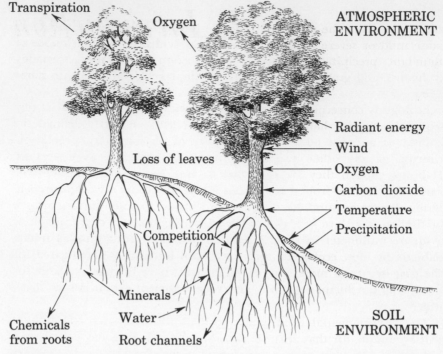

Transpiration

Oxygen

ATMOSPHERIC
ENVIRONMENT

Radiant energy

Wind

Oxygen

Carbon dioxide

Temperature

Precipitation

Loss of leaves

Competition

Minerals

Water

Chemicals
from roots

Root channels

SOIL
ENVIRONMENT

FIGURE 1–1 Reciprocal ecological relationships transpiring between a living organism and the surrounding environment.

Ecology is a field of study concerned with the relationship between the environment and living organisms. Any concise, simple definition may contain hidden implications that might be overlooked if we didn't take a closer glance. First of all, it must be understood that any phase of ecology involves a reciprocal relationship between an organism and its environment. If we consider a pine tree in its natural forest setting (Figure 1–1), we find that the pine is subject to environmental influences such as soil water, wind, soil minerals, the amount of soil oxygen, atmospheric carbon dioxide, the amount of sunlight, the prevailing temperatures, and countless other **abiotic,** or nonliving, factors. In addition, there are the **biotic,** or living, elements of the environment such as bark beetles, birds, squirrels, soil bacteria and fungi, worms, and parasites of various types—all of which may directly or indirectly affect the tree. The tree, in turn, will modify the surrounding environment: the shade produced will alter temperatures; its limbs will prevent the free flow of air; transpiration, or water loss, from leaf surfaces will alter the humidity of the air; its roots will penetrate the soil, opening up soil channels; and root hairs will extract water from soil spaces, so that the entire soil environment will be modified. We have used a plant to illustrate reciprocal activity. An animal also will exert an influence on the surrounding environment by grazing, predation, burrowing, trampling vegetation, and so on. Even the nonliving (abiotic) factors of the environment can cause mild or severe changes in an area as evidenced by continuous or abundant precipitation (floods), wind action (hurricanes, tornados, typhoons), and gravitational activity (earthquakes, land slides), to name a few.

Ecology is concerned to a great extent with the **habitat** and is, consequently, applied habitat biology. Elton (1949) succinctly defined the habitat as an area possessing uniformity of physiography, vegetation, climate, or any other quality the investigator assumes is important. Habitats, though they are restricted in area, will exhibit considerable variability in size—from a coniferous forest or oceanic area measured in terms of acres or hundreds of square miles to an exposed surface of rock or the lower surface of a twig a few square centimeters or a fraction of a square millimeter in area. The latter two examples are called **microhabitats** by most ecologists; they have been intensively investigated for the past twenty or more years as instruments have become available for measuring the fluctuations in the **microenvironment** extant in such localities.

The environmental conditions prevalent within any specific habitat will be unique for that area, though similar conditions may prevail in a habitat of the same type a fraction of a mile or thousands of miles distant. For example, temperature, wind movement, fauna and flora present will be similar in any particular type of deciduous forest for any specific time of year, but all of these conditions will not be exactly the same for any two such habitats. Furthermore, conditions within any habitat will vary from place to place. For example, there would be in a forest environment different temperatures, humidity, and wind movement in the treetop area (forest canopy) than there would be near the forest floor or in the soil. Finally, to compound the situation, seasonal differences will exist in any habitat throughout the year. In a pond habitat, the temperature of the water, oxygen content, amount of **plankton** (including diatoms, algae, and bacteria as well as small and often immature crustaceans and various aquatic worms) and fish population will be quite different in the **vernal** (spring) period than they would be in the **aestival** (summer) aspect of the year.

BRIEF HISTORY OF ECOLOGY

Our account would be incomplete without at least a brief examination of the history of ecology. The vague beginnings of ecology may be traced back to prehistoric man, who utilized environmental information to hunt food, trap animals, find edible vegetation, and locate shelter to survive the hardships imposed by nature. An increased knowledge of the importance of environmental conditions led quite naturally to religious rituals, worship of weather gods, and rain dances. Paleontological evidence gathered in different parts of the world indicate the continual migration of some social groups and tribes to escape unfavorable temperatures or the harsh effects of storms.

The early Greek philosophers and scientists were aware of the importance of environmental studies. Hippocrates, the father of medicine, published a paper entitled *On Airs, Waters and Places*. One portion of the work reads: "Whoever wished to investigate medicine properly, should proceed thus: in the first place to consider the seasons of the year, and what effects each of them produces (for they are not all alike, but differ much from themselves in regard to their changes)." In his writings on natural history Aristotle refers to the habits of animals and environmental conditions prevailing in certain areas. One of Aristotle's students, Theophrastus, an accomplished botanist, is considered by many as the first true ecologist, for he wrote about plant communities and the types of plants found in different areas. These communities were considered with respect to the environment in which they were located, such as marine aquatic plants, marine littoral plants, marsh plants, and so on.

After the intervening centuries of intellectual stagnation, referred to as the "dark ages," natural history studies were resumed by a number of workers. The Frenchman, Reaumur (1683–1757), published six volumes on the natural history of insects (*Memoires pour servir a l'historie des insects*), which contained a great deal of ecological information about insects. But it was during the nineteenth century that natural history studies became more numerous and knowledge began to accumulate at a rapid pace. Two groups of investigators established themselves in the literature during the early part of the century: the continental naturalists and the island naturalists. An outstanding worker of the former group, Baron Alexander von Humboldt, spent five years exploring tropical and temperate South America. He traveled along the largest rivers in South America—the Amazon, the Orinoco, and the Negro; he explored the **llanos** (plains) of Venezuela, the mountains of Ecuador, and the valleys of Peru. Humboldt collected plant specimens and recorded local environmental conditions, including air temperature, elevation above sea level, and the abundance and type of flora. Upon his return to Germany in 1804, he published 26 volumes based on data collected while he was in South America. Humboldt's prolific writing not only helped to establish the science of plant geography, but also stimulated other naturalists to investigate the flora and fauna of South America. Of the many naturalists who explored this portion of the world, the youngest was Henry W. Bates, who, at the age of twenty-three, started an eleven-year search for insects and covered 1400 miles over the rugged landscape of this continent. His most famous publications were on the termites, warrior ants, and parasol ants. Other investigators included Richard

Spruce, who explored the Amazon and Negro rivers, and Alcide d'Orbigny, who arrived in Uruguay in 1826 and collected specimens of fossils and living organisms in the Andes Mountains and Bolivia.

Other naturalists journeyed to other areas of the world during this period. Edward Forbes, a British naturalist, investigated the flora and fauna of the Mediterranean Sea as well as fossil deposits. The flora and fauna of the polar continent, Antarctica, were investigated by Joseph Hooker for three years, while he was with the Sir James Ross Expedition. A Swiss-born naturalist, Louis Agassiz, came to the United States in 1846 and taught at Harvard University from 1848 until his untimely death in 1873. Agassiz's energy and philosophy were contagious for he stimulated a "back to nature" movement in this part of the world. He believed in first-hand nature study in the field rather than in relying

FIGURE 1–2 View of the Duke University Marine Laboratory located on Piver's Island, Beaufort, North Carolina. Docking facilities are in the foreground; laboratories and dormitories are in the background.

solely on laboratory work or on textbook accounts. His travels included a trip through the United States and resulted in the publication of *Contribution to the Natural History of the United States.* A later journey through Brazil in 1865 stimulated the tireless Agassiz to publish, three years later, *A Journey in Brazil.*

One of Agassiz's most important achievements was founding the first marine laboratory in the United States (1873) at Penikese Island, Wood's Hole, Massachusetts. Dohrn had established the first marine laboratory in the world a year earlier at Naples, Italy, which he called the Statione Zoologica. Though Agassiz's station started from humble beginnings, it was to become the dominant marine laboratory along the Atlantic Coast. The growth of oceanographic information in the western Atlantic area owes much to the imagination and foresight of this one naturalist, Louis Agassiz. A number of marine biological stations have been established by colleges or universities interested in the research potential offered by the existence of such an installation. The Duke University Marine Laboratory (Figure 1–2) located on the North Carolina coast is an excellent example of a marine biological station supported by university funds and staffed by university personnel.

As continental areas were being explored in scattered parts of the world, insular areas did not escape intensive investigation by a group known as the "island naturalists." These individuals worked in continental regions as well, but many of their notable contributions were on insular life. The H.M.S. *Beagle,* with Charles Darwin aboard as naturalist, visited many scattered islands—Cape de Verde, Tahiti, Galapagos Islands, New Zealand, St. Helena, Ascension, and the Azores, to name a few—during its five-year voyage around the world. Darwin published a work entitled *Journal of Researches into the Natural History, and Geology of the Countries Visited during the Voyage of H.M.S. Beagle.* He postulated that at some time in the geological past many of the present islands and island chains had been connected to continental areas by land bridges that permitted unrestricted movement by the flora and fauna back and forth. With the geological recession of these connecting links, organisms were isolated in the insular areas with different types of environmental conditions. This led to a natural selection for certain structures or traits, resulting in different characteristics for the insular life as contrasted with continental species of the same ancestral type.

Edward Forbes, who had earlier dealt with the natural history of the Mediterranean area, published a paper in 1846 dealing with the paleoecology of the British Isles (*On the Connexion between the Distribution of the existing Fauna and Flora of the British Isles, and the Geological Changes which affected their Areas*). Forbes believed that plants as well as animals had moved across land bridges between Europe and the British Isles in the geological past. The accumulation of information

FIGURE 1–3 The East Indies, indicating the location of Wallace's Line (dashed line).

about land bridges and the emphasis placed upon their importance with respect to distribution and natural history by Darwin, Forbes, and others impressed a close friend of Darwin, Alfred R. Wallace. Wallace toiled in the Malay Archipelago for over eight years and published three books, *The Malay Archipelago, Island Life,* and *The Geographical Distribution of Animals.* He found that two island groups with different faunal and floral origins existed in this portion of the world. A western group of islands, including Borneo, Sumatra, Java, and Bali, contained species of an oriental origin, implying the existence of a land bridge with southeastern Asia. An eastern group of islands, including Celebes, Lombok, New Guinea, and other smaller islands with occidental species had been connected, according to Wallace's deductions, with Australia at one time in the geological past. A channel of ocean water, narrow but deep, between Bali and Lombok separated the two groups of islands with their living indigenous populations. A line (Wallace's Line) separated the two island groups (Figure 1–3), though it is doubtful that Celebes belongs to the eastern group, because some of the fauna displays a considerable affinity with the organisms found on Borneo and Sumatra.

Wallace's Line, though it was intended originally as a geographic boundary, has evolved into a more important concept of distribution in this part of the world.

In 1859, Geoffrey Saint Hilaire used the term **ethology** to refer to the study of relationships between the organism and the environment, but the term was never generally accepted by the earlier ecologists. Ethology has been resurrected in recent years as an important part of ecology dealing with the field of animal behavior. Nine years later, Reiter introduced the term **oekologie** derived from the Greek *oikos* meaning "home," and *logos,* a "discussion or study." Ernst Haekel is often falsely credited with the derivation of the term because he defined it in the literature a year later. The term has since been anglicized to "ecology."

The community concept of study, which materialized toward the latter part of the nineteenth century, heralded the birth of modern ecology as distinct from the important but more generalized nature studies of preceding eras. A community, in the most limited sense, may be represented by two species living together or in close proximity to one another, though in actuality many species are generally involved. However, as regards community studies, the fact that two or more species are living together in a limited area is not only obvious but superficial. The importance of community work, in the ecological sense, is the study of interaction between species and its effect on longevity and changes in the surrounding environmental conditions. Various aspects of community interaction—parasitism, predation, and other vital heterospecific and reciprocal relationships—are presented in later sections of this text. Botanists of this period realized the importance of plant communities some time before zoologists became aware of the value of aggregate interactions. Le Coq, Sendtner, and Kerner are a few of the botanical investigators involved with community work in nature. Karl Mobius (1877), in studying oyster bed communities, stated: "Every oyster bed is . . . a community of living beings, a collection of species, and a massing of individuals, which find everything necessary for their growth and continuance. . . . Science possesses, as yet, no word by which such a community where the sum of species and individuals, being mutually limited and selected under the external conditions of life have . . . continued in possession of a certain definite territory. I propose the word Biocoenosis for such a community." Thus, Mobius was one of the first animal ecologists to recognize the significance of communities and propose a synonym for the term community—a **biocoenosis.**

Shortly after the turn of the century, community studies increased in number. Davenport (1903) published a paper on the animal ecology of Cold Spring Harbor, and S. A. Forbes (1907) wrote about the distribution of Illinois fishes; both men used the community approach. E. Warming (1909), a Danish plant ecologist, recognized the interdependence and close relationships that often exist between plant and animal communities and cautiously recommended dealing with plant and animal communities as entities rather than separately, as had been done in the past. V. E. Shelford (1907, 1908) accepted Warming's cautious proposal and included pertinent data on both botanical and animal components of the environment in his now famous tiger beetle work.

As the years have passed, an immense amount of literature of an ecological nature has been published. During the first third of this century, the total volume of ecological work surpassed by a healthy margin all of the written material on ecology and natural history produced during all of the preceding centuries of recorded history. A tendency toward increased specialization in ecology has occurred as is evidenced by the establishment of such disciplines as **paleoecology,** a study of environmental conditions and life as it existed in past ages. Pollen analysis, radioactive dating, and paleontology have aided the paleoecologist.

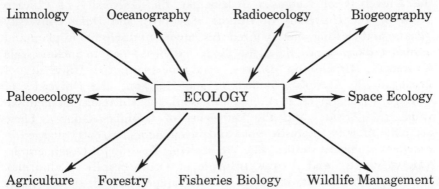

FIGURE 1–4 Graphic representation of relationships between the trophic levels of a nutritional series.

Other specialized fields of ecology are **zoogeography,** the scientific study of the geographic distribution of animals; **oceanography,** the study of the biotic and physical conditions existing in oceans, bays, and estuaries; and **limnology,** the study of the living and nonliving components of inland waters. With the establishment of specialized disciplines, the value of applied ecology has become apparent to farmers, agricultural extension workers, and foresters as many of the basic principles of ecology have been applied in solving problems such as dust bowls, soil erosion, wildlife management, and other conservation problems throughout this country and other parts of the world. A few of the relationships that exist between ecology and related fields of study are represented in Figure 1–4. This graphic presentation is far from exhaustive, but reciprocal exchanges between ecology and a related discipline are represented by double arrows.

Recently, statistical studies on populations, sampling techniques, and community problems have increased in the ecological literature. Current emphasis on community and population studies stem from several important texts published in the second decade of this century: Lotka's *Elements of Physical Biology*, Elton's *Animal Ecology*, and Volterra's work, which appeared in translated form in Chapman's *Animal Ecology*. Following these initial studies, Gause's *The Struggle for Existence* and Bodenheimer's *Problems of Animal Ecology* emphasized the importance of existing problems in population and community investigations. More recently Slobodkin's interest in population dynamics and the general field of energetics, particularly with regard to *Daphnia*, have helped to broaden and enrich the general field of population studies. Ecological thought is no longer dominated by a few schools in this country, but is fortunately shared by an increasing number of institutions scattered throughout the United States. During the earlier part of this century, the University of Nebraska (Clements), the University of Chicago (Cowles), the University of Illinois (Shelford), and Duke University (Pearse and Oosting) monopolized this important discipline in plant and animal ecology. Since then, the circle has broadened to include Yale University (Hutchinson, Deevey, and Lindeman), the University of Michigan (F. E. Smith, Slobodkin, and Hairston), the University of Chicago (T. Park, O. Park, and Emerson), the University of Pennsylvania (MacArthur) and the University of Georgia (Odum). These are only a few of the institutions and investigators currently engaged in excellent ecological studies. The Wood's Hole Institute of Oceanography (Massachusetts) and Scripps Institute of Oceanography (California) remain the important centers of oceanographic research, though many smaller installations, many of them supported or affiliated with inland colleges and universities, are rapidly establishing a reputation in the current literature.

An excellent group of papers by outstanding population and community ecologists has recently appeared in a publication, *Readings in Population and Community Ecology*, edited by W. E. Hazen. Several reference texts have been published in the past fifteen years. One of the classic works, *Principles of Animal Ecology*, by Allee, *et al.* (1949), deals with all of the major aspects of ecological work. *Natural Communities*, by Dice (1952), properly deals with the community problem in terms of physical factors, territoriality, food, succession, and community evolution. A most recent scholarly work by Andrewartha and Birch, *The Distribution and Abundance of Animals* (1954), covers a number of phases of ecological thought never before presented in a single volume; however, much of the material pertains to entomological research. A complete discourse on the physical and physiological analysis of environment is followed by a reasonably thorough discussion of quantitative ecology, including material on sampling, population fluctuations, distribution, and periodicity. This excellent work is concluded by a consideration of the genetic aspects of ecology.

At the present time ecological investigations stand on the threshold of the vast unexplored realm of space ecology. The possibility of a trip to and return from neighboring planets is approaching closer to reality, with the expectation that many may investigate the climatic, biotic (?), and related abiotic conditions that exist on these unexplored planets. Studies dealing with radioactive materials and its effect on the environment and organisms have begun and are yielding information at the present time. The ecologist of the future will truly have exciting and important discoveries to divulge relative to space and radioactivity.

Many societies and organizations have been established in the past and are destined to materialize in the future as ecological investigations continue. Countless natural history museums, clubs, and associations have been formed for the dissemination of information in published form or through group discussions. Two of the oldest and more prominent organizations dealing solely with ecological material are the British Ecological Society founded in 1913 and the Ecological Society of America established in 1916.

FACETS OF ECOLOGY

Methods of study vary in regard to ecological investigations. An ecological hierarchy has been established that becomes more restrictive as we pass downward from one hierarchical level to another. The **ecosystem** includes all of the living and nonliving components of the environment, so that the entire world could be considered a giant ecosystem; however, it is rather impractical for purposes of study. A pond, a forest, and a desert area are examples of ecosystems, each containing living organisms. A pond ecosystem would likely contain algae, insects, crustaceans, bacteria, seed plants, snails, and fish as its living component. Then the ecologist must consider all of the abiotic factors of the environment such as sunlight, cosmic radiation, temperature, oxygen concentration of the water, mineral content, type of substrate, and other related factors. At the **community** level, as distinguished from the ecosystem, the ecologist is primarily concerned with the plant and animal life in an area, and though abiotic factors cannot be excluded from an environmental study, only the more important elements would be investigated in any detail. Going a step further down the ecological hierarchical ladder, **population ecology** deals with a species or at times several closely related species. Once again, the nonliving elements of the environment are never disregarded, but only the more critical interactions are studied. Population

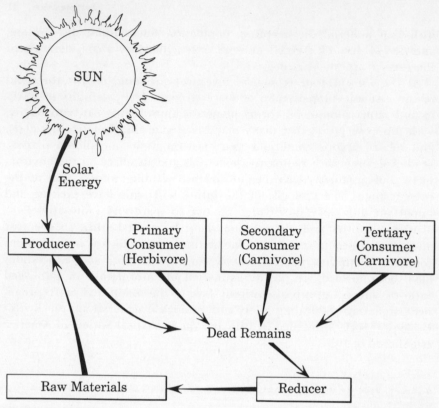

FIGURE 1–5 Simple diagrammatic representation of relationships between the trophic levels of a nutritional series.

dynamics, concerned with the number of factors affecting population growth, decline, cyclic changes, and other important changes in a population structure, has become an integral part of this field of study.

A recent development is the study of differences and similarities in food relationships among living organisms; it has been referred to as the **productivity approach** in modern ecology. In this type of study, the community is studied in terms of **trophic levels,** which indicate the organism's relationship to the food web in any natural environment. The basic trophic levels in any area will include the following groups (Figure 1–5): **Raw materials** consisting of nonliving substances such as soil minerals, water, and carbon dioxide are the first link in the food chain. These raw materials that comprise the first trophic level are utilized by the **producer** organisms, which are mostly plants because very few animals are involved with food production. The producers generally produce food by photosynthesis, using available energy from the sun or selected spectral portions of artificial light sources to combine the raw materials and yield carbohydrates, fats, and proteins, plus vitamins. **Consumers** (with very few exceptions these are animals) make up the third trophic level, which must be subdivided into two major groups on the basis of feeding habits: the **herbivores** and **carnivores.** Herbivores consume the producer group and transform some of the material into body tissue, thus increasing the mass of the individual; some of this food will be utilized as an energy source and some will pass through the digestive tract unused by the organism and eliminated as fecal wastes. Carnivores also utilize the producer level, but in an indirect way; they feed on the herbivores (or other carnivores), transforming their body tissues into usable food materials. Another obvious alternative is the existence of **omnivores,** groups of animals feeding on producers (herbivorous feeding) and preying on the consumers (carnivorous feeding). It should be equally obvious that there may be a number of links in the carnivorous portion of the consumer level. For example, herbivorous insects may be caught by a frog or toad (primary carnivore), which may in turn be consumed by a snake (secondary carnivore), which could be caught and eaten by an owl (tertiary carnivore). Eventually a producer or consumer, if not eaten or captured by another organism during its lifetime, will be killed by unfavorable environmental conditions such as intolerable temperatures, oxygen concentration (in aquatic environments), or disease. Whatever the cause, death is inevitable, and this allows another trophic level, the **reducer** organisms, comprised of fungi and bacteria, to transform dead organic materials back to raw materials that may be used by the producer element to begin the cycle over again. Productivity studies in the past have yielded much information relative to carrying capacity, biomass, consumer-producer ratios, and cyclic changes in productivity.

The terms **autecology** and **synecology** have been introduced into the ecological literature to clarify the investigator's method of approach to a specific problem. An autecologist is interested in a single species or at best a few closely related species and the manner in which they affect and are affected by the environment. The ecologist who follows such an approach is, in actuality, a population ecologist. This has been the more recent approach to ecological studies, for by gaining more information about the individual species and its requirements in nature, we shall learn more about the community or ecosystem of which they are a part. Synecology, on the other hand, is primarily a community type approach, in which all life, including plants and animals as well as the pertinent abiotic elements, are studied. Both methods of investigation have much to offer regarding future studies, just as they have provided biologists in past periods with important environmental data.

Ecology, as a scientific discipline, cannot divorce itself from other scientific fields of endeavor any more than an organism can become segregated from the surrounding environment. Most ecologists must rely on information derived from the physical sciences; the well-entrenched disciplines—chemistry, physics, meteorology, climatology, geology, geography, and mathematics—can often provide the ecologist with essential material. Meteorological studies and climatological data for certain geographic localities allow for a more subtle interpretation of results. **Pedeology,** the study of soils, their acidity, alkalinity, humus content, mineral content, soil type, and so on, is often of importance to the terrestrial ecologist. If an investigator restricts his studies to forest communities, a basic knowledge of forestry can be invaluable in terms of forest type distribution, floristic composition, and prevalent environmental factors.

Statistical data are becoming more important in interpreting the reasons for activity, population increases, migrations, probability of ecological events occurring in a particular area, sampling techniques and reliability of results. Ecology is also closely allied with a number of biological disciplines; in fact, there are few biological disciplines that cannot be utilized by some ecologists in a phase of laboratory or field work. Some biological studies are of prime importance to the ecological investigator. Paleontology provides information about the ancestral organisms and environmental situations prevalent in the past. Without the knowledge of the functional aspect (physiology) of life, the ecologist would generally have a very incomplete idea of the critical environmental factors and their effects on the biota. Systematics provides the means of identifying the organism (s) under investigation as well as information about the effects of isolation and geographic races. Evolution and genetics are utilized to interpret the reason for organic changes when linked with environmental conditions, establishment of new populations and species, environmental effects on genetic populations, and so on.

The reliance on information supplied by a number of basic disciplines has led to the remark that ecology is not a full-fledged subdivision of biology, but rather "a way of thinking or a type of biological philosophy." Such a statement is not valid in view of the general interdependence of other biological disciplines. For example, an embryologist relies on knowledge culled from many related fields of science: cytology, histology, biochemistry, biophysics, and physiology. No biological discipline of recognized rank stands as an island of knowledge, completely divorced from other branches of investigation. Ecology, it is true, relies on a greater number of disciplines than do the other biological disciplines, but it should nevertheless be regarded as a basic branch of biology rather than a nebulous philosophy. The fact that ecology does rely on an impressive array of biological, physical, and mathematical fields of study would strengthen its position in biology. Ecology, along with genetics and evolution, gives any student a greater depth of understanding or a new dimension that allows for more critical and valid interpretation of biological events.

Selected References

Allee, W. C., A. E. Emerson, O. Park, T. Park, and K. P. Schmidt. *Principles of Animal Ecology* (Philadelphia: W. B. Saunders, 1949), pp. i–xii, 1–873.

Andrewartha, H. G., and L. C. Birch. *The Distribution and Abundance of Animals* (Chicago: Univ. of Chicago Press, 1954), pp. i–xv, 1–782.

Bodenheimer, F. S. *Problems of Animal Ecology* (Oxford: Oxford Univ. Press), pp. i–vi, 1–183.

Chapman, R. N. *Animal Ecology with Especial Reference to Insects* (New York: McGraw-Hill, 1931), pp. i–x, 1–464.

Davenport, C. B. 1903. The animal ecology of the Cold Spring Harbor sand split, with remarks on the theory of adaptation. Decennial Publ. Univ. Chicago, **10**:157–176.

Dice, L. R. *Natural Communities* (Ann Arbor, Mich.: Univ. of Michigan Press, 1952), pp. i–x, 1–547.

Elton, C. 1946. Competition and the structure of ecological communities. J. An. Ecol., **15**:54–68.

———. 1949. Population interspersion: an essay on animal community patterns. J. Ecol., **37**:1–23.

Forbes, S. A. 1907. On the local distribution of certain Illinois fishes: an essay in statistical ecology. Bull. Ill. Lab. Nat. Hist., **7**:1–19.

———. 1925. The lake as a microcosm. Bull. Ill. Nat. Hist. Survey, **15**:537–550.

Gause, G. F. *The Struggle for Existence* (Baltimore: Williams & Wilkins, 1934), pp. i–ix, 1–163.

Hazen, W. E. (ed.) *Readings in Population and Community Ecology* (Philadelphia: Saunders, 1964), pp. i–x, 1–388.

Lotka, A. J. *Elements of Physical Biology* (Baltimore: Williams & Wilkins, 1925), pp. i–xxx, 1–460.

Mobius, K. 1877. Die Auster und die Austernwirtschaft. Berlin. (Translated, 1880. The oyster and oyster culture. Rept. U.S. Fish. Comm. [1880]), pp. 683–751.

Shelford, V. E. 1907. Preliminary notes on the distribution of the tiger beetles *(Cicindela)* and its relation to plant succession. Biol. Bull., **14**:9–14.

———. 1908. Life histories and larval habits of the tiger beetles (Cicindellidae). Linn. Soc. Jour. Zool., **30**:157–184.

Slobodkin, L. B. 1954. Population dynamics in *Daphnia obtusa* Kurg. Ecol. Monogr., **24**:69–88.

Volterra, V. 1928. Variations and fluctuations of the number of individuals in animal species living together. Jour. du Conseil intern. pour l'explor. de la mer III, Vol. I. Reprinted in R. N. Chapman, *Animal Ecology* (New York: McGraw-Hill, 1931).

Warming, J. E. B. *Oecology of Plants* (Oxford: Clarendon Press, 1909), pp. i–xi, 1–422.

II. Basic Principles
of Ecology

Every scientific discipline has its own technical terminology and principles that must be understood and appreciated if the student is to have a clear, concise grasp of the subject matter. In this chapter, I shall attempt to define some of the terms that are used frequently in the ecological literature and present some of the guiding principles that have evolved from past ecological observations and investigations. With regard to the use of words, it should be pointed out that, as is often the case with many things biological, words such as *always* and *never* are dangerous terms, because too often we find exceptions in nature. C. C. Adams, the naturalist, once made the comment that nature seldom draws a clear line; often it is blurred and far from clear with respect to many phases of biological activity. One basic reason for exceptions within the natural environment is the sizable complex of factors governing practically every facet of biological activity. With this in mind, it follows that with the greater number of interactions, the probability of one of these factors varying to a greater or lesser degree is increased proportionately.

LIMITING FACTORS

All living organisms, plant or animal, will have a range of tolerance for certain environmental factors. That is, the organism will be able to survive provided the temperature, humidity, or some other important element is maintained within critical limits. In some instances, the range of tolerance is narrow and the organism is considered **stenoecious** relative to that particular factor. The prefix *steno-* is derived from the Greek *stenos,* meaning "narrow," "little," or "close." This same organism, though it may be **stenothermal** (able to tolerate a relatively narrow temperature range), may at the same time be **euryoecious** (the prefix *eury-* means "broad" or "wide") with regard to some other environmental factor. Some marine organisms are designated as **euryhaline**, meaning that they have a broad range of tolerance for salts in water. A euryhaline

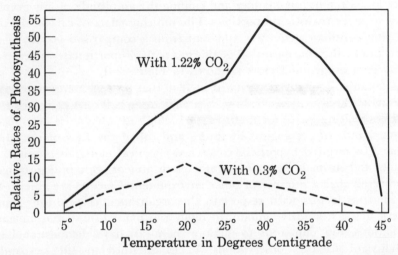

FIGURE 2–1 Rates of photosynthesis in potato leaves in relation to temperature and the concentration of carbon dioxide. Calculated from data by H. G. Lundegardh from *Textbook of Botany* by Transeau, Sampson, and Tiffany (Harper & Brothers, 1953).

organism, provided other environmental factors are adequate for its existence, may be found in an estuary where the salt content might be 14 parts per thousand or in the open ocean with a salt content of 35 parts per thousand. If an environmental factor essential for life is absent or depleted below the critical minimum, or if that factor exceeds the maximum tolerable level for the species, it becomes a **limiting factor**. In other words, it is this condition that will prevent an organism from successfully invading an environmental area; or under less severe circumstances, although the organism may be able to exist in the area, it may affect the general metabolism of the organism. An example of the latter condition may be cited with regard to many photosynthetic plants. In terrestrial areas, carbon dioxide is very often a limiting factor with regard to photosynthetic rate. Carbon dioxide is present in a concentration of about three parts per 10,000 parts, or .03 per cent, of air. If this amount of carbon dioxide is increased above the normal level, which has been done in greenhouse and field experiments by piping the gas into the plant beds or fields, often a 100 to 150 per cent increase in plant yield is noted. In some forest areas, under a thick canopy of trees, the carbon dioxide content of the atmosphere may be 0.08 per cent rather than the normal 0.03 per cent. The high percentage of carbon dioxide in this area may partially compensate for the reduced light intensity in some of the lower strata of forests. A logarithmic curve indicates the effect of carbon dioxide concentration on photosynthetic rate. A log curve is most convenient in tabulating results because it tends to exhibit data in a straight-line manner and confine the amplitude of any graphic scale to more realistic proportions. The limiting effect of carbon dioxide on photosynthetic activity is apparent from a comparison of very slight increases in the concentration of this gas with proportionate increases in other environmental factors as shown in Figure 2–1.

A botanist, Justus Liebig, stated in 1840 that any environmental factor that most closely approached the critical minimum for a species will tend to be a limiting factor for that species. Liebig's idea has since been incorporated into the ecological literature and called the Law of the Minimum. His original hypothesis concerned chemical materials required by plants and animals in their natural environment. But biologists have discovered that a number of other environmental factors are able to act as limiting factors with respect to the organism. Temperature, atmospheric gases, humidity, amount of light, and many other environmental conditions, too numerous to mention here—all have demonstrated the validity of Liebig's observations. V. E. Shelford in 1913 expanded Liebig's observations to include the maximal limits of an environmental factor. Thus Shelford's Law of Tolerance states that a value below a critical minimum (Liebig's Law of the Minimum) or a quantity or factor in excess of the critical maximum would exclude certain organisms from environmental areas. Any value lying between these critical limits falls within the range of tolerance for an organism; if the limits of tolerance are exceeded for a particular species, it will lead to the disappearance of the species from that area as long as the condition persists.

Since the publication of Shelford's Law of Tolerance over a half century ago, a considerable amount of additional information has come to light. A plant or animal may have a wide range of tolerance for one factor in the environment, but a relatively narrow range of tolerance for another condition. Thus we find that some species of freshwater fish are eurythermal (have a wide range of tolerance for temperature), but they are stenohaline (have a narrow range of tolerance for salt). We find that in some instances, reciprocal effects are apparent; if conditions are not suitable with regard to one condition, the limits of tolerance may be reduced with regard to another. Broekema (1941) reported that lowering the temperatures of brackish waters tended to reduce the tolerance of estuarine species to low salinities. In the Blackwater Estuary off the southeastern coast of Ireland, workers found that oyster drills (*Urosalpinx*) died at low temperatures because they were unable to tolerate the salinity values within this thermal range. Under normal temperature conditions, however, these same salinity values would have been well within the range of tolerance. In some cases, the range of tolerance for a particular condition increases as the age of the organism increases. We find that young seedlings or larval insects will often have a relatively narrow range of tolerance to temperature or moisture values (stenoecious), but as they mature the range broadens, often surpassing both the critical minimum and critical maximum established for immature stages. Any organism will have an optimal point or range within the range of tolerance, as shown in Figure 2–2, within which the maximum rate of growth and activity will occur.

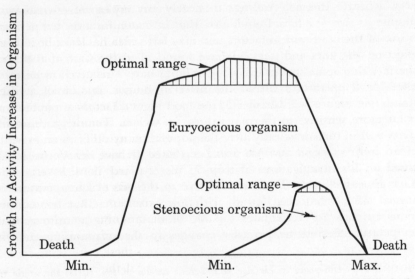

FIGURE 2–2   Tolerance diagram with optimal range and minimal-maximal limits for an euryoecious and stenoecious organism with the same maximal limits of tolerance.

The range of tolerance and optimal conditions, particularly the latter, will vary for geographical races of the same species. The common meadow or leopard frog (*Rana pipiens*) has a geographic range extending from Panama to Canada. The conditions that exist throughout this unusually broad geographic range vary considerably, but over the course of many thousands of years natural selection, genetic change, and adaptation have altered the populations to the extent that the critical minima, maxima, and optimal range are found to be quite different when individuals from different areas are compared. These differences become more extreme as we approach the two limits of the geographic range. Such locally adapted populations are referred to as **ecotypes** by the ecologist. Turesson (1922) defined *ecotype* as "the product arising as a result of the genotypical response of an ecospecies to a particular habitat." He distinguished the genetically different populations from the physiological or functional response to a particular area by employing the term **ecophene** to the latter group. We find that the frogs at the northern limit of the geographic range do not produce viable embryos when bred with southern frogs. Eggs of northern frogs undergo a rapid development at a lower water temperature; southern frog eggs display a much slower development at higher aquatic temperatures.

One abiotic factor that has received more attention in the ecological literature than any other is temperature. Undoubtedly, one reason for this is the ease with which such measurements may be made. By means of thermisters and electrical resistance recorders, it is possible to secure very accurate thermal readings in nearly any ecological environment, despite its size. We have found, also, that in many instances temperature is one of the most critical factors and may have either a direct or indirect effect on the flora and fauna. I have found in my research that despite the fact that some springtails (Collembola) have a relatively wide tolerance for temperatures within the litter or humus stratum of a forest stand (see Figure 3–3, Chapter 3) the food ingested by these populations is far more sensitive to thermal values (as well as humidity); this sensitivity will in turn drastically alter the population size. This is an example of an indirect effect and has also been cited by van der Vecht (1953) based on his investigations of tropical insect populations. Several rules have appeared in the literature relative to the effect of temperature on animal size. It has been found, with few exceptions, that homoiothermous animals (or vertebrates capable of maintaining a uniform body temperature despite temperature changes in the surrounding environ-

FIGURE 2–3 Difference in ear size of different species of fox. (Left) the arctic fox (*Alopex lagopus*) (center) the red fox (*Vulpes vulpes*) of temperate regions; (right) the desert fox (*Megalotis zerda*). Reprinted from *Ecological Animal Geography* by W. C. Allee and K. Schmidt by permission of John Wiley & Sons, Inc., 1951.

ment) tend to be larger in northern climates. There is less surface area in proportion to body weight, and hence less heat is lost for the same body weight during cooler periods. This principle is called Bergmann's Rule. Another principle, known as Allen's Rule, states that the length of the extremities of homoiothermous animals, such as ears, legs, and tails, is reduced proportionately as one travels northward (Figure 2–3). Allen's Rule holds even for laboratory populations; we find that the tails of a species reared in a temperature range of 15.5° to 20° C. are noticeably shorter than are those of members of the same species raised in a temperature range of 31° to 33.5° C.

STRATIFICATION AND ZONATION

STRATIFICATION

In ecological terminology, the term **stratification** refers to a vertical layering of organisms or environmental conditions within a biotic community. Stratification may be considered as one of the integral properties of nearly every natural community; it should not, however, be confused with zonation, which more properly refers to the horizontal arrangement of biotic or abiotic factors. Stratification of the biotic element is obvious even to the casual observer because the living components can readily be identified and counted. The abiotic factors, on the other hand, are seldom seen, nor are they often measured with ease.

A forest community is an extreme example of terrestrial stratification because there are a number of well-recognized strata above and below the soil surface. A typical forest (Figure 2–4) will have an **overstory stratum** comprised of trees that are forty or more feet in height in mature stands. These trees will form the **canopy**, which may be open or closed, depending upon the relative proximity of trees. Below this protective canopy, there is often an **understory stratum** that extends from twenty feet in height to a short distance below the overstory. The trees in this stratum are generally shade-tolerant species that never grow to the height of the overstory species; they are often more sparsely represented than the overstory flora. A **transgressive stratum** extending from about four feet to twenty feet or more is comprised of shorter shade-tolerant species or species that in the course of germination and growth are passing through the transgressive stratum and will eventually increase the density or replace those species making up the overstory and understory strata. The transgressive stratum is dependent, in part, upon a **seedling stratum** that begins at the soil level and extends to the lower limit of the transgressive stratum. These seedlings are hardwood species in a well-developed upland forest because softwoods as a rule are not shade tolerant. Even in a thick forest, there is the **herbaceous stratum,**

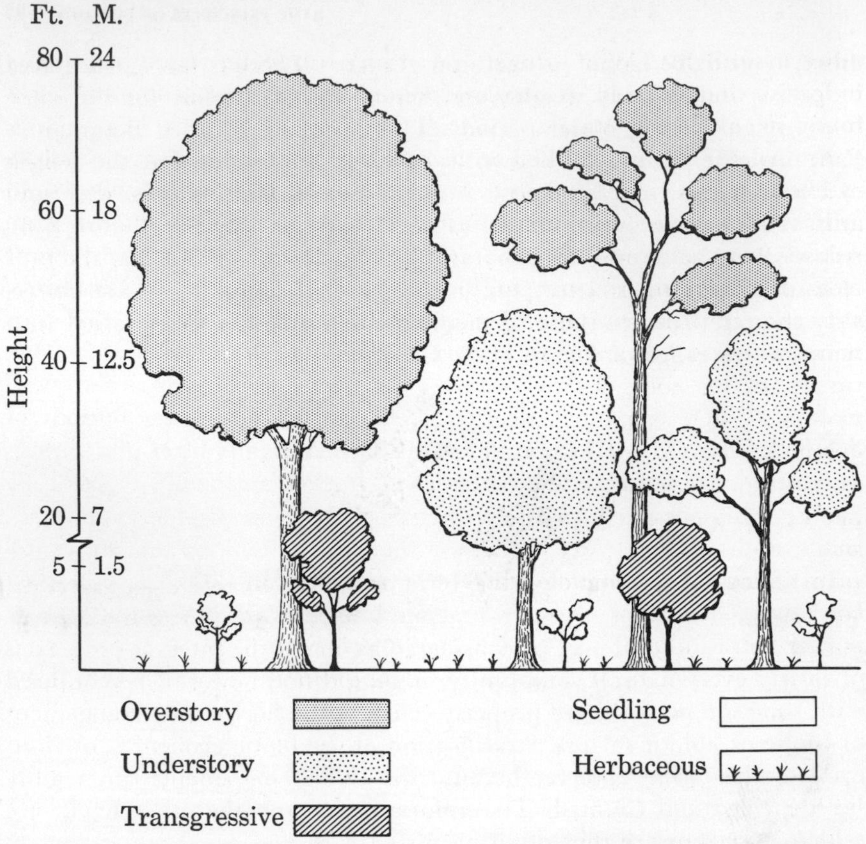
Ft.
M.
80
24
60
18
Height
40
12.5
20
7
5
1.5
Overstory
Understory
Transgressive
Seedling
Herbaceous

FIGURE 2–4 Stratification of vegetation in a deciduous forest stand.

which contains nonwoody plant growth. A grassland area where trees or shrubs are scattered and usually located at considerable intervals with respect to one another is known as a **savanna.** In savannas, the herbaceous stratum may be quite thick and luxuriant because of the increased amount of light reaching the soil surface. Below the herbaceous stratum is the humus-soil stratum containing bacteria and fungi.

In a typical oak-hickory forest, such as would be found in the southeastern portion of the United States, white oak (*Quercus alba*) and post oak (*Q. stellata*) are the predominant species of oak in the overstory. Several species of hickory are common in this stratum (*Carya alba, C. carolinae-septentrionalis, C. glabra*). The understory will be comprised of the species mentioned, as well as scattered representatives of red maple (*Acer rubrum*). The transgressive stratum includes sourwood (*Oxydendrum*), dogwood (*Cornus*), red cedar (*Juniperus virginiana*), and black gum (*Nyssa sylvatica*). Seedlings will consist primarily of oaks and hickories as well as of representatives of the transgressive stratum. Herbaceous species are sparse, primarily as a result of reduced insolation (direct sunlight). Wild ginger (*Asarum*), carpenter weed (*Prunella vulgaris*), and tickseed (*Coreopsis major*) are the most common herbs found in oak-hickory stands.

Animal life is also stratified within plant communities, but the stratification is not so rigid because of the mobility of these organisms. Often animals will move from one stratum to another in search of food or in response to numerous abiotic factors. Arboreal species that may move from the seedling stratum to higher strata are insects, snails, birds, squirrels, and the opossum, to name a few. Animals that are seldom or never arboreal but are most commonly situated above the soil include turtles, snakes, some lizards, certain insects, some birds, and a variety of mammals such as rabbits, deer, wolves, and foxes (during periods of greatest activity). Another faunal stratum inhabits the litter and humus microstrata of the soil. These organisms include springtails, beetles, fly larvae, millipedes, centipedes, pseudoscorpions, mites, spiders, annelids, snails, and sow bugs. At a still lower level in the mineral soil are protozoans, nematodes, annelids, and some springtails.

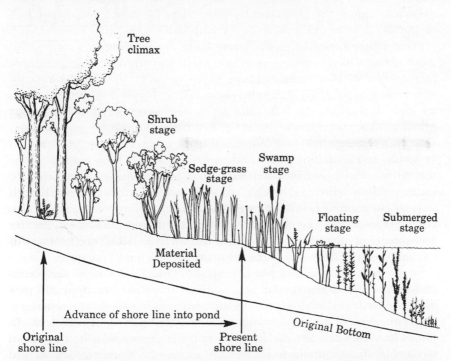

FIGURE 2–5 The stratification of freshwater vegetation from the completely submerged type (far right) to the floating stratum and the emergent hydrophytes located in shallow water. Zonation in keeping with depth of water as well as stratification are represented following the successional pattern through to the completely mesophytic shrub and tree stages (far left). From *Botany* by Carl L. Wilson and Walter E. Loomis (Holt, Rinehart & Winston, Inc., Third Edition, 1962). Used by permission.

Aquatic communities will exhibit vegetative stratification, as shown in Figure 2–5. Emergent hydrophytes located around the periphery of ponds and lakes are partially submerged in water, but a large portion of the plant extends above the water's surface; cattails (*Typha*), bulrushes (*Scirpus*), reeds and sedges are examples of such a stratum. Floating leaf aquatics, which include water lilies (*Nymphaea*) and water hyacinth (*Eichornia*), will often shade out submergent vegetation in shallow water, but their distribution is limited by water depth. A stratum that is located entirely within the aquatic environment and that is also limited in distribution by water depth are the algae, which are often microscopic in size. These organisms are numerous in the upper strata of any mature pond or lake, but decrease in quantity with increasing depth as a result of reduced light penetration and consequently the inability to carry on photosynthesis. Submerged vascular vegetation comprises a stratum relatively close to the shoreline, for this vegetation is rooted, yet unable to carry on sufficient photosynthesis to compensate for metabolic losses at increased depths for the very same reason that algae are absent below certain depths. These submerged vascular plants include water weed (*Elodea*), tape grass (*Valisineria*), pickerel weed (*Pontederia*), mil foil, or parrot's feather (*Myriophyllum*), and water crowfoot (*Ranunculus*).

Some animals, unlike plants, move from one stratum to another, but most of them spend more time in one particular stratum. The positional relationship of the various groups based on their location in a freshwater environment is graphically presented in Figure 2–6. On this basis we may distinguish the following categories: the neuston is the faunal group closely associated with the surface film covering a body of water. Usually such organisms are found in lentic (quiet water) situations such as ponds, lakes, shallow pools, and backwater areas along streams where the surface film is not in a continual state of turbulence. Aquatic birds, water striders, whirligig beetles, spiders, and egg rafts of mosquitoes— all are commonly associated with the upper surface of the film; this faunal aggregation, therefore, may be termed the supraneuston. Another assemblage of organisms, the infraneuston, will come in contact with the submerged surface of the film—which includes mosquito larvae ("wrigglers"), mosquito pupae ("tumblers"), aquatic snails, and some cladocera (*Scupholebris*). An aggregation of plants and animals that float aimlessly at various depths or swim too feebly to maintain a constant position against any appreciable water current is called plankton. This vast quantity of living material is often comprised of many species of algae and bacteria; the latter may be found at any depth, but living algae will be limited to the surface waters above the compensation depth for reasons mentioned previously. This plant material is called phytoplankton to distinguish it from the zooplankton, which contains only faunal representatives. The zooplankton typically contains protozoa, jellyfish, shrimp larvae, rotifers, and certain annelids. These

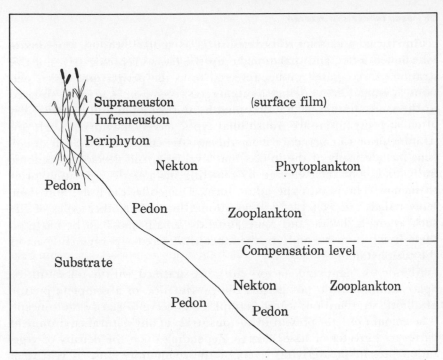

FIGURE 2–6 Diagrammatic representation of the stratification of freshwater fauna in a lentic environment.

organisms may be found at different times and in different stages of their life cycles from the surface film to the bottom, so that the plankton, when considered in its entirety, occupies a very broad stratum, especially in some of the deeper marine areas. **Nannoplankton,** which is so called because of its exceedingly small size (too small to be taken in a fine mesh net), exceeds in total volume the larger planktonic forms in many areas.

Another group of organisms occupying the same stratum is the **nekton.** These organisms are active swimmers; they are not at the mercy of currents, tides, and waves as are the plankton. A variety of organisms from some of the more advanced phyla belong to this category, including arthropods (mature shrimp, some crabs, diving beetles, giant water bugs, back swimmers, water boatmen), mollusks (squid, scallops, sea hares), and the chordates, including a tremendous variety of bony and cartilaginous fish, amphibians, reptiles (crocodiles, alligators, turtles), and mammals (seals, walruses, whales, porpoises, muskrats, beavers). The lowest stratum of aquatic faunal life is designated as the **pedon** and includes all of the bottom-dwelling individuals or organisms that spend a majority of their time moving, feeding, or resting on the bottom or the burrowing types that live within the substrate. Some protozoans, coelenterates, flatworms, annelids, arthropods (crabs, lobsters, crayfish, midge larvae, dragonfly larvae, damselfly, caddisfly, and stonefly naiads), echinoderms, and some chordates such as tongue worms, amphioxus, lobe-finned fishes, and snakes make up the faunal representatives of this stratum. A recognized group, referred to as the **periphyton,** which pertains to animal life clinging to submerged vegetation, is actually situated in the same stratum as that occupied by the plankton and nekton. Very often such organisms are transitional types, merely moving through this stratum prior to emergence from the aquatic environment. Such organisms include many of the insects that live, feed, and develop as pedonic individuals, but then emerge by crawling up aquatic vegetation prior to metamorphosis into the adult form. Dragonfly, caddisfly, and damselfly naiads are examples of transitional biota, but other types of life such as snails, hydra, and some annelids remain and feed or move on these living supports and are therefore considered a permanent part of the periphyton.

Abiotic, or nonliving, factors are also stratified within communities. Space limitations do not permit the presentation of a complete picture of abiotic stratification; a few examples may serve to clarify the concept. The amount of light present in various strata of any natural environment varies to a greater or lesser degree, depending upon the density of vegetation present in overlying layers of the community. Just as is true of the extreme stratification of floral elements in a forested situation, the same extreme degree of photic stratification is found in this same community type. The surface of the crown, or canopy, will receive the greatest intensity of illumination, with a decreasing quantity as we approach the forest floor. The density of different strata, type of vegetation, openings in the forest crown, and so on—all will lead to variations in the number of foot candles of light received. Below a thin layer of compact litter, there is no recordable light penetration at all.

In aquatic communities, marine or freshwater, light stratification is most definitely apparent, even in shallow bodies of water. About 10 per cent or more of the light striking the surface of the water is lost in reflection or absorbed within the first inch or so of the surface. When light is reduced to 1 per cent of its surface value, this depth establishes the lower limit (phytic limit) for photosynthetic plants, for below this level the light energy is not great enough to allow for an appreciable rate of photosynthesis. Of course, one factor should be kept in mind in this regard: most aquatic plants exhibit an optimal photosynthetic rate when exposed to only 6 to 12 per cent of full sunlight. Suspended matter such as silt, plankton, and submergent or emergent vegetation will radically affect the amount of light penetration in aquatic areas. Seasonal and diurnal differences in angle of the sun's rays as well as seasonal changes in planktonic populations and diurnal movements of some planktonic organisms to deeper waters during the midday period also affect the intensity and depth of light penetration. Many organisms are definitely sensitive to light penetration; *Mytilus edulis,* the common mussel, opens its valves only when light intensity is reduced. The chiton (*Chiton tuberculatus*) is negatively **phototaxic** (moving away from a light source) when young, but it becomes positively phototaxic as it reaches maturity. A brown marine alga (*Fucus vesiculosis*) inhabits the north surfaces of rock and coral or becomes attached to solid surfaces where the amount of illumination is relatively low.

There is a differential transmission of different parts of the visible spectrum in water as shown in Figure 2–7. We find that in the clearest lake or ocean water the red, or longer, wavelengths rarely penetrate more than the upper 5 meters of surface water; orange light is reduced to 7 per cent of its surface value at 10 meters; yellow light to 6 per cent at

FIGURE 2–7 Differences in intensity of spectral sunlight penetration at different depths in optically pure water. *R*, red rays; *O*, orange rays; *Y*, yellow rays; *V*, violet rays; *G*, green rays; *B*, blue rays. From "The Utilization of Solar Energy by Aquatic Organisms," G. L. Clarke, AAAS Publ. No. 10 (Problems in Lake Biology), 1939, p. 28. Used by permission of the American Association for the Advancement of Science and the author.

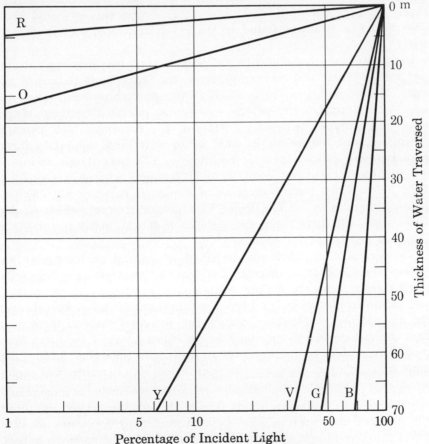

70 meters; green light to 45 per cent; and blue light to 70 per cent of surface value at the same depth. In most temperate ponds and lakes of the Northern and Southern Hemispheres, we find that fine particles suspended in the water tend to scatter the blue parts of the spectrum, with the result that the green wavelengths of light are most penetrating in these areas. Since infrared and red portions of the light spectrum are so readily absorbed in the surface water, the heating effect of illumination is apparent only in surface water, or in the intertidal zone and tide pools of marine areas, or in shallow parts of lakes and ponds. Ultraviolet light is also absorbed in surface waters, which is fortunate for many aquatic forms because this invisible cool light of short wavelength is capable of causing rapid breakdown of organic compounds, vitamins, and so on. The distribution of plants correlates with spectral penetration of light. The green marine alga *Enteromorpha* carries on a high rate of photosynthesis in red light, a lower rate when exposed to blue light, and the lowest rate in green light. *Delessaria sinuosa,* a red marine alga, exhibits equally high rates of photosynthesis in red and green light, but a slightly lower value in blue light. In keeping with these facts and the depth of penetration of various spectral components, we find that *Enteromorpha* is always found in shallow water, *Delessaria* in deeper water.

Deep freshwater communities and oceanic areas may be simply stratified into a photic and an aphotic layer, the latter being devoid of all light. Marine ecologists are inclined to recognize three basic zones: an upper well-illuminated **epipelagic stratum,** an intermediate **mesopelagic** level, and a deeper **bathypelagic stratum.** The epipelagic layer extends down to about 200 meters in clear ocean water and supports a large photosynthetic phytoplanktonic population. The mesopelagic region is a twilight area extending from 200 to 5,000 meters, with often very little light below 1,000 meters, certainly not enough to allow for efficient photosynthetic activity. The lower bathypelagic stratum, which in the open ocean will have the greatest depth (5,000 to 10,000 meters) is a region of permanent darkness.

Temperatures are obviously stratified in natural environments. In terrestrial environments, thermal stratification is most obvious in heavily forested areas, with the highest temperatures located above the canopy and becoming progressively cooler as we approach the forest floor during the diurnal period. However, during the nocturnal interval there may be a thermal reversal as the sun sets; the upper layers of the forest may cool more rapidly, while the lower strata remain somewhat warmer for some time. In open areas, such as open fields, rock outcrops, and sandy areas, the surface stratum may increase to a maximum temperature at about three o'clock in the afternoon as a result of direct heat absorption and subsequent radiation and reflection of heat (particularly on rock and sand surfaces). In fact, the temperature near the surface of a light-

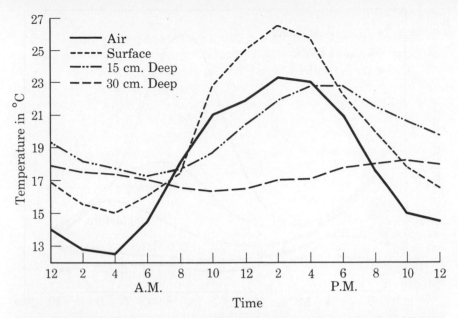

FIGURE 2–8 Temperatures taken at different levels in a sandy soil and air in June in Greenville, North Carolina. Note the decrease in temperature variation in deeper soil strata throughout a twenty-four-hour period. Note the diurnal temperature lag; minimal temperatures occur two and four hours (at 15 cm. and 30 cm., respectively) after they are recorded at the soil surface. Maximal temperatures at 15 cm. depth occur two hours after they are recorded at the soil surface and eight hours later at 30 cm.

colored soil, sand, or rock may be a number of degrees higher than in the overlying blanket of air only a few inches above the surface. This surface heat will penetrate the soil and exhibit diurnal (daily) fluctuations to a depth of about 3 feet, though the thermal values several inches below the soil surface are considerably lower than surface temperatures. Rock surfaces cool rather slowly (though they absorb and transfer heat rapidly), so temperatures in this region will cool more slowly than the overlying atmosphere. Within the soil there is a definite temperature lag (Figure 2–8)—that is, the soil temperature does not drop as rapidly after dark as do surface temperatures. This same thermal lag is apparent during the early part of the day because temperatures do not reach their maximum in deeper soils until sometime after surface maxima have been attained. Thermal stratification can be altered or completely destroyed by wind movement in terrestrial areas above soil level.

Thermal stratification in aquatic communities has received considerable attention because it affects the biotic community to an extreme degree during certain portions of the year. Radiation from the sun is the only major source of heat for natural bodies of water. As was previously mentioned, the infrared portion of the spectrum is absorbed in the upper surface waters; thus it is this area that increases in tem-

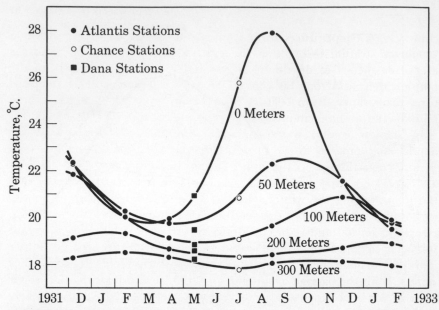

FIGURE 2–9 Temperatures at various depths throughout the year in the North Atlantic accumulated from data by the Atlantis, Chance, and Dana Expeditions. From C. O'D. Iselin, "A Study of the Circulation of the Western North Atlantic," Papers Phys. Oceanogr. Meteorol. Mass. Inst. Technol. and Woods Hole Oceanogr. Instit. 4:1–101, 1936. Used by permission of the author.

perature with increased exposure to sunlight. In the open ocean, there is a mixing of surface water as a result of wind and wave action. These surface waters, averaging some 5 to 10 meters in depth, undergo seasonal thermal changes, depending upon the angle of incidence of the sun's rays and the number of hours of full sunlight. In the North Atlantic, surface water (0 meters) will vary from a February temperature of 20° C. to a maximum of 28° C. in early September, dropping to about 21.5° C. in late November. At 50 meters depth, February and November readings are relatively close to surface water values, but the September readings (annual maxima) are only about 22° C. (Figure 2–9). At 100 meters, the annual minimum is attained in May (19° C.), and an annual maximum of about 20.9° C. occurs in late November. At 200 and 300 meters, the thermal change displays far less amplitude throughout the year, with a February maximum of 19.2° C. and 18.4° C. and an annual minimum in mid-July of 18.3° C. and 17.9° C. for the two depths, respectively. As we compute values and periods of the year for different layers similar to conditions encountered in the soil, it becomes quite obvious that there is a definite thermal lag. Often these upper layers (from 1 meter to 100 meters) are designated as **seasonal thermoclines** in the open ocean, since there is a noticeable temperature change during one season of the year, from early July to late October, through this upper stratum of water. Below 500 meters, there is a permanent thermocline where temperatures drop from about 20° C. to 6° C. within a 700-meter stratum throughout the year. This is a change of 2° C. for every 100 meters of depth. In deeper water, from 1,200 meters to the bottom, there is a zone between 1,200 and 2,000 meters where temperatures drop slowly from 6.0° to 3.5° C.; but from 2,000 meters to the bottom, the water is about 3.0° C. everywhere.

In shallow coastal waters, seasonal temperature changes reach all depths, as compared to the open ocean where seasonal changes in temperature are limited to the upper layers. In coastal areas, tidal action and increased wind and the subsequent wave activity thoroughly mix the water during the winter, yielding a uniform temperature from top to bottom, with minimal temperatures in February. In spring, with increased radiation and reduced salinity of surface waters owing to runoff following spring rains (these waters of reduced salinity will be lighter and will remain near the surface), temperatures increase in surface waters. With the passage of summer and continued insolation, this upper layer of water becomes warmer, reaching a maximum in August or early September. At this time, there is an upper warm stratum of water, a thermocline (zone of rapid temperature change), and a stratum of cooler water below the thermocline. In late September and October, strong winds bringing about an increased stirring of the water, coupled with reduced radiation, gradually destroy the thermal stratification that had been established, so that by late November the coastal waters are of nearly uniform temperature.

Deep ponds and lakes exhibit a thermal stratification and seasonal

FIGURE 2–10 The three recognized thermal strata of deep water lakes and ponds. Depth and thermal values are drawn to scale.

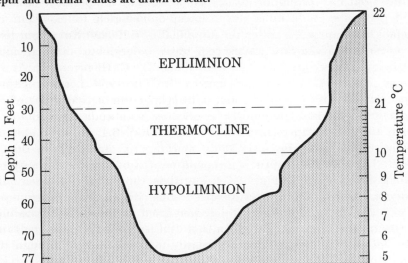

changes that are roughly comparable to conditions transpiring in coastal waters. In midsummer, solar radiation warms a surface layer known as the **epilimnion.** In this particular layer, the continual stirring of the water by surface winds results in a fairly narrow temperature range. The large numbers of phytoplanktonic organisms that reside in this stratum will maintain a relatively high oxygen concentration as a result of their photosynthetic activity during the daylight hours. In a typical pond or lake of this type, the epilimnion may extend down to a depth of 30 feet, with temperatures of perhaps 21° to 22° C. throughout the entire stratum as shown in Figure 2–10. Below this rather uniform layer is a contrasting zone of rapid temperature change (the **thermocline**). In a typical lake of the temperate zone, this may be a 15-foot stratum (30 to 45 feet from the surface). Temperatures may drop from 21° C. to 10° C., a drop of nearly 0.7° per foot of depth! In many bodies of freshwater, nearly 50 to 65 per cent of the temperature change may occur within this narrow zone during the summer. Below the thermocline and extending to the bottom of the pond or lake is the **hypolimnion,** an aphotic region of still water with a slow drop of temperature toward the bottom, a typically low oxygen concentration, and a high carbon dioxide content. This is a stagnant zone of water where temperatures at the bottom may be in the range of about 5° C.

With the arrival of autumnal conditions in temperate areas, water of the epilimnion begins to cool. Since water reaches its maximum density at 4° C., it begins to sink as temperatures in the epilimnion approach this value (Figure 2–11). This sinking of surface water destroys the thermal stratification established during the summer and allows the lighter water, varying in temperature from 5° to 10° C. in the hypolimnion, to reach the surface. This slow cyclic movement of oxygen-rich water from the epilimnion to deeper portions of the pond or lake and the passage of stagnant water (carbon dioxide-rich water) from the depths to the surface is called the **autumnal,** or **fall overturn.** In northern temperate areas, surface waters cool until ice begins to form at about 0° C.; since this cooler water is lighter than the water below, which will range from 0° C. near the surface to 4° C. near the bottom, ice will float on the surface of the pond. Throughout this period many of the organisms hibernate in mud or overwinter in a cold-resistant cyst or spore stage. As temperatures rise during early spring, the ice thaws and water gradually warms, eventually reaching its maximum density at 4° C. The **spring overturn** is a repetition of conditions that transpired in the fall, for the heavier (4° C.) surface waters descend toward the bottom as the cooler, lighter, deeper waters rise, gradually warming to 4° C. and then dropping into deeper layers. This continual mixing helps to distribute the gases throughout all levels of the pond, bringing an end to winter stagnation. As surface waters continue to warm above

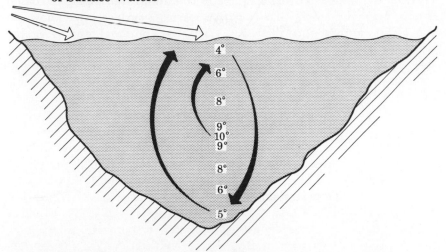

Wind Stirring and Cooling
of Surface Waters

4°
6°
8°
9°
10°
9°
8°
6°
5°

FIGURE 2–11 A transect of a deep water pond showing how it begins to lose its thermal stratification with a cooling of surface waters and wind action in temperate areas. Surface waters with temperatures of 4° C. (maximum density of water) begin to drop toward the bottom, indicating the overturn that destroys the stratification that existed.

the critically dense 4° C. level, they begin to remain in what gradually becomes the epilimnion, with the advance of summer completing the summer stratification and the annual cycle.

TERRESTRIAL ZONATION

In the ecological sense, zonation refers to the horizontal placement or arrangement of abiotical and living components. Thus we find that in nearly every environmental situation there are distinct zones where the ecological conditions will vary from one place to another, as they do in stratification or vertical layering. Deserts and open oceanic areas closely approach an azonal situation, but even here if we observe carefully, we find differences arising in what we might superficially consider a homogeneous region.

A familiar type of vegetational zonation is evident in mountainous areas. Montane zonation consists of a number of vegetational belts located at various altitudes along a mountain slope. The distribution of these vegetational zones is governed by temperature and rainfall. In a montane area, temperature decreases correspondingly at higher altitudes, thus producing communities (animal and vegetational types) located along the slopes similar to the more spacious biome types that occupy extensive areas within certain latitudes from the equator to the poles.

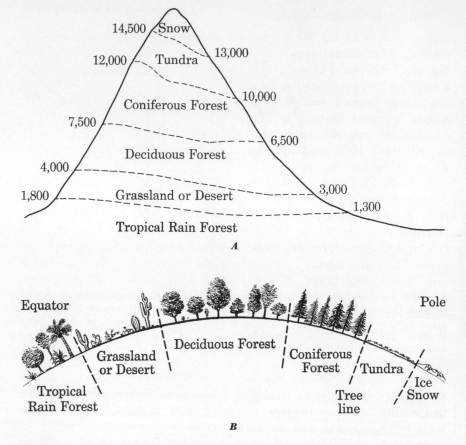

FIGURE 2–12 Vegetational zonation in montane areas (*A*) and the similarity with latitudinal zonation (*B*). Note that vegetational zones vary in altitudinal extent and location, depending on whether it is located on a north- or south-facing slope. Elevations in Diagram *A* are in feet.

Mean air temperature decreases about 1° F. for every degree of latitude north of the equator; mean air temperature will decrease 1° F. for every 300 feet of altitude. With these facts in mind, it is easy to see how Mount Popocatepetl in Mexico, with an altitude of 17,874 feet, possesses the same life zones that may be encountered by traveling from tropical forests of equatorial regions to the barren snow and ice of polar areas. Although the illustrated diagram (Figure 2–12) is a hypothetical mountain in terms of vegetational distribution and altitudinal zones, similar conditions do in actuality exist in nature. It will be noted that comparable zonal limits along the south slope of any mountain are located at a somewhat higher altitude, since the amount of insolation and consequent thermal values are also somewhat higher.

Montane zonation varies with regard to the faunal and floral inhabitants throughout the world in keeping with the climatology and geological history of the area. Zonation of this type practically excludes **ecotones** (transitional areas) of any extent (see the section titled "The Ecotone," Chapter IX) and will virtually isolate the faunal inhabitants located at varying altitudes, for, with the exception of some birds and insects, the fauna is unable to tolerate the ecological conditions prevalent in adjacent zones. The Ruwenzori Range of mountains in equatorial Africa contains a zonation quite different from the zonation in the Northern Hemisphere. At the base of this range and extending up to an altitude of about 5,500 feet is a lush savanna-type community (grasslands with scattered flat-topped *Acacia* trees) and elephants as the dominant biota. A rain forest (150 inches of annual rainfall) extends from the savanna area to 7,500 feet, with giant ferns, wild bananas, and forest buffalo. This suddenly changes at altitudes of 7,500 to 9,500 feet to a bamboo forest zone containing bamboo and the duiker as the major floral and faunal inhabitants. From 9,500 to 12,000 feet, a heath zone, with giant heath 40 feet high, lichens, mosses, and liverworts exposed to almost a continual drizzle, form a thick mass of junglelike vegetation. Leopards are indigenous in this area. A barren alpine zone is located above 12,000 feet. Black lichens, brown mosses, carex tussock, and senecio add a somber touch to this desolate region. A small rock *Hyrax* manages to eke out an existence in this harsh environment.

Latitudinal zonation of vegetation is influenced by thermal zonation and precipitation. Isotherms (lines connecting points of equal [mean] temperature) tend to run east and west. They are modified in coastal areas because warm or cold currents of water flowing along coastal regions will modify the terrestrial temperatures. A **frost line** extends through central Florida, along the Gulf Coast, and across southern California. Plants and animals must be frost hardy—that is, be able to produce seeds, spores, or cysts that are cold resistant or hibernate periodically—to endure conditions above the frost line. A more complete discussion of latitudinal zonation is presented in a future section of the text dealing with biomes and their geographic distribution (see the section titled "Biomes and Biome Types," Chapter XI).

FRESHWATER ZONATION

Lakes and ponds are zoned, as shown in Figure 2–13, primarily on the basis of water depth and type of vegetation that will appear over the course of time in freshwater areas. At times, a zone just above the edge of standing water is designated as the **supralittoral zone.** This zone, although it is not submerged, will be exposed to wave action and splash along the margins of larger ponds and lakes during windy periods (spring and fall) of the annual cycle. As a result of wave action and the subsequent abrasive effect of sand or pebbled shorelines, life is often sparse in this zone. Bulrushes, sedges, insects, and some annelids will

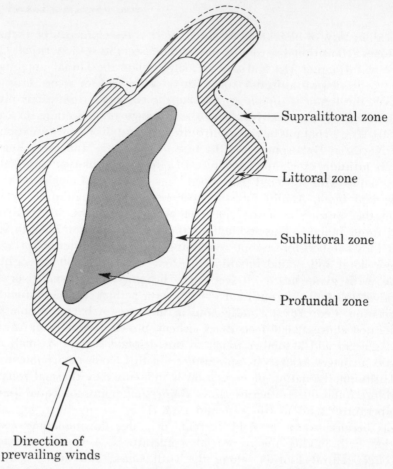

Supralittoral zone

Littoral zone

Sublittoral zone

Profundal zone

Direction of
prevailing winds

FIGURE 2–13 Zonation of a freshwater pond as seen from above. Solid line represents the permanent shoreline; other lines denote limits of each zone. Note that prevailing winds produce a splash zone (supralittoral zone) along the shore opposite the incoming direction of prevailing winds.

tolerate such conditions. From the water's edge to a depth of about 6 meters is the **littoral zone** as shown in Figure 2–14; all of the rooted hydrophytes, whether emergent or submergent, are limited to this zone. In shallow ponds, rooted vegetation may fill the entire body of water, in which case the pond is monozonal—that is, it contains but one zone (littoral zone). The zoological representatives of this zone are directly or indirectly dependent on the vegetation present. Aside from the planktonic organisms, this is the most productive zone in any lake or pond. The vegetation is very beneficial to the fauna that thrive in this area, for it anchors and stabilizes the substrate and serves as an anchorage for many of the aquatic animals (periphyton) as well as a holdfast for egg masses of snails and insects. Even sparsely populated vegetative areas will reduce wave action in the area, which in turn will minimize turbidity. But more important is the production of oxygen and reduction of carbon dioxide by photosynthetic activity of the submerged hydrophytes.

Beyond this zone of rooted vegetation is the **sublittoral zone,** extending from the 6-meter level out to the average upper limit of the hypolimnion. This area will contain the zooplankton and phytoplankton as well as debris from adjacent rooted vegetation that will often litter the bottom. Generally, the lower limit of the sublittoral zone marks the **compensation level**—that is, the level where the photosynthetic rate equals the respirational rate of the flora, limiting the photosynthetic organisms to these zones and the strata above these depths. The sublittoral area is often designated as the **shell zone** because of the large populations of mollusks that inhabit this region (snails, mussels, clams). Freshwater crustaceans such as water fleas (*Daphnia*), crayfish (*Cambarus*), and fairy shrimp (*Eubranchipus*) are quite common in this zone. The deepest water zone of ponds and lakes, the **profundal zone,** is not well developed unless the body of water is thermally stratified. Extending from the average upper limit of the hypolimnion to the deepest portions of the area, it is characterized by a deep muddy substrate. Conditions are radically different from those in the adjacent shallow water zones, for the water temperature and dissolved oxygen are low. The amount of light, particularly in turbid waters, penetrating into the upper reaches of the profundal zone is extremely low and there is often a

FIGURE 2–14 A transect of a deep freshwater pond or lake, indicating the location of various zones.

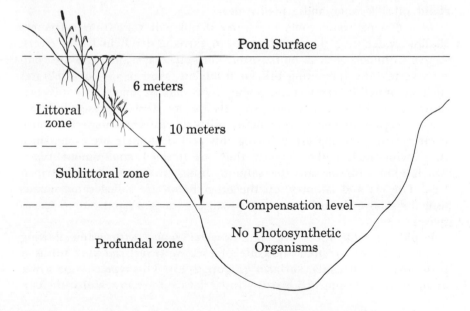

high hydrogen sulfide content in the lower waters. Usually this zone renders an acid reaction with pH values considerably lower than those of adjacent waters. Despite these adverse conditions there are often few species, but large numbers of organisms representing each species. Mollusks and immature insects belonging to the Orders Diptera, Odonata, Ephemeroptera, and Heteroptera are common pedonic forms in this zone, though populations undergo considerable seasonal variation because of the periodic emergence of insects from the water as they metamorphose to adults.

The German limnologist, Thienemann, classified lakes on the basis of their productivity. Productivity, however, is correlated with zonation. Thienemann designated two main types of lakes: **oligotrophic** and **eutrophic** lakes. Oligotrophic lakes are relatively deep, young lakes characterized by low productivity. Very often there is a relatively narrow littoral and sublittoral zone, but an extensive profundal area with many fish and not subject to the severe oxygen depletion that often typifies the deeper portions of such zones. Eutrophic lakes are shallower, older lakes, with a far less extensive profundal zone and a highly productive littoral and sublittoral region. Usually such lakes are very similar to old ponds in that there is a well-established littoral vegetation and dense populations of phytoplankton and zooplankton.

Lotic, or stream-type, communities, such as brooks, creeks, and rivers, lack the well-defined zonation apparent in lentic areas. Very often, the limits of such zones are poorly defined, arbitrary, or of a transitional nature. In other words, the criteria used to designate zones in quiet or standing water communities simply do not apply in streams. The three basic zones in streams may be designated as a flowing water zone; a rapid, or riffle zone; and a pool zone.

In a flowing water zone, the water depth will vary from extremely shallow water near the shoreline to an extreme depth in larger rivers. Active swimmers such as mink, otter, muskrat, snakes, and fish are common vertebrates inhabiting this environment. Most of the invertebrates such as annelids, crustaceans, some insect larvae, snails, and bivalves move along the bottom where currents are not swift or possess holdfast organs to prevent being swept many miles downstream. Some fish move upstream to spawning areas during this period of their life cycle; since they swim against the current they are termed **anadromous** types. Anadromous fish include the salmon, brook trout, shad, and striped bass. The eel and lamprey, on the other hand, are called **catadromous** fish; they move downstream (swim with the current) and out to sea to spawn.

Rapid, or riffle zones are shallow-water zones, with water flowing rapidly over an irregular substrate of rock or gravel, spewing up as it passes over the irregular surfaces (Figure 2–15). This type of zone serves as an ideal environment for many insect larvae for two reasons: the cur-

FIGURE 2–15   A freshwater riffle or rapids zone located along a stream.

rent is relatively rapid and will carry greater quantities of food per unit
period of time through the zone, and the water is well oxygenated because it is mixed with atmospheric gases as it spews up some distance
into the atmosphere. Most of the living organisms normally found in
this zone, where currents are usually rapid, are sedentary forms possessing structures for attachment, or body forms adapted for life in swift
currents. Many animals and plants are found on the lower surfaces of
rocks or on the downstream side of fixed objects where the current is not
as strong and the organisms are not exposed to the full force of current.
Snails, insect larvae, filamentous algae (*Cladophora*), stonewart (*Chara*),

FIGURE 2–16   A pool zone located along a freshwater stream. The pool is located in the background; the rapidly flowing portion of the stream can be seen in the foreground, tumbling over a rocky substrate.

mosses (*Fontinalis, Hypnum*), and diatoms often produce dense populations on rocks in these areas. The riverweed (*Podostemum*) often harbors large numbers of invertebrates on its leaves and stems.

Pool zones as shown in Figure 2–16 are often numerous along older rivers, especially where the downstream gradient is not steep. These zones are frequently referred to as river ponds, pools, bayous, or swamps, provided they are directly connected to moving streams of water. The current in pool·zones is extremely slow or practically nonexistent as compared with the current in riffle zones. Water depth is greater than that found in riffle areas and the substrate is usually a fine sand, silt, or clay suited for burrowing types of animals. Water striders and whirligig beetles are common on the surfaces of these pools, and bivalves, snails, annelids, and dragonfly, horsefly, and mayfly larvae are located on vegetation such as submerged hornwort (*Ceratophyllum*), tape grass, river bulrush, duckweed, lotus, water lilies, and watershield (*Brasenia*) or burrow in the fine-grained substrate of the pool bottom. Mayfly larvae are one of the principal burrowers and make up approximately 20 per cent of the fish food during certain parts of the year. Drifting plankton that is often swept into these pool zones from adjacent ponds and lakes connected to the stream system is referred to as **potamoplankton** in lotic communities. This aggregation, which often enters pool zones in great quantities during periods of heavy rainfall and subsequent flooding, consists of bacteria, blue-green algae, diatoms, green algae, protozoa, and rotifers. These helpless organisms that are completely at the mercy of currents lead a hazardous life once they enter lotic areas, for they may be swept many miles downstream into an entirely different and at times an intolerable biological location.

MARINE ZONATION

The oceanic community can be subdivided into two provinces (which are in actuality two basic zones): a **neritic province** of limited extent (less than 1 per cent of the entire marine biome) and an **oceanic province** of considerable magnitude. The neritic province extends from the high-tide mark to a depth of about 200 meters, which marks the outer limit of the continental shelf in many areas. This province contains illuminated water in most areas, and has received more careful study compared to the oceanic province because of the relative ease of collection and recording of environmental measurements in these waters as contrasted with deeper waters. As is indicated in Figure 2–17, the neritic province (or near-shore waters) is comprised of a number of more restrictive zones, one of which is the **intertidal zone** (Figure 2–18). This zone is delimited by the high- and low-water marks of spring tides; this means that the intertidal zone will have the greatest possible width because spring tides have the greatest amplitude. That is, the high tides are highest and the low tides are lowest because the sun and moon are working together in harmony in regard to overall attraction for the earth's water. Since this zone is more accessible to biologists, it has been investigated more thoroughly by taxonomists and ecologists. Certainly, this is one of the most complex zones in terms of types of living organisms and the diverse nature of the habitat. Some of the unfavorable characteristics of this zone are that tides periodically cover and uncover this area twice every day. As a result, there is considerable variability

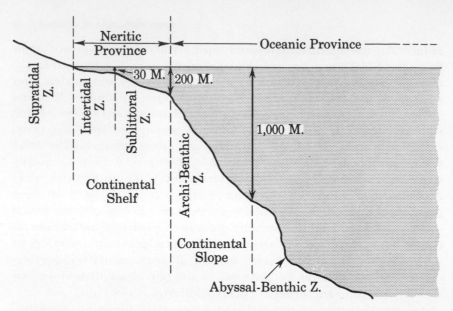

FIGURE 2–17 Zonation of overlying bodies of oceanic water into two marine provinces; the neritic province and the oceanic province. The zonation of the substrate and arbitrary limits of depth (in meters) are represented, but will vary from one geographic locality to another.

in temperature, light, evaporation, and salinity in keeping with the movement of tidal water. Temperatures range from air temperature to water temperature, though the range is reduced in rocky areas because rocks act as heat reservoirs. Evaporation of water from tissues will also

FIGURE 2–18 The intertidal zone of a marine environment at low tide.

reduce the temperature differential during the warmer portions of the year. Intertidal areas lying near the mouths of rivers will experience even greater variations in salinity values as nonsaline water from these streams dilutes the salt content of adjacent regions. In addition to the adverse conditions mentioned, the physical force of tidal water moving over the substrate, combined with wave action, can cause frictional action that many organisms are unable to tolerate. Of course the hold-fast organs of algae, the byssal threads of bivalves, and the cementing secretion of barnacles help to counteract the frictional effect. The exposure of organisms to air and the subsequent desiccation that inevitably occurs introduces a problem of duration. For example, an animal or plant may be able to tolerate a six-hour exposure to air without ill effects, but a seven- or eight-hour duration may prove fatal; hence, the organism's tolerance to exposure will definitely determine the location of the organism within the intertidal zone—that is, whether it will be situated closer to the high-tide or low-tide line.

To counterbalance some of the hardships of living in the intertidal zone, there are certain benefits. The relative shallowness of water (seldom exceeding 30 meters) allows a considerable amount of light to penetrate the water, thus insuring greater productivity by photosynthesis. The constant mixing of this body of water by waves and tidal action creates a circulation of oxygen and nutrients that is impossible of attainment in deeper waters. The type of substrate flooring any intertidal region will

FIGURE 2–19 A tide pool environment showing the rippled sand of the intertidal zone in the foreground. Part of a long tide pool is visible, beyond which are the remaining intertidal beach and rolling surf.

determine the type of life found in the area. Many marine organisms are sessile or burrow and depend on the type of substrate available. A rocky substrate favors the sessile types, whereas sand or mud is utilized by burrowing types of organisms. Along rocky shores, during the low-tide period, inhabitants are subject to varying environmental conditions, particularly evaporation, except where intertidal pools exist or when the organism is protected by a shell, or exoskeleton, or a burrow. Rock pools or intertidal pools (Figure 2–19) exhibit changes of salinity because as evaporation of water takes place the salinity may increase well above the normal salinity of sea water. Animals and plants occupying these areas must be able to tolerate this change in salinity in order to survive. Loose rocks are moved frequently, causing a continual abrasion of the surfaces and eliminating most sessile forms. Larger, stable rocks often have a heavily populated lower surface in the intertidal zone because this portion of the rock is not exposed to insolation and the subsequent salinity changes and so usually remains damp or quite moist.

The biota inhabiting the upper limits of loose rock areas are spring-tails (Collembola) and crustaceans such as *Gammarus* and *Orchestia*. In the lower reaches of a loose rock intertidal region, annelids (*Eulalia, Cirratulus, Nereis*), hermit crabs, starfish (*Asterias*), and sea urchins (*Echinus*) are common. Large stable rocks are inhabited by solid rock borers such as boring spongers, annelids, lamellibranchs, sea urchins, and barnacles—all of which live in burrows bored out of solid rock. Upper limits of stable rocky coasts are populated by barnacles (*Belanus, Chthamalus, Tetraclita*) and lichens (*Verrucaria*), and the lower part of a stable rock intertidal zone will include such organisms as sponges (*Halichondria, Grantia*), tunicates, bryozoans, mussels (*Mytilus*), and scallops (*Pecten*).

Sandy regions are characterized by a uniform topography, with none of the sharp irregularities of rocky shores. Particle size of sand grains tends to be smaller along sheltered parts of the beach and toward the low-water mark. Pore space in mixed sandy substrates (mixed particle size) is roughly 20 per cent of the volume; this allows for good drainage of water, carrying nutrients and oxygen downward as the tide moves out. Of course, capillary water rises above the water table; the finer the texture of the sand, the higher it rises. There are generally small changes in salinity within a sandy substrate because sand acts as a barrier to insolation and the subsequent evaporation of moisture. Sand does not have the stability that rocky substrates have, because the small mineral particles are washed and moved by waves and tides. Sandy areas, in general, are rather sterile with respect to the biota; some lamellibranchs such as *Tellina,* burrowing copepods, and mole crabs are characteristic inhabitants. If silt is mixed with sand to form a muddy sand substrate, then the quantitative and qualitative aspects of the biota increase. Lamellibranchs such as *Macoma haltica, Cardium edule, Mercenaria mercen-*

aria, and *Mya arenaria,* the polychaet lugworm *Arenicola marina* with its peculiar U-shaped burrow, and a number of crustaceans such as shrimps, amphipods, and isopods abound. As the silt increases, the species and density of organisms gradually decrease, but the burrowing habit is more common in this type of substrate (muddy sand) than in shifting sand or soft sandless mud.

A silt substrate (mud flats, Figure 2–20) is located in regions where there is little water movement other than the gentle flood and ebb of tides; silt particles are exceedingly fine and would be swept away by any gross movement of water. Muddy substrates are endowed with a high organic content, but there is very poor circulation of interstitial water as well as a poor exchange between subsurface muds and overlying water with regard to temperature changes, salinity, and oxygen concentration. This latter condition leads to anaerobic conditions within the substrate. A muddy substrate presents a problem for crawling organisms; without specially adapted structures, they become buried in these soft oozes. The very texture of the substrate makes burrowing easier, but the organism must be anaerobic, live near the surface of the mud, or be able to obtain oxygen from the overlying water in order to survive. The bivalve *Mya,* mud snails (*Nassa*), boring whelks (*Murex*), starfish (*Asterias*), and the annelids *Sabella* and *Myxicola* are common inhabitants of mud flats. Mangroves and eel grass (*Zostera*) flourish in these areas because of their well-developed root systems.

FIGURE 2–20   Mud flats at ebb tide along coastal North Carolina.

A **sublittoral zone** extends from the lowest low-tide mark out to a 200-meter depth. The substrate is usually of a rather soft consistency— a mixture of sand, silt, and clay, with small rocks or shells scattered over the surface. Zones of seaweed such as *Laminaria* and *Lithothamnion* are found in shallow waters out to a depth of 120 meters. Brown algae such as *Saccorhiza, Alaria,* and *Himanthalea* are found in great quantities in certain areas. Red algae are common in deeper waters. In the Pacific, many of the sublittoral regions are dominated by the giant kelps such as *Macrocystis* and *Nereocystis.* These giant kelps are of ecological interest: they tend to reduce wave action shoreward, they stabilize the bottom by means of numerous holdfasts, and they provide points of attachment for small epiphytes and epizooids such as barnacles. Finally, they are an important source of oxygen in these areas, for even though they are fastened in dimly lit waters, the upper parts extend into well-lit waters, where photosynthesis may occur at an increased rate.

Animals of different types are quite numerous in the area: Protozoa (Foraminifera), sponges *(Clione)*, worms including sipunculids, nemertines, polychaets *(Chaetopterus)*, coelenterates (sea fans, sea pens), arthropods such as spider crabs *(Maia)*, hermit crabs, rock lobsters *(Palincerus)*, and stone crabs *(Menippe)*. Mollusks of many types, whelks *(Buccinum)*, boat shells *(Scaphander)*, scaphopods *(Dentalium)*, bivalves *(Pecten, Cyprina)*, cephalopods *(Octopus, Eledone)*, echinoderms, including crinoids, brittle stars, and starfish—all abound in this zone of the ocean.

The sublittoral zone extends seaward to a depth of 200 meters, which along most continents is the edge of the continental shelf (see Figure 2–17). Beyond the continental shelf is a continental slope with a much sharper drop-off. Within this continental slope, with depths ranging between 200 and 1,000 meters, is the **archibenthic zone.** Near the bottom of this zone the water temperature is relatively constant, with practically no seasonal change; water pressure throughout this zone will average about 400 pounds per square inch. Only a small amount of blue-violet light reaches the lower layers of this zone, certainly not enough light energy for photosynthesis; thus it is found that the photosynthetic plants (planktonic algae) are limited to the upper strata, and bacterial organisms exist at all depths. Animal life in this zone is sparse, for animals must depend on food material drifting out from the intertidal or sublittoral zones or plant material settling out from the upper, well-illuminated portion of the ocean. Sponges *(Geodia)*, sea cucumbers, starfish, brittle stars, brachipods, and bivalves are the principal types of animal life in this zone.

From approximately 1,000 meters out to the very depths of the ocean is the **abyssobenthic zone,** which seldom exceeds depths of 10,000 meters, except in the deepest trenches of the Pacific Ocean. This is the portion of the ocean beyond the continental shelf, with no seasonal change in temperature (average temperature, 0.5° C. to 3.0° C.), little dissolved oxygen, no light, pressures in excess of one ton per square inch, and seldom any gross movement of water in the lower stratum. The vegetation is similar in distribution, though more sparse, to the flora of the archibenthic zone. Animal life is also sparse, with perhaps one or two organisms per meter at great depths; in shallower water (1,600 to 2,000 meters) there are scattered forests of sponges (*Cladorhiza*). Organisms at great depths are exposed to tremendous pressures and are seldom able to survive the ascent to surface where pressures are much reduced, although some that have been brought up in dredges by oceanographic expeditions did survive. More recently underwater photography has been employed, so that many of the organisms living at these great depths may be photographed in their natural environment.

Two important obstacles in addition to those previously mentioned must be overcome by organisms living at these great depths. The substrate covering the ocean floor at these great depths are primarily soft oozes with no firm substrate. Thus these abyssobenthic forms must be burrowers (annelids), sessile forms possessing long stalks (long-stem hydroid sea pens, long-stem crinoids, alcyonarian corals, bryozoans, and tunicates), or have body extensions or appendages that tend to distribute body weight over a large area and prevent the animal from sinking into the soft ooze. Active organisms of the latter group include broad-footed gastropods (*Neopalina*), sea cucumbers, long-legged pycnogonids, and one of the largest living crustaceans, a crab (*Kaempfferia kaempfferi*), with a leg expanse of over 5 meters.

The other obstacle encountered is the amount of organic material settling from the upper (epipelagic) stratum. Aside from the bacteria that exist at all levels, photosynthetic plants are limited to the upper horizon of the sea, and bottom dwelling forms depend upon this phytoplankton for existence. One common characteristic of deep-sea fish and invertebrates is the large extensible oral opening; food is scarce in these deeper strata and therefore they must be able to swallow any food encountered, large or small. In these deep, permanently dark areas bioluminescent organisms are common; the light emitted by these organisms may be used as a lure for prey or as a source of recognition for individuals of a species. Below the 1,000-meter depth, organisms lose pigmentation, gradually becoming white or pale yellow because under conditions of permanent darkness, pigmentation of the body serves no valid function as protective coloration or as protection against ultraviolet radiation. In the deeper trenches or at depths in excess of 10,000 meters, there are no predators or suspension feeders; the fauna is limited to bottom deposit feeders.

The substrate of the archibenthic and abyssobenthic zones is comprised of terrigenous deposits, oozes, clays, or varying combinations of these three primary types. The approximate percentage of the three most common types of marine sediments are presented in Table 2–1. Terrigenous

TABLE 2–1. *Percentage Amounts of Sediment Types in Oceanic Areas**

TYPE OF SEDIMENT	PERCENTAGE OF EACH SEDIMENT TYPE		
	INDIAN OCEAN	PACIFIC OCEAN	ATLANTIC OCEAN
Calcareous ooze	54.3	36.2	67.5
Siliceous ooze	20.4	14.7	6.7
Red clay	25.3	49.1	25.8

* From H. U. Sverdrup, M. W. Johnson, and R. H. Fleming, *The Oceans: Their Physics, Chemistry and General Biology* (Englewood Cliffs, N. J.: Prentice-Hall, 1942), pp. i–x, 1–1087. Used by permission.

deposits, as the name implies, are materials carried from continental areas into the sea by rivers. The basic component is silica, and though much of it is deposited near the mouths of rivers in intertidal or sub-littoral zones, the finer particles are often carried out to sea. Coloration of terrigenous deposits varies, depending on the principal components: volcanic dust and iron oxides are reddish, manganese oxides are blue, and silicates of iron or potassium are green. Oozes are organic remains of living organisms located primarily in the epipelagic and mesopelagic strata that gradually settle and blanket the ocean floor throughout a large portion of the two deeper zones of the ocean. There are several types of recognized oozes classified according to the principal substances present. Radiolarian oozes are comprised of the siliceous shells of radiolarian protozoans located in deeper waters, from about 1,500 meters to the deepest parts, of the Indian and tropical Pacific oceans. Diatomaceous oozes, common in the northern Pacific and Antarctic seas, are made up of the dead remains (siliceous diatom shells) of this populous algae. In the archibenthic waters of the tropical Atlantic and its appendage (Caribbean Sea) are pteropod oozes that are primarily calcareous, derived from pelagic mollusks (pteropods and heteropods). The most extensive oozes, covering well over a third of the abyssobenthic zone from 2,000 to 5,000 meters, are the calcareous globigerina oozes. These oozes are basically calcareous (60–70 per cent) and are derived for the most part from shells of the tiny protozoan *Globigerina bulloides,* which attains fantastic proportions in the planktonic masses that populate the open ocean.

Red clay deposits cover roughly one third of the ocean floor. This type of substrate is inorganic in origin, containing silicates of iron, manganese, and aluminum. Sources of such material are primarily volcanic and meteoric dust, usually the former. Vast expanses of the Pacific Ocean are covered with this substrate, which because of its inorganic material, is usually barren.

Selected References

Blackman, F. F. 1905. Optima and limiting factors. Ann. Bot., 19:281–295.

Brady, F. 1943. The distribution of the fauna of some intertidal sands and muds on the Northumberland Coast. Jour. An. Ecol., 12:27–41.

Broekema, M. M. 1941. Seasonal movement and the osmotic behaviour of the shrimp *Crangon crangon* L. Arch. Neerl. Zool., 6:1–100.

Browne, C. A. 1942. Liebig and the law of the minimum, Liebig and after Liebig. Publ. AAAS, 16:71–82.

Daubenmire, R. F. 1946. The life zone problem in the northern intermountain region. Northwest Sci., 20:28–38.

Oosting, H. J. 1942. An ecological analysis of the plant communities of Piedmont, North Carolina. Amer. Midl. Nat., 28:1–126.

Shelford, V. E. *Animal Communities in Temperate America* (Chicago: Univ. of Chicago Press, 1913), pp. i–xiii, 1–368.

Southward, A. J. 1958. The zonation of plants and animals on rocky sea shores. Biol. Rev., 33:137–177.

Taylor, W. P. 1934. Significance of extreme or intermittent conditions in distribution of species and management of natural resources, with a restatement of Liebig's law of the minimum. Ecology, 15:374–379.

Thorson, G. 1955. Modern aspects of marine level-bottom animal communities. Jour. Mar. Res., 14:387–397.

Turesson, G. 1922. The species and the variety as ecological units. Hereditas, 3:100–113.

Turrill, W. B. 1946. The ecotype concept. A consideration with appreciation and criticism, especially of modern trends. New Phytol., 45:34–43.

Van der Vecht, J. 1953. On some aspects of the numerical variation of insects in the tropics. Internat. Congr. Ent. Trans. IXth, 2:272–276.

Welch, P. S. *Limnology* (New York: McGraw-Hill, 1952), pp. i–xi, 1–538.

III. Abiotic Factors — The Terrestrial Environment

The term *abiotic* means simply without life. In this chapter and the one following, only some of the more pertinent nonliving elements of terrestrial and aquatic environments will be discussed; an exhaustive treatment of the nonliving portion of an ecosystem would be a major undertaking and beyond the scope of this text. Although climatic factors would fall under the realm of nonliving portions of the environment, they are not considered in any detail at this time, since the basic principles of climatology are discussed more fully in another portion of the text (Chapter V).

SOIL

A substrate is the surface upon which an organism will move or settle. Or it may be a solid material within which an organism will live. This surface may serve as a means of transport, food, shelter, support, resting place, or a combination of several of these functions. An edaphic substrate (soil) is the most common type of surface encountered on land, though many organisms may spend but a brief period or no time at all in contact with this universal material so indicative of the terrestrial environment. Living structures such as grasses, trees, and animals may serve as a perfectly suitable substrate for a variable period of time; this

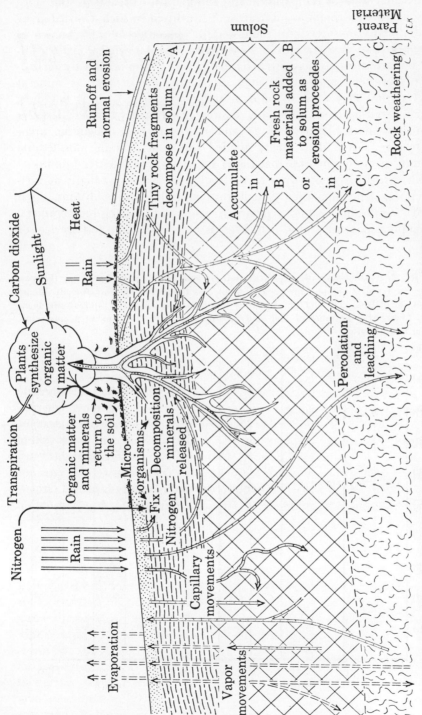

FIGURE 3–1 Hypothetical soil profile showing some of the more common processes tending to alter the chemical and physical nature of soils. From *The Soils That Support Us* by C. E. Kellogg (The Macmillan Company, 1941).

is particularly so for ectoparasitic and endoparasitic organisms. But since the soil is such a common substrate and is utilized by such a varied array of life, let us consider it in some detail. The study of soils, known as **pedology**, is an important branch of science. The knowledge made available by soil scientists may often receive practical application by agriculturists, foresters, and nurserymen. Soils may be defined as mineral material that may exist in solid or unbroken form, such as boulders, gravels, large outcrops, solid sills of stone, or as finely divided particles of mineral matter referred to as sands, silts, or clays, depending upon the texture. Often these finely divided soils will contain considerable amounts of organic matter that forms a very rich, productive humus.

Soils, which originate from rock, develop or evolve gradually at variable rates, depending on the ecological and climatic conditions, often called "weathering," where repeated freezing and thawing temperatures, in combination with water (which seeps into fine cracks and crevices of

FIGURE 3–2 Diagrammatic representation of soil classification based on the percentage of textural components present. Sand, less than 15% clay and/or silt; loamy sand, 15% to 20% clay and/or silt; sandy loam, 21% to 50% clay and/or silt; loam or silt loam, 51% or more of clay and/or silt; clay–loam, 20% to 30% clay; clay, 31% or more clay.

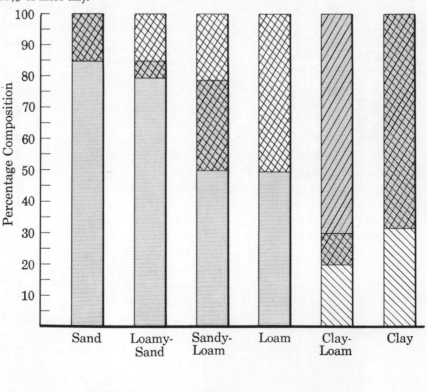

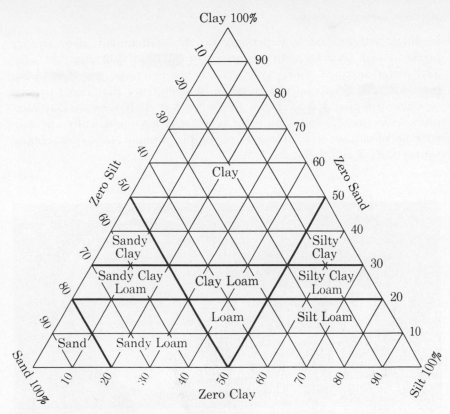

FIGURE 3–3 A soil texture triangle used for determining the principal textural classes of soils. From *Forest Soils* by Harold J. Lutz and Robert F. Chandler, Jr. by permission of John Wiley & Sons, Inc., 1946.

the rock), brings about the physical breakdown of rock into finer particles. Chemical substances, particularly organic acids, added to the soil by the flora and fauna in the immediate area, alter the parent rock and help to subdivide and dissolve the mineral components (Figure 3–1). Soils are constantly altered over periods of time by the addition and incorporation of organic detritus from plants and animals, the chemical decomposition of minerals, and finally the leaching of certain mineral and chemical substances from surface layers to deeper zones by the percolation of soil water (gravitational water) through the soil profile. Soils will change as climatic conditions and the associated plant and animal communities change, because different chemical and physical forces will definitely alter the mineral and organic substances.

The texture of a soil is determined by particle size and the proportional amounts of these different-sized particles within any one soil sample. Particle size is determined by the diameter of individual soil fragments. According to the international system of soil classification, soil particles with a diameter larger than 2.0 mm. are gravel soils; those with diameters ranging from 0.02 mm. to 2.0 mm. are sands (coarse, medium, and fine sands, depending on the predominant size category present); soil particles with diameters of 0.002 to 0.02 mm. are silts. The finest textured soils, with particle diameters of less than 0.002 mm., are clays. Soils with a number of size classes that make up the substrate are classified as shown in Figure 3–2. Soils with silt-clay mixtures, as is true of sandy and loam types, may have practically any proportion of silt or clay, from a negligible amount to overwhelming proportions of either (Figure 3–3).

FIGURE 3–4 A nest of soil sieves used to separate the soil particles on the basis of size in ecology and soil science laboratories.

Soil scientists and ecologists employ a number of methods to determine soil texture. The simplest method consists of oven-drying a soil sample at 105° C. to 110° C. for twenty-four to forty-eight hours, then weighing the oven-dry sample. The soil sample is then introduced into a nest of soil sieves, as shown in Figure 3–4. Each sieve will have a different mesh diameter, with the largest mesh size situated at the top. The sieves are then agitated by hand or by a mechanical shaker that separates the different soil particle sizes. By weighing each sieve separately, the percentage weight of each soil size class can be ascertained and the type of soil present in a particular area is then known. For example, suppose we weigh a sample of soil after oven-drying and find its total weight is 500 grams. The 500-gram sample is introduced into a nest of sieves and after agitation and weighing, we find no soil above the 2.0 mm. mesh sieve; thus we have no gravel in our sample. However, 140 grams is present in the sieve with a 0.02 mm. mesh (sand); 90 grams is present in the sieve with a 0.002 mm. mesh (silt); and the remaining 270 grams (clay) is located in the collecting pan below this smallest sieve. We find that the percentage of sand is $\left(\dfrac{140 \text{ gms.}}{500 \text{ gms.}} \times 100 = 28.0\% \right)$ 28 per cent, the percentage of silt is $\left(\dfrac{90 \text{ gms.}}{500 \text{ gms.}} \times 100 = 18.0\% \right)$ 18 per cent, and the

percentage of clay is $\left(\dfrac{270 \text{ gms.}}{500 \text{ gms.}} \times 100 = 54.0\% \right)$ 54 per cent. Thus,

according to our scheme of classification represented in Figure 3–2, we

FIGURE 3–5 Differences in surface area owing to differences in particle size; the smaller particles present a much greater surface area per unit weight than do larger particles of the same weight. Notice the extremely small amount of surface area presented by soil particles of larger size (sand), even though sand exceeds by weight the other two size classes (silt and clay). From *The Soils That Support Us* by C. E. Kellogg (The Macmillan Company, 1941).

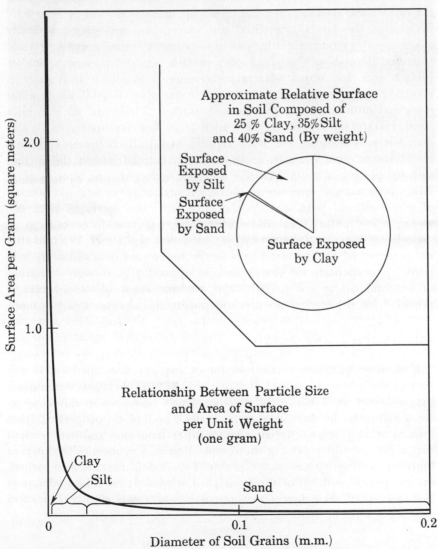

have a clay soil, since over 30 per cent of the total volume by dry weight is clay. More exacting methods of texture analysis may be achieved by the hydrometer method recommended by Bouyoucos (1936, 1937a, 1937b), which is used in many soil laboratories. The pipette method (Wright, 1939) is not so rapid, but is used widely in this country and abroad.

Soil texture is of considerable ecological interest, for the dominant particle size present in any area will have a considerable effect on the flora and fauna of an area. We find that coarser textured soils allow the roots of plants to penetrate the substrate more readily and will facilitate the passage of burrowing animals through the soil. As a rule, loam soils (soils of intermediate texture) are more favorable for forest growth than either coarse sands or fine clays. Some of the advantages of the coarser textured soils are that rainfall penetrates the soil more rapidly because of the larger interstitial soil spaces, and soil gases, primarily oxygen and carbon dioxide, can diffuse more rapidly owing to the increased porosity of the soil. Larger particle size also presents a smaller surface area for water adsorption (Figure 3–5). Since less water is adsorbed by the surface of soil particles, more water is available to plant roots and animals inhabiting the soil stratum. There are, on the other hand, certain advantages to be gained from fine textured soils. Water does not pass through fine textured soils as rapidly because of gravitational forces; consequently, more water is retained within the surface soils for plant and animal use for a longer period of time after rainfall. The evaporation of moisture from the soil surface is not as rapid because of decreased soil pore size. At the same time the decreased pore size within a fine textured soil allows water to rise greater distances from an underlying water table as a result of increased capillarity. We find that the presence of fine textured soils in the lower part of a soil body may partially compensate for coarser soils in upper layers, though a mixture of fine and coarse soil particles can combine many of the advantages provided by either type texture and nullify the obvious disadvantages.

SOIL PROFILE AND DEPTH

If we were to take a vertical section of any well-developed soil in any part of the world, we would find that this soil profile consists of a number of layers, or horizons, of variable depth. Soil profiles differ, sometimes radically, in their chemical, physical, and biotic properties, from area to area. Just as different profiles differ from one another, we find that there are differences in the composition and properties of different horizons making up any single profile. Figure 3–6 presents a hypothetical soil profile with all of the principal horizons. It must be understood that not all of these layers are present in any single profile, but every profile has some of them.

Horizon	Description
A_{00}	Loose leaves and organic debris, larely undecomposed.
A_0	Organic debris partially decomposed or matted; frequently divided into subhorizons.
A_1	A dark colored horizon, containing a relatively high content of organic matter, but mixed with mineral matter. A thick horizon in Chernozem and very thin in Podzol.
A_2	A light colored horizon, representing the region of maximum leaching (or reduction) where podzolized or solodized. The "bleicherde" of the Podzol. Absent in Chernozem, Brown soils, Sierozem and some others.
A_3	Transitional to B, but more like A than B. Sometimes absent.
B_1	Transitional to B but more like B than A. Sometimes absent.
B_2	A usually deeper colored horizon, representing the region of maximum illuviation where podzolized or solodized. The "orstein" of the Podzol and the "clay-pan" of the solodized-Solonetz. In Chernozem, Brown soils, and Sierozem this region has definite structural character, frequently prismatic, but does not have much if any illuviated materials and represents a transition between A and C. Frequently absent in the intrazonal soils of the humid regions.
B_3	Transitional to C.
G, C_c, C, C_s	Horizon G represents the glei horizon of the intrazonal soils of the humid region, usually between A and C. (Horizons lettered C_c and C_s represent possible layers of accumulated calcium carbonate or calcium sulphate found in Chernozem and other soils. Commonly, but not always, C_c is between B and C.)
D	Underlying stratum.

Left-side groupings:

Organic debris lodged on the soil, usually absent on soils developed from grasses.

The SOLUM
(This portion includes the true soil, developed by soil-building processes.)

Zone of eluviation (of removal of materials dissolved or suspended in water).

Zone of illuviation (of accumulation of suspended material from A, as in podzolic soils). (Exclusive of carbonates or sulphates; in Chernozem, Brown soils and Sierozem this horizon is considered as essentially transitional between A and C.)

The weathered parent material. Occasionally absent i.e., soil building may follow weathering such that no weathered material that is not included in the solum is found between B and D.

Any stratum underneath the soil, such as hard rock or layers of clay or sand that are not parent material but which may have significance to the overlying soil.

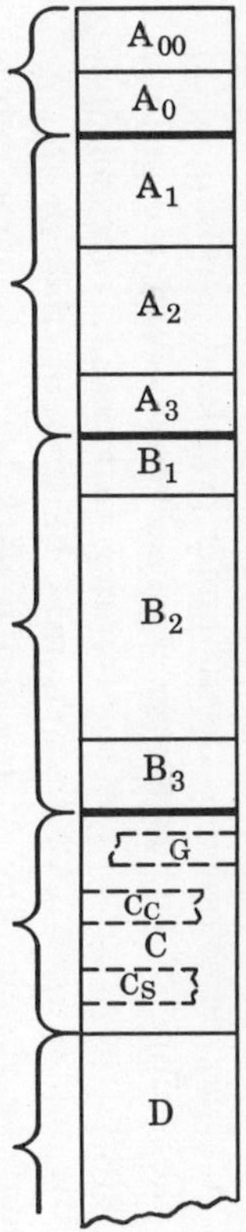

NOTES:
1. Important subdivisions of the main horizons are conveniently indicated by extra numerals, thus: A_{21} and A_{22} represent subhorizons within A_2; G_1 and G_2 subhorizons within G, etc.
2. Boundaries between horizons may be sharp or indistinct, smooth or irregular.
3. In some soils genetic horizons cannot be determined without laboratory study.

FIGURE 3–6 A hypothetical forest soil profile showing the principal horizons and the general physio-chemical conditions characteristic of each stratum. From *The Soils That Support Us* by C. E. Kellogg (The Macmillan Company, 1941).

57

The main divisions of a soil profile consist of a lettered series: the **A horizon** (the topmost layer), the **B horizon** (the layer beneath the A horizon), the **C horizon** (the layer beneath the B horizon), and the **D horizon** (the lowest layer). Each horizon in turn may be subdivided into several sublayers. In the A horizon, an upper A_{oo} **region** is well developed in forest communities, especially in the few months following leaf fall in deciduous stands. It consists of fresh leaf material and other organic detritus that has not undergone any chemical or mechanical breakdown, and is often referred to as the litter, or forest litter layer. Below this is an A_o **level** containing organic matter in a variable state of decomposition. The upper portion contains detritus in the initial stages of decomposition, but the source material is readily recognizable— that is, leaves of oak, beech, and so on. This is commonly referred to as the **F layer,** or **fermentation level.** The lower portion of the A_o horizon is called the **H, or humus** level) ; here annelids, insects, fungi, and other soil organisms have chemically and mechanically acted upon the material to such an extent that the source from which the material was derived is no longer identifiable. Upper layers of the soil horizon just described (A_{oo} and A_o) may be completely absent under grassland stands.

Below these upper layers is the mineral soil, or **solum,** the genetic soil developed from the various soil-forming processes. Three subdivisions of the top soil, A_1, A_2, and A_3 may be present, though the A_3 horizon may be absent. The A_1 horizon is dark because organic debris is mixed with the mineral material from the overlying humus. An A_2 layer is light in color, for this is a zone of maximum leaching, meaning that **eluviation,** or loss of certain chemical compounds and organic material, is occurring here as they are carried down into deeper layers by the passage of soil water to lower depths by gravitational force. A layer that is often absent, the A_3 horizon, is intermediate between stratum A and stratum B, but is more like stratum A than B. Stratum B can be subdivided into three layers—B_1, B_2, and B_3—similar to the subdivision of the overlying mass of soil. B_1, if present, is transitional between the leached A type layers and the B horizon, though it is darker in color, indicating the presence of leached chemicals. B_2 is the layer containing the maximum amount of leached material; this then is the zone of maximum **illuviation,** the collection of materials that have been transported downward by gravitational water. A B_3 layer will contain some leached materials, but not nearly the quantity found in the B_2 layer. This lower level may contain rather large chunks of parent rock material that are in a gradual process of weathering and chemical breakdown. In general, we may say that the B horizon is characterized by deeper colors because of illuviation and coarser textured mineral matter.

A C horizon may be present in the normal soil profile, though it is occasionally absent because soil building may follow the weathering process so rapidly that there is no stratum located between the B horizon and parent rock material (horizon D). The C horizon is often thick, if present, consisting of large masses of weathered mineral material. The upper portion of the C stratum in some areas may become **gleyed,** meaning that an accumulation of water (water logging) and lack of oxygen have caused a uniform gray soggy layer. Below the gleyed levels there may be thin layers of calcium carbonate (hard pan) or calcium sulfate; this is particularly characteristic of grassland soils. The lowest horizon of a soil profile is the D horizon, comprised of unweathered rock or possibly a clay or sand (the latter two are not parent materials but they may often be of significance to overlying layers).

The depth of various horizons within the soil profile shown in Figure 3–6 cannot and should not be represented because of the extreme variability even in the same locality. The depth of each horizon depends upon a vast complex of physical, biological, and chemical conditions within the region. The depth of the solum, or unconsolidated soil material, is most important in governing the vegetation and consequently the animals that will exist in any area. Where parent rock material is slightly weathered (bare rock ledges, rock outcrops, rocky cliffs, Figure 3–7), only

FIGURE 3–7 Slightly weathered rocky outcrop with pioneer vegetational communities including lichens and mosses. Mosses have become established along the left margin of the rock where weathering of rock has allowed its establishment.

hardy plants (pioneer species, such as mosses and lichens) can endure the harsh climatic conditions that prevail, but deeper soil will support a varied and often flourishing plant and animal assemblage. Soil depths, based on the depth of A and B horizons, are arbitrarily classified by soil scientists, as shown in Table 3–1. It might be well to mention at this point that one should differentiate between the physical depth of soils and their physiological depth. Soils may be relatively deep in the physical sense (depth of A and B horizons) but physiologically shallow because of hard pan layers or high water tables that prevent full use of all of the soil available by the root system of plants or by other soil organisms.

TABLE 3–1. *Classification of Soils on the Basis of Stratal Depth**

CLASSIFICATION	DEPTH	
Very shallow	Less than 0.15 meter	(Less than 6.0 inches)
Shallow	0.15 to 0.30 meter	(6 to 12 inches)
Moderately deep	0.30 to 0.60 meter	(12 to 24 inches)
Deep	0.60 to 1.20 meter	(24 to 48 inches)
Very deep	More than 1.20 meters	(More than 48 inches)

* From H. J. Lutz, and R. F. Chandler, Jr., *Forest Soils* (New York: John Wiley & Sons, Inc., 1946), pp. i–xi, 1–514. Used by permission.

Humus, which is formed and located in greatest quantity in the lower portion of the A_0 section of the soil profile, is one of the most important constituents of the soil, particularly from the standpoint of plant growth and nutritional relationships that exist with regard to certain soil-dwelling animals. As we have mentioned, humus is organic in origin, derived from plant and animal remains that combine with mineral parts of the soil in the A_1 horizon to form the complex colloidal structures within the soil. The importance of humus layers lies in the fact that it provides food for soil organisms as well as chemical elements such as carbon, nitrogen, phosphorus, calcium, iron, and manganese that are essential for proper plant growth. Humus soils also tend to impede the leaching of nutrient substances from upper soil layers. The amount of humus in any particular soil will vary with the vegetation and climate. In general, prairie soils contain the greatest quantities of humus, forest soils somewhat lesser amounts, and desert soils have the smallest amount. Classification of humus layers follows no consistent pattern, for in the literature we find many examples of loose and inconsistent nomenclature. Two primary types of humus, however, are universally recognized. One is called **mull.** In this type, the humus material is mixed with mineral soil to such an extent that there is no definite, separate humus layer distinct from the A_1 horizon. Mull is characteristic of warmer temperate zones and generally supports hardwood forests. The other type, **mor, is** humus that is not incorporated into mineral soil, but remains matted above with an A_1 stratum, often becoming blackened by the leaching of organic detritus from the distinct organic layer (H layer of A_o stratum). Mor is characteristic of colder parts of the temperate zone, especially at the higher elevations on mountain ranges or in southern areas where either excessive moisture or dryness fosters the conditions requisite for this type of humus development.

SOIL CLASSIFICATION

Soils are classified according to the soil series and soil class to which they belong. A **soil series** is based on the type of soil profile and named for the locality in which the profile was first identified. All soils of the same series have developed from the same parent rock material. **Soil class** is based on the size of soil particles in the surface layer, such as gravel, sand, silt, or clay. A particular class of soil in a given series is called a **soil type.** Needless to say, the different types of soil series and soil classes throughout the world are so vast in number that it would require a map of considerable size to denote their distribution. In a text of this scope, it is obviously impossible to cover the overall distribution of soil types. For convenient discussion, therefore, we shall consolidate soil classes and soil series into more all-inclusive units known as **soil groups.** The distribution of these major soil groups throughout the world is shown in Figure 3–8.

Tundra soils occur in northern Alaska and Canada, skirting the southern shores of Hudson Bay and the northern edge of Newfoundland. This same soil group skirts the southern edge of Greenland, the southwestern tip of South America, and extends across northern Russia and Siberia. The overlying vegetation consists of soil lichens, mosses, a variety of herbs, and dwarf shrubs. These soils have poor drainage, low temperatures (permafrost permeates the subsurface layers), and a peaty surface layer. Mineral soil below the peat layer is gray, mottled with brown, gradually grading into deeper soils of a slate-blue or green-blue coloration. **Podzol** soils develop in relatively cool, humid climates, where percolation of water is sufficient to cause the leaching of chemicals from surface layers (A horizon). These soils are quite acid as a result of acid organic detritus in upper layers. This organic debris may accumulate to a depth of twelve inches or more on the surface, producing an extremely thick A_{oo} and A_o stratum. Mineral soil in the A horizon is characteristically gray (and acid); the B horizon is brown or dark brown in color. Iron and aluminum compounds are leached in large quantities from the A horizon and accumulate in the B horizon. Podzol soils extend from

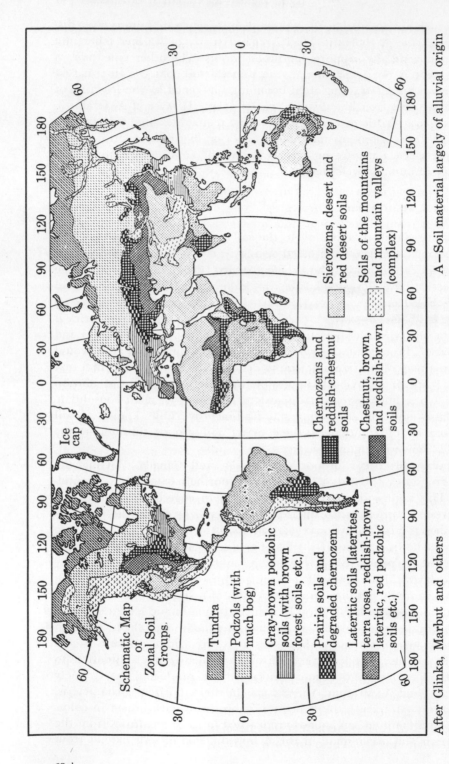

Schematic Map of Zonal Soil Groups.

Tundra

Podzols (with much bog)

Gray-brown podzolic soils (with brown forest soils, etc.)

Prairie soils and degraded chernozem

Lateritic soils (laterites, terra rosa, reddish-brown lateritic, red podzolic soils etc.)

Chernozems and reddish-chestnut soils

Chestnut, brown, and reddish-brown soils

Sierozems, desert and red desert soils

Soils of the mountains and mountain valleys (complex)

Ice cap

After Glinka, Marbut and others

A—Soil material largely of alluvial origin

FIGURE 3–8 The distribution of zonal soil groups throughout the world from *The Soils That Support Us* by C. E. Kellogg (The Macmillan Company, 1941).

central Alaska and Canada across the northern Lake States and northern New England. In the Eastern Hemisphere, this same soil group is found in the western part of the British Isles, most of Sweden, Finland, central Russia, Siberia, northern China, and Japan. **Brown** and **gray-brown podzolic** soils and **brown forest** soils appear in regions south of the podzol soils. These soil groups are found in the northeastern part of the United States, the eastern half of the British Isles, northern and central Europe, southern Japan, eastern China, and much of New Zealand. There is less intense leaching of aluminum and iron compounds from the A horizon because of more temperate climatic conditions. The A horizon varies from a dark gray to grayish-brown in color; the B horizon also varies, from yellowish-brown to a very deep dark-brown. Although illuviation occurs here, no organic matter reaches these lower zones of the soil.

Lateritic type soils are groups that have very thin organic and organic-mineral strata overlying leached reddish soils. The parent rock material is often rich in iron oxides or hydrates of aluminum and has only sparse amounts of silica. True lateritic soils are not found in the continental United States; they develop in humid tropical environments. In a broad transitional area between the gray-brown podzolic soils of humid temperate areas and the true laterite soils of the humid tropics are red and yellow podzolic soils. **Red podzolic** soil, characteristic of the drier areas of the southeastern United States and West Indies, have a thin layer of unincorporated organic matter above a gray or brownish-gray A_1 stratum. A yellowish or pinkish-gray more or less sandy A_2 layer lies above a red or brownish-red clay soil of the B horizon, which may be 3 feet or more in thickness. **Yellow podzolic soils** develop under more humid conditions (Coastal Plain of the southeastern United States) than do red podzols. The A_1 layer is often dark in color owing to the inclusion of organic debris, but this grades into a pale yellow A_2 stratum. The B horizon is yellow or a light reddish-yellow in color. Lateritic soils (including the red and yellow podzolic types) are widespread, as is shown in **Figure 3–8.** They occupy the southeastern United States, the West Indies, the eastern coast of Central America and much of northern South America. In the Eastern Hemisphere, these soil groups girdle central Africa, southern and eastern India, southeastern Asia, the East Indies, and the northeastern and southwestern corners of Australia.

Prairie soils develop in cool, moderately humid climates, with rather weak podzolization. They support tall grass vegetation and are extensive in the Midwest, the east coast of South America, and small isolated thin strips in eastern Europe, Russia, Africa, and Asia. Although a small amount of leaching occurs in prairie soils, the grasses return sufficient calcium to surface layers. The surface strata are usually dark brown or gray brown in color. **Chernozem soils** develop in temperate to cool sub-humid environments. These soils are characterized by a distinct calcium carbonate (hard pan) stratum in the C horizon. The A horizon is nearly black, high in organic content and slightly acid, overlying a lighter colored B horizon. Tall and mixed grasses flourish on this soil group. A narrow zone of chernozem soil extends west of the prairie soils from central Canada to the Gulf Coast in the United States. In South America there is a fingerlike intrusion of this soil type west of the pocket of prairie soils. Scattered areas are also situated in central and southern Africa, eastern Europe, central and southern Russia, central India, and eastern Australia.

Chestnut and **brown soils** occupy extensive areas west of the chernozem type in the United States and South America. A belt of this soil group extends across central Africa (below the Sahara Desert), through southern Russia, and central Asia. Less extensive areas are found in central India and southwestern and eastern Australia. These two soil groups are situated in temperate or cool areas with arid or semiarid conditions. These soils characterized by brown or dark-brown surface soils overlying lighter colored B horizons are like the chernozem soils in that there is a zone of hard pan (calcium carbonate accumulation) in the C horizon.

The last group of stratified soils we shall discuss are the **sierozem** (gray desert soils) and **desert soils.** Sierozem soils develop in semidesert areas with temperate to cool temperatures and dry conditions. Surface soils are brownish gray, grading into lighter-colored subsoils, with a calcium carbonate stratum layer only a foot or so from the soil surface. Desert soils develop in temperate to cool areas under very dry conditions; surface soil is light gray or brownish gray, with a calcium carbonate layer very close to the surface (often less than twelve inches from the surface). Sierozem soils support desert shrubs and grasses, but desert soils have only scanty vegetation. Desert or semidesert areas throughout the world have these soil groups. The southwestern portion of the United States, northern Mexico, southeastern South America, central Australia, northern Africa, and huge areas of southwestern and central Asia have sierozem and desert soils.

Azonal soils—that is, soils having no well-defined strata or profile, exist along coastal areas (sand dune regions) and in mountainous areas. Montane areas of western Canada, the United States, southern Mexico, western South America, Norway, southern Europe, and the mountainous regions of southern Asia—all support azonal soils.

SOIL CLIMATE

Within the soil—in this permanently dark environment—temperature, humidity, and gases differ, often radically, from those in the atmosphere above the soil. In discussing the soil atmosphere—that is, the gaseous element of this area—it is necessary to understand that there are spaces or cavities within the soil that will vary considerably in size in keeping with soil texture, types of vegetation, biota present, and the frequency of cultivation (Figure 3–9). The **air capacity** of soils may be defined as the amount of air present in a particular volume of soil. Air capacity is related to soil texture; coarser textured soils will have a greater air capacity because of their larger pore space. It follows, then, that soils with a higher air capacity are more suitable for vegetation and soil organisms because there will be a more rapid exchange of gases between the soil and atmosphere above and a more rapid percolation of water, which prevent air depletion and water logging. We find that the soil

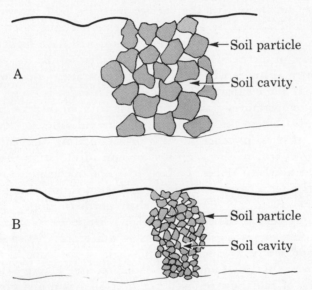

FIGURE 3–9 Magnified section of a coarse textured soil (*A*), such as sand and a fine textured soil (*B*), showing differences in the size of soil cavities or pores caused by differences in particle size. Average soils have 40 to 60 per cent of their volume taken up by pores.

atmosphere differs from atmospheric air in that there is, in general, less oxygen in proportion to the amount of carbon dioxide and a greater amount of water vapor in the soil. This is logical, since oxygen is continually used by plant root tissues and the vast array of minute soil organisms, while carbon dioxide is liberated as a waste product by living cells of these organisms. Soil aeration, or the degree to which a soil is supplied with oxygen, will vary. Compact soils inhibit aeration because the soil pore spaces are smaller and so reduce the amount of oxygen that can enter the soil. Furthermore, the smaller pore spaces slow down the passage of oxygen through the soil from one area to another. The passage of gases through the soil atmosphere is dependent on diffusion gradients identical to the gaseous transport mechanism operative in the overlying atmosphere. In other words, gases (oxygen and carbon dioxide) will pass from areas of higher concentration to regions of lower concentration.

Soil temperatures are the result of a balance between heat gained and heat lost from the soil surface. Most of the heat gained is a result of absorption of solar heat energy, but infiltration of warm air and warm rain water are additional agents of heat energy. Heat is lost by radiation from the soil surface, by convection currents set up within the soil atmosphere and gradually reaching the soil surface, or by a rather slow conduction of heat energy from one soil particle to another until this heat energy finally reaches the surface particles. Soil temperatures are controlled and altered by a number of external and internal factors. Obviously, soils in the region of the equator will have higher temperatures because of increased periods of solar radiation. By the same token, soils at lower altitudes will have higher temperatures than will soils at higher levels for comparable periods and latitudes because the neighboring air temperatures gradually decrease with an increase in altitude.

In any area where the terrain displays irregularities or deviations in elevation (that is, presence of hills or mountains), the southern and western slopes will receive a greater amount of radiation than will the eastern and northern slopes. In fact, it is not uncommon for southern slopes to register a maximum surface soil temperature that is 11° C. to 14° C. (20° F. to 25° F.) higher than northern slopes. In general, southern and western slopes register higher temperatures than do northern or eastern slopes, with the greatest differences recorded between northern and southern exposures. The angle of the slope in relation to the sun governs the total amount of radiation (see Figure 3–10) because the amount of radiation received per unit area is proportional to the cosine of the angle formed between a perpendicular to the surface and the direction from which the radiation comes. As the angle increases, the amount of radiation decreases. Living and nonliving material covering the soil surface will definitely alter soil temperatures in contrast to denuded soils under the same conditions of insolation. The overall effect is stabilization of soil temperatures. Vegetation reduces diurnal and seasonal amplitudes, lowering the diurnal and summer maxima and preventing the extreme minima that occur throughout the nocturnal or winter periods in denuded soils. Snow and ice cover, as well as unincorporated organic debris, serve as insulators that minimize thermal changes in the soil strata.

Thus far, we have mentioned the external factors involved in soil temperatures and their variability. There are internal or intrinsic factors as well. The **specific heat,** or the number of calories of heat energy necessary to raise a unit weight (one gram) or a unit volume (one milliliter) of a substance one degree centigrade, varies, depending upon

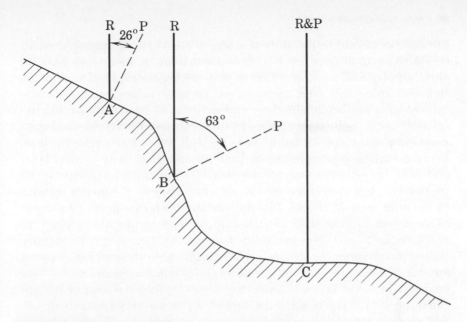

FIGURE 3–10 Three different angles presented by a slope with respect to the direction of radiation *(R)*. The amount of radiation varies inversely with the degree of the angle formed by the dotted line *(P)* drawn perpendicular to the surface of the slope; thus area *C* receives the greatest amount of radiant energy, and slope *B* the least amount.

the composition of the soil. Sand has a relatively high specific heat (0.292 per unit volume); clay is somewhat lower (0.233); and humus, with a specific heat of 0.165, is lower still. The preceding figures simply mean that it would take a greater amount of heat energy to raise a given volume of sand one degree centigrade than would be necessary to raise the same volume of humus an equivalent amount. With the addition of water to any of these materials, we would find that the specific heat would increase proportionately, so that damp soils have a higher specific heat than do dry soils of the same type. This is readily demonstrated when we compare the hot, dry sand with the considerably cooler, wet sand along a beach area after both areas have been exposed to the same amount of solar radiation. This is owing to the fact that if we change the physical state of water from a solid (ice) to a fluid and then from a fluid to a gas (water vapor), the changes in physical state involve heat absorption. Thus if we change a solid (ice) into a fluid, there is latent heat of fusion; or a solid into vapor, there is latent heat of sublimation, or a liquid into vapor, there is latent heat of vaporization. It involves the absorption of a considerable amount of heat energy to bring about these changes, as shown in Table 4–2. The conductivity of heat through the soil varies with the type of soil material. Sand has a higher thermal conductivity than clay. Adding organic matter to a dry soil lowers its thermal conductivity, but wetting a soil will increase its conductivity of heat energy. Rock has a higher thermal conductivity than does dry soil. Areas with rock or rocky soils heat up more rapidly and cool more slowly than do areas devoid of such material. Soil color will have an effect on thermal values because darker-colored soils are better absorbers and emitters of heat than are lighter-colored ones. Soil temperatures exhibit diurnal (daily) and seasonal variations, rising and falling in keeping with atmospheric temperatures. Diurnal variations are greatest in summer and smallest in winter. Heat and cold in surface strata are conveyed to lower layers primarily by conduction, but convection of soil air currents will aid in the transfer of warm or cool air masses. Diurnal variations may be noted to a depth of three feet in some soils, but the amplitude of temperature change, as is shown in Figure 2–8, gradually becomes smaller at greater depths. As one investigates the deeper strata, a noticeable **thermal lag** becomes apparent. The time at which maximal or minimal temperatures are recorded in lower layers is somewhat later (lag) than is true of surface conditions. This lag results in a three-hour delay at a two-inch depth, and over six hours at depths of six inches in some soils. In the summer, it is not uncommon for dark soils with no vegetational cover to record maximal temperatures that are higher than maximal air temperatures, but these same soils never exhibit a temperature drop comparable to minimal, nightly air temperatures.

Seasonally, soils heat up during spring and summer and gradually cool in fall and winter. As one reaches the lower strata, it becomes apparent that there is a seasonal thermal lag that grows more pronounced with proportionately greater distances from the surface. The depth at which seasonal thermal changes disappear is proportional to the degree of seasonal amplitude of soil temperatures. In other words, the greater the amplitude in seasonal temperatures, the greater the depth at which these seasonal changes can be detected. Soil temperatures are of paramount ecological importance because the germination of seeds, the growth of plants, and the degree of activity of soil animals (most of them are poikilothermous) depend upon this vital factor. In addition to controlling the general metabolic activities of plants and animals living in the soil, thermal conditions govern the rate of water absorption by plants and animals. Low temperatures inhibit water uptake, but if high temperatures prevail, water loss by evaporation may be excessive and have a lethal impact upon the soil biota.

Soil moisture, as we have mentioned previously, influences the physical, chemical, and biological properties of soils. Soil water is a nearly perfect solvent; it dissolves many substances that would not be available to living organisms in a solid state. It also serves as an excellent medium of transport of plant nutrients as well as moistening the surface membranes of plant and animal cells, allowing for the diffusion of gases as well as nutrients and waste materials. Soil moisture is retained by the substrate as a result of two attractive forces. The most powerful attractive force is known as **adhesion,** a binding force exerted by molecules of unlike substances when they are brought in contact. This water is held with such force that it is unavailable to plants. Around this film of water, which is held by an adhesive force equivalent to several thousand atmospheres, additional molecules of water will gradually congregate. These molecules of water are attracted to one another by a second force, known as **cohesion.** As the water film surrounding soil particles increases in thickness (Figure 3–11), the cohesive force holding these molecules becomes progressively weaker. Consequently, as soil moisture increases in quantity, the force needed to remove water from the soil decreases proportionately.

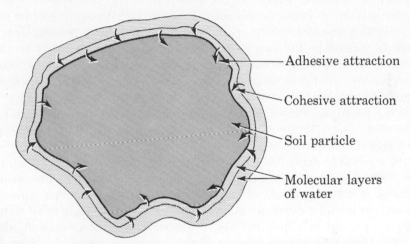

Adhesive attraction

Cohesive attraction

Soil particle

Molecular layers
of water

FIGURE 3–11 Adhesion holds a molecular layer of water to the surface of a soil particle with many atmospheres of force; cohesion binds molecular layers of water to one another, but the force decreases toward the periphery.

Soil scientists recognize three basic categories in the classification of soil water. During a gentle rain most of the water enters the soil and gradually enters deeper and deeper soil strata as it percolates down through the soil pores or cavities. This water that continues to move down into deeper strata by gravitational force is aptly called **gravitational water** and exists in surface soil layers for only a very brief period after a rain. **Capillary water** is retained around soil particles (by cohesive attraction) and in capillary (minute) pores of the soil structure after gravitational water has left the area. This is the most important component of soil water, for it is the capillary water that is important in chemical and biological activities within the soil. Capillary water is readily available to plants and animals. A thin film of water surrounding soil particles, fifteen to twenty molecules thick, is referred to as **hygroscopic water.** The adhesive and cohesive forces are of such values that this water is unavailable to plants and animals.

Soil water moves through the soil in a liquid or vapor state. Gravitational attraction allows water to percolate through soil pores to an impermeable layer (hard pan) or to the water table. The number, size, and continuity of soil cavities regulate the rate of movement. We find that air entrapped in soil spaces will slow the rate of percolation; this often occurs when heavy rains follow periods of drought. Water in the liquid state may also be transported in a vertical or horizontal direction by means of capillary tension. Extremely small soil spaces (capillary pores) must be present to promote this movement. Water rises vertically in capillary pores in inverse proportion to the size of the pores; consequently, water will rise a greater distance in clay soils (smaller soil particle size, smaller capillary pores) than it will in sandy soils. Water vapor may move from the soil into the overlying atmosphere or in the reverse direction, depending upon the value of the vapor pressure deficit that is present in the two areas. **Vapor pressure deficit** refers to the amount of moisture necessary under existing conditions of temperature and pressure needed to saturate a particular volume of air or to increase the relative humidity to 100 per cent. Whether this vaporous water is leaving, entering, or moving through the soil, it always obeys the physical law of diffusion. It always moves from an area of high vapor pressure to a region of lower vapor pressure.

At a variable depth below the soil surface, there is a zone in which the soil or impermeable material is saturated with water. The water present is called **ground water,** and the upper level of this zone of saturation is called the **water table** (Figure 3–12). At times ground water may be present in a position above the main zone of saturation; this is called **perched ground water** and the upper surface of this layer is

FIGURE 3–12 Ground water and perched ground water strata in a diagrammatic soil profile, with the accompanying capillary fringes.

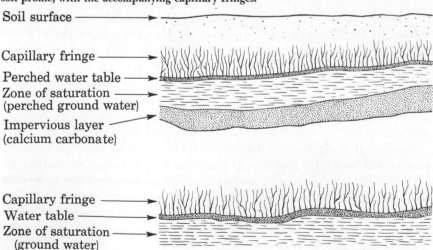

Soil surface

Capillary fringe

Perched water table
Zone of saturation
(perched ground water)

Impervious layer
(calcium carbonate)

Capillary fringe
Water table
Zone of saturation
(ground water)

aptly called the **perched water table.** A perched mass of ground water is the result of an impervious layer of material, usually calcium carbonate, located some distance above the main water table, which prevents the normal passage of gravitational water down through this zone. Extending above the water table, whether it is the main water table or a perched water table, is a **capillary fringe.** In this area, the small pores of the soil are filled with water, held in the pores by capillarity opposing the force of gravity. The thickness of this fringe will vary with soil texture; fine textured soils (silts and clays) will have a much thicker capillary fringe than that of coarser texture (sand). The water table may be relatively close to the soil surface in areas adjacent to ponds and lakes; in this case, trees and other vegetation may use this water by the growth of root systems into regions of this capillary fringe. At higher elevations, in regions where drainage is excellent, or where industry has utilized ground water from deep wells, the water table may be so deep that it cannot be used by vegetation. The position of the water table is seldom stable; seasonal fluctuations causing increased transpiration, evaporation, precipitation, temperature, and atmospheric pressure—all will affect the level of the water table. In general, we find that the water table is lower in summer and higher in winter.

Soils vary in their hydrogen ion concentration or pH values. A pH value of 7.0 indicates neutrality; values below this figure (0–6.9) indicate acid conditions. The lower the figure, the more acid the substrate. Hydrogen ion values above 7.0 indicate alkaline conditions (7.1–14.0), the higher values indicating that a more basic or alkaline condition exists. Plants and animals vary with regard to their pH tolerance. Some organisms are unaffected by a rather broad range of pH values; others may exhibit considerable intolerance to even minor variations in the pH. Bog organisms must live in an acid environment, whereas desert organisms are exposed to alkaline soils. The hydrogen ion concentration of the soil will control the rate at which many plants are able to absorb soil nutrients. The type of organic litter covering the soil or organic debris that becomes incorporated with mineral soil will modify the pH values of surface soil strata. In coniferous stands, the soil is acid in reaction, which promotes a rich fungus population but often a sparse soil fauna. Deciduous stands have a less acid litter and a richer soil fauna but a smaller number of fungi.

In certain soils the amount of salt present may restrict the flora and fauna present to only the most tolerant species. Along ocean fronts exposed to salt spray or in salt lake areas the dominant salt is usually sodium chloride, but other salts may also be present. In arid regions, the small amount of precipitation allows salts to accumulate in surface soils rather than be leached into lower strata by gravitational water. Added to this set of circumstances is the great evaporation of moisture from surface soils that concentrates these salts, forming alkali deserts in some areas where very few plants and animals can survive.

OTHER SUBSTRATES

Snow and ice are temporary substrates in temperate areas, except at extreme altitudes. Arctic, antarctic, and tundra areas may possess a snow or ice substrate permanently or for extensive periods of time. Ice will offer a firmer surface for movement. Whether the substrate is ice or snow, water is usually unavailable (physiological drought), since it is present in solid or flake form and must thaw or melt before it can be utilized. Most living organisms furnish a biotic substrate for a number of different plants and animals, many of which the organism is unaware of because many of the ectoparasitic and endoparasitic forms cause only minor damage. Trees and many other large masses of vegetation, as well as grasses, may furnish a permanent substrate for other plants (parasites and epiphytes) or animals. Man harbors a vast variety of parasites and mutualistic organisms within and on his body, as is true of many other animals. Certainly the microenvironmental conditions throughout the body of any organism (plant or animal) vary to such an extent that it defies description in a general textbook.

ATMOSPHERIC GASES

The atmosphere, or gaseous envelope, surrounding the earth is relatively constant in composition within reasonable limits of altitude. The percentage composition of atmospheric gases is represented in Table 3–2. Obviously, the amount or percentage of water vapor in the atmosphere

TABLE 3–2. *Percentage Composition of Atmospheric Gases**

GAS	PER CENT COMPOSITION
Nitrogen	78.03
Oxygen	20.99
Argon	0.94
Carbon dioxide	0.03 (approx.)
Hydrogen	0.01
Neon	0.0018
Helium	0.0005
Krypton	0.0001
Xenon	0.000009
Water vapor	variable

* From P. McCorkle, *The Physical World* (New York: McGraw-Hill Book Co., 1950), pp. i–vii, 1–450. Used by permission.

varies, not only from one locality to another, but from one time unit to the next as atmospheric and climatic conditions change. In certain industrial areas, air pollution will often alter the percentage composition of the atmospheric gases by inclusion of more carbon dioxide or sulfur compounds. If such industrial plants do not employ some method for air purification, there is the danger that it may be fatal to some forms of life and consequently exclude the distribution of some organisms. There are localities where atmospheric gases have become so radically altered that animals cannot survive. One region is the Dieng Plateau of Java, known as a famous death valley. Carbon dioxide spews from fissures in the ground, and since carbon dioxide is heavier than oxygen, it becomes concentrated at ground level, with only a very slow diffusion into the surrounding atmospheric areas.

Selected References

Baver, L. D. *Soil Physics* (New York: John Wiley, 1940), pp. i–xi, 1–320.

Bouyoucos, G. J. 1936. Directions for making mechanical analyses of soils by the hydrometer method. Soil Sci., **42**:225–229.

———. 1937a. A sensitive hydrometer for determining small amounts of clay or colloids in soils. Soil Sci., **44**:245–247.

———. 1937b. The high degree of accuracy of the improved soil hydrometer used in the mechanical analysis of soils. Soil Sci., **44**:315–317.

Edlefson, N. E., and W. O. Smith. 1944. The determination of moisture in undisturbed soil. Proc. Soil. Sci. Soc. Amer. 1943, **8**:112–115.

Hilgard, E. W. *Soils, Their Formation, Properties, Composition and Relations to Climate and Plant Growth in the Humid and Arid Regions* (New York: Macmillan, 1906), pp. i–xxvii, 1–593.

Joffe, J. S. 1932. Lysimeter studies: I. Moisture percolation through the soil profile. Soil Sci., **34**:123–143.

Keen, B. A. *The Physical Properties of the Soil* (New York: Longmans, Green, 1931), pp. i–vii, 1–380.

Kellogg, C. E. 1936. Development and significance of the great soil groups of the United States. U.S.D.A. Misc. Publ. **29**:1–40.

———. 1937. Soil survey manual. U.S.D.A. Misc. Publ., **274**:1–136.

Kubiena, W. L. *Micropedology* (Ames, Iowa: Collegiate Press, 1938), pp. i–xvi, 1–243.

Lebediev, A. F. 1924. On the moisture properties of the soil. Soil Sci., **17**:423–426.

Lutz, H. J., and R. F. Chandler, Jr. *Forest Soils* (New York: John Wiley, 1946), pp. i–xi, 1–514.

MacKinney, A. L. 1929. Effects of forest litter on soil temperature and soil freezing in autumn and winter. Ecology, **10**:312–321.

Romell, L. G., and S. O. Heiberg. 1931. Types of humus layer in the forests of northeastern United States. Ecology, **12:**567–608.

Russell, E. J., and A. Appleyard. 1915. The atmosphere of the soil: its composition and the causes of variation. Jour. Agric. Sci., **7:**1–48.

Stefferud, A. (ed.) *Soil* 1957 Yearbook of Agriculture (Washington, D.C.: Government Printing Office, 1957), pp. i–xiii, 1–784.

Waksman, S. A. *Humus: Origin, Chemical Composition and Importance in Nature* (Baltimore: Williams & Wilkins, 1938), pp. i–xi, 1–526.

———. *Soil Microbiology* (New York: John Wiley, 1952) pp. i–x, 1–356.

Wright, C. H. *Soil Analysis: A Handbook of Physical and Chemical Methods* (London: Murby, 1939), pp. i–x, 1–276.

IV. Abiotic Factors — The Aquatic Environment

The aquatic environments (marine and freshwater) cover over 75 percent of the earth's surface. The oceans are two and one half times more extensive than land, and provide over 300 times the living space, since they are habitable throughout their entire depth by certain groups of organisms. Water is obviously heavier than air, which imparts a greater buoyancy to the aquatic medium, enabling organisms to float at variable levels. Since water supports the weight of aquatic organisms, it enables some of these animals and plants to attain a bulk and size that would be impossible in a terrestrial environment. Some of the giant squid (the largest known invertebrates), whales (the largest vertebrate), and the giant kelps (the largest primitive plants) bear this statement out in dramatic fashion—all of them inhabit the marine environment. Comparative densities are represented in Table 4–1. With a little mathematical calculation, it becomes evident that sea water is more than 850 times as dense as air. It is little wonder that masses of water in rapid motion are far more destructive than air.

TABLE 4–1. *Comparative Densities of Various Environmental Media*

MEDIUM	DENSITY IN GRAMS PER MILLILITER AT $4°$ C.
Air (sea level)	0.0013
Distilled water	1.000
Pond water	1.001
Seawater (35‰)	1.028

From G. L. Clarke, *Elements of Ecology* (New York: John Wiley & Sons, Inc., 1954), p. 26. Used by permission.

PHYSICAL PROPERTIES OF WATER

TEMPERATURE

One well-known physical fact relative to temperature and water is that a considerable amount of heat energy is required to convert water from one phase to another. Not only are large amounts of heat energy required to change water from a solid to a liquid to a gas, but a great deal of heat must be lost before the reverse set of reactions can occur—that is, from a gas to a fluid to a solid. (See Table 4–2.) We find that a change of temperature, whether warming or cooling a body of water, such as a pond, a lake, or a body of salt water, will occur at the water's surface initially. No one has ever seen ice forming on the bottom of a pond or lake while the surface waters remained fluid; if a body of water freezes, it always does so from the surface downward. The reason for this is that the maximum density of water is reached at $4°$ C., meaning that water at this temperature (somewhat above freezing) sinks to the bottom, while cooler water (below $4°$ C.) rises toward the surface, and water at the freezing point ($0°$ C.) forms ice on the surface. The notable exception is sea water with a salinity of 24.7 parts per thousand or higher. Water with these salinity values has no maximum density, but instead the colder

TABLE 4–2. *Physical Properties associated with a Change of State of Water*

	HEAT REQUIRED	RESULT
Heat of fusion	79.7 cal./gm.*	Converts 1 gm. of water to ice with no change in temperature
Heat of vaporization	539.6 cal./gm.	Converts 1 gm. of water at 100° C. to water vapor with no change in temperature

* The calorie is the amount of heat required to raise 1 gm. of water 1° C.

it becomes the more dense it becomes. If ice were to form in water of these higher salinity values, it would sink to the bottom; this of course is hypothetical, because when saline water freezes, crystals contain but a small amount of salt and consequently float on the surface of the heavier saline water in the immediate area.

Aquatic temperatures vary from the scalding temperatures of hot springs to the freezing temperatures of arctic and antarctic seas. In shallow lakes of the temperate zone, thermal values will vary seasonally. Under severe climatic changes they may display considerable differences within a twenty-four-hour period, although the variation will not be so great as that occurring in the surrounding atmosphere owing to the high specific heat of water. Freshwater areas seldom drop below 0° C. without freezing, but sea water may drop to −2.5° C. before it freezes, since the presence of salts in sea water lowers the freezing point. The average temperature range for sea water varies from about 30° C. in tropical waters to −1.5° C. in arctic and antarctic areas (36.0° C. is the highest temperature recorded for deep-sea surface waters, though temperatures may run higher in shallow water areas such as tide pools, bays, and estuaries). Thermal values control the distribution of many organisms. For example, many corals do not flourish where temperatures drop below 21° C., while the bivalve *Portlandia arctica* is not found in water above 4° C. and the scallop (*Pecten groenlandicus*) of eastern Greenland is never present in waters above 0° C. In contrast to this, we find the blue-green alga, *Phormidium hijahense* and *Oscillaria filiformis*, living in freshwater at a temperature of 85.2° C., and some bacteria in water at 88.0° C., though these organisms are living close to the upper limits of heat tolerance. While we are discussing temperature and distribution of organisms, it might be well to mention the fact that temperature exerts an indirect effect by altering the viscosity and solubility of gases in freshwater and marine environments. The viscosity of water rises as the temperature decreases. If the temperature of sea water drops from 30°C. to 0° C., the viscosity of the water doubles. This same thermal drop, however, will double the solubility of oxygen in sea water, which often controls the distribution of certain biota.

A number of biological processes are definitely affected, if not controlled, by thermal values extant in aquatic areas. Feeding, growth, respiration, reproduction, and general physical activity are often altered by temperature extremes, maximal or minimal, which may be close but nonetheless somewhat below or above, respectively, the temperatures at which death would occur. Geographically, there is a nonbreeding fringe within the absolute distribution of a species where the temperatures are either too high or too low for breeding. In these areas, distribution is dependent upon the migration of larval or adult organisms into these regions. In marine areas, the poleward distribution is dependent on the minimal winter temperature, which determines survival, and the max-

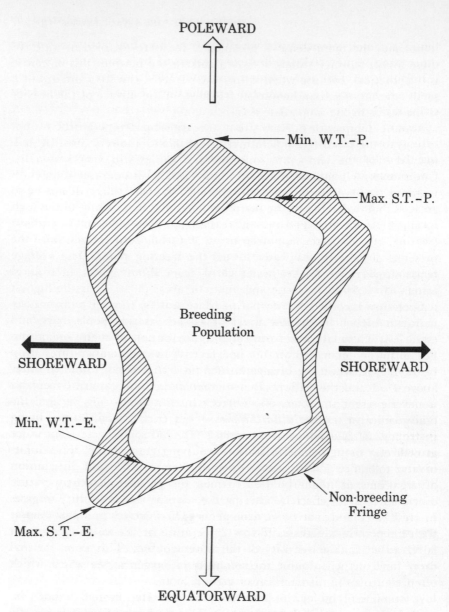

POLEWARD

Min. W.T.-P.

Max. S.T.-P.

Breeding
Population

SHOREWARD ← ← SHOREWARD →

Min. W.T.-E.

Non-breeding
Fringe

Max. S. T.-E.

EQUATORWARD

FIGURE 4–1 Hypothetical absolute geographic distribution of a marine species limited by aquatic temperatures. Nonbreeding fringe is the diagonally lined area; the breeding area for actively reproducing forms is left unlined. Min. W. T.—P represents minimal winter temperature preventing the poleward movement of the species. Max. S. T.—P is maximum summer temperature preventing the poleward movement of the breeding population. Min. W. T.—E is the minimal winter temperature preventing the equatorial movement of the breeding population. Max. S. T.—E is the maximal summer temperature limiting the southern distribution of nonbreeding portions of the population. Shoreward distribution is limited by water depth and intrinsic temperatures. It must be noted that this is a static diagrammatic representation of a hypothetical marine invertebrate and does not take into account the dynamic shifts recorded over a time span of many years.

imum summer temperature, which governs breeding activity. On the other hand, equatorial distribution is governed by a summer maximum controlling survival and a winter minimum dictating the breeding temperatures necessary for successful reproduction (Figure 4–1). Successful spawning involves the maturation of spermatozoa and ova within the gonads of the organism, followed by the release of these products. Each activity involves critical temperatures that must be satisfied. But following the release of these genital products, critical temperatures with narrow ranges of temperature tolerance for early cleavage stages will be followed by progressively wider ranges of tolerance for larval and adult periods. Stauber (1950) has noted that oysters (*Ostrea*) of one species have several physiological races that spawn at about the same time each year in different geographic localities. Critical minimal temperatures necessary for a successful spawn for this particular species are 25° C. in Delaware Bay, 20° C. in the Bideford River Estuary, and 16.4° C. in Long Island Sound.

Growth rate, to a great extent, is controlled by temperatures because various metabolic processes governing growth react to critical temperatures. Generally, in freshwater and marine areas, animals and plants inhabiting cooler waters tend to be larger. Whether this is due to a more rapid growth rate or a long-continued growth process is not definitely known, but undoubtedly both explanations may be valid, depending upon the organism involved. There are exceptions: diatoms are generally larger in warmer waters; a sea urchin (*Echinus esculentus*) and a gastropod (*Urosalpinx cinerea*) are also larger. Suitable temperatures for growth may exist for only a brief interval of time in cooler waters. The bivalve *Ostrea virginica* grows all year off the coast of Florida and attains a size in one year that would take two or three years in northern waters. The cirri of the barnacle *Balanus balanoides* carry food to the organism. From 2° to 21° C., the movement of these cirri increase proportionately with temperature increases. Below 2° C. or above 21° C. the movement is irregular, and above 27° C. all movement ceases. Since these cirri carry food to the barnacle, an indirect relationship exists pertaining to temperature and growth. Fluctuating temperatures characteristic of shallow freshwater and marine environments are often more favorable for growth than are fixed thermal values. This is true because different life processes (enzyme activity, digestion, respiration, muscular activity, and other vital processes) have different optimal temperatures, and fluctuating temperatures increase the probability that an optimal thermal value would exist for a brief time for many of these vital and necessary activities.

In aquatic areas, as well as terrestrial environments, the rate of respiration increases as temperatures increase until an optimal temperature is reached; then the rate of respiration decreases until the lethal temperature is attained. Some organisms such as the anomuran, *Emerita talpoida*

(Edwards and Irving, 1943), displays a seasonal adaptation to temperatures, so that the winter respiratory rate recorded at 3° C. was identical to the summer rate when water was 15° C. Sparck in 1936 noted that bivalves in the Greenland area exhibited the same respiratory rate as lamellibranchs from the warmer Mediterranean area at quite different local average temperatures.

In any body of water—lakes, rivers, inland seas, and oceans—there is a critical depth, known as the **compensation point,** at which there is just sufficient illumination for the photosynthetic process to balance the respiratory requirements of the plant. However, we find that the compensation point varies with temperature. For example, at 10° C. the compensation point would be located at a depth where the illumination would be about 250 to 300 meter-candles for a certain species of plant, but at a higher temperature (16° C.); when the metabolic activity is accelerated and the requirements for continued life are proportionately higher, the illumination must be about 350 to 400 meter-candles.

Mobile organisms are able to leave areas where temperatures become intolerable, but sessile animals and plants will die if thermal conditions exceed the lethal point. Populations of the marine gastropod *Littorina littorea* that extend into arctic localities move seaward from the intertidal zone during the arctic winter to deeper, warmer waters. Freshwater and marine zooplankton exhibit diurnal, vertical movements in order to escape severe thermal conditions. During the early daylight hours there is a gradual descent to deeper strata as the illumination (and surface temperatures) increase. This descent will continue until a minimal thermal barrier is reached; then, in the late afternoon, these organisms begin their ascent as surface waters gradually cool. Intertidal algae gradually die along the upper limit of distribution as thermal values reach their seasonal peaks along coastal areas.

High and low temperature mortality have been recorded, in a number of instances, even for mobile forms that are unable for some reason to escape or where such vast areas of water have exceeded lethal high or low thermal values that no immediate safe zone is accessible. Off the Dry Tortugas, high temperatures ranging from 33° to 38° C. caused, sometime ago, the wholesale destruction of *Fissurella* (gastropod), *Diadema* (sea urchin), and *Octopus.* It is generally believed that widespread mortality of certain species of freshwater and marine plants and invertebrates are often the result of enzymatic failure associated with respiration. Mollusks along the coast of Denmark—namely *Mytilus edulis* and *Littorina littorea*, suffered 100 per cent mortality as a result of two months of freezing weather. It is important to remember that though certain temperatures may not be lethal for short periods of time, these same thermal values may exact a considerable death toll if exposure is prolonged. Freezing temperatures in freshwater ponds and lakes result in ice formation that will cut off the oxygen supply. In shallow bodies of freshwater, prolonged periods of icing-over may kill many fish and other vertebrates as the oxygen supply is gradually exhausted. Many of the freshwater plants covered by ice will not receive enough illumination, and the cooler temperatures will have reduced photosynthetic activity to the point that oxygen cannot be resupplied in great enough quantity to keep pace with the demand. Low temperatures in estuarine areas reduce the tolerance of indigenous organisms to cope with reduced salinities in these areas.

SALINITY

Obviously, the salinity, or salt content, is higher in sea water than in freshwater. The composition, in terms of the common ions present, differs somewhat, as is evident from Table 4–3. As indicated, the ions in greatest abundance are the same for sea water and soft freshwater, but car-

TABLE 4–3. *Concentrations of the Most Common Ions Found in Different Aquatic Areas**

	GRAMS PER LITER	GRAMS PER LITER
Seawater	Chloride—19.3	Sodium—10.7
Soft freshwater	Chloride—0.019	Sodium—0.016
Hard freshwater	Carbonate—0.119	Calcium—0.065

* Modified from G. L. Clarke, *Elements of Ecology* (New York: John Wiley & Sons, Inc., 1954), pp. i–xiv, 1–534. Used by permission.

bonate and calcium are more abundant in hard freshwater. In addition, there are varying amounts of potassium, manganese, and sulfate ions present, though soft freshwater seldom has measurable amounts of potassium or manganese. Open ocean water has a relatively constant salinity value of 35 to 36 parts per thousand, but in regions where evaporation is high and contact with the high seas is limited, as in the Mediterranean or Red Sea, salinity values are often as high as 40 parts per thousand. In coastal areas, river estuaries, bays, and harbors where there is an influx of freshwater, salinity values are not only variable, depending upon the climatic conditions (precipitation) in terrestrial areas, but also are lower than those encountered seaward. The Baltic Sea has a salinity of about 8 parts per thousand because a great deal of freshwater enters this particular body of water.

Salinity conditions will of course involve osmotic regulation in an organism. We find that the salt content of the cells of many marine organisms is relatively close to the salinity of sea water, so that the problem of osmoregulation is reduced to a considerable extent. Many fish have chloride cells or glands to rid the body of excess salts, and of course it has become known recently that many birds, including the gulls, albatrosses, and penguins that frequent salt water areas drink seawater with no ill effects because of the presence of salt glands, located in the nasal area, that are capable of excreting a salt solution nearly twice the concentration of seawater. Seawater and food with high salt content that are normally ingested by the bird have salts removed by the salt gland, which liberates the concentrated salt through the nasal cavity and external nares. Large sea turtles have salt glands, located close to the eye, with a duct that liberates the salt solution into a passage opening at the corner of the eye. Some of the marine mammals (seals and whales) will either subsist on fish or marine invertebrates. The kidneys are capable of producing urine that is more concentrated than the surrounding seawater, and the organism consequently maintains its salt balance by effective renal function. Estuarine species often resolve the problem of osmoregulation by a corresponding decrease in saline values very similar to those of the surrounding water (isotonic condition).

Under extreme estuarine conditions (where salt concentration is extremely low and approaches the salinity of freshwater) or in freshwater areas, we often find there is a reversal of conditions that prevail in marine areas. In these instances, the salt concentration of the animal or plant tissues exceeds that of the surrounding water, so that there is a tendency for water to continually enter the cells. This means that the organism must rid itself of excess water through increased excretory activity. Other mechanisms may aid the organism in solving the continual environmental problem of osmoregulation. Many freshwater organisms are surrounded by exoskeletons, cuticular sheaths or scales that are impervious to or impede the free passage of water. Cell membranes of some organisms have intrinsic structural components that tend to reduce the quantity of water entering the cell over a unit period of time.

Some plants and animals are physiologically adapted to areas where salinity values change rapidly and frequently, such as tidal pools where rainwater or evaporation can alter the salinity from 10 to 105 parts per thousand within a twenty-four-hour period. The marine gastropod *Puperita,* and the algae *Ulva* and *Cladophora* have been found living under such conditions. Additional environmental factors often alter the organism's ability to tolerate saline conditions. *Gunda ulvae,* a platyhelminth, commonly located under stones and other debris in intertidal areas, can migrate into freshwater areas provided calcium is present in a concentration of 5 mgms. of calcium per liter of water. Calcium, in this case, is essential for osmoregulation. The eggs of the shore crab (*Carcinus maenas*) can tolerate lower salinities at higher temperatures. The minimal tolerance has been recorded as 25 parts per thousand in water at 10.0° C., but only 20 parts per thousand in water at 16.3° C. In certain groups of algae, it has been discovered that the rate of respiration will increase if salinity values drop for any appreciable period. The photosynthetic rate is doubled if *Fucus* and *Ulva* are exposed to a salinity that is reduced by a third (24 parts per thousand).

PRESSURE

Pressures increase with increased depth of water at the rate of one atmosphere (760 mm. of mercury) for every 10 meters of descent. Organisms normally inhabiting the floor of deep-sea areas at depths of 10,500 meters are exposed to pressures of about one ton per square centimeter. Fishes, birds, and mammals will experience a change in shape and size of air-filled chambers within the body. The swim bladder of a fish will decrease to one half of its surface volume at a depth of 10 meters; consequently, those fishes that possess swim bladders are often limited with respect to vertical distribution. Birds and mammals have an additional respiratory problem; they must surface periodically to expel the accumulated carbon dioxide and replenish their supply of oxygen. For this reason, dives are limited to 100 meters in depth for humans and to 400 to 1,000 meters for whales. Most organisms living at great depths lack air-filled cavities; any cavities or spaces that may exist are filled with fluids.

MASS MOVEMENT OF WATER

Waves. Waves are masses of water in vertical and horizontal movement. As early as 1820 there was a great deal of theoretical work done on waves by French scientists. This theoretical work, which was later pursued by English oceanographers, contains a large terminology and a tremendous number of theoretical formulae. We find, for example, that the height of a wave is the distance from the trough to crest, but amplitude is only one-half the wave height, or the distance from the undisturbed surface to the crest of a wave as shown in Figure 4–2. The period of a wave (time interval between crests), the wavelength (distance from crest to crest), and the speed of a wave can be determined, if any two of the forementioned factors are known, according to the following formula:

$$C = \frac{L}{T},$$

where C = speed of the wave, L = wavelength, and T = period of the wave. Thus if the interval between crests were 24 centimeters and the period of the wave were 12 seconds, the wave would be traveling at a speed of 2 centimeters per second. A wave by definition is a displacement of the water surface from one of equilibrium. Three forces tend to main-

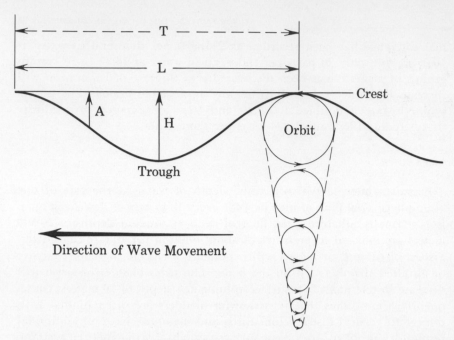

FIGURE 4–2 Diagram of a wave showing 1½ wavelengths. *L* is the wavelength from crest to crest, *H* is the height of the wave measured from crest to trough, and *A* is the amplitude of a wave, or ½ the height of a wave. The period, or *T*, is the time required for one wavelength (*L*) to pass a particular point. Circles represent orbits of water particles, which gradually decrease with depth. Surface orbits are of the same diameter as the wave height.

tain this equilibrium or to act as a collective restoring force (restoring a condition of equilibrium), as shown in Figure 4–3: Gravity, buoyant force, and surface tension—all are involved, but to varying degrees, depending on wave size. In large waves, we find that gravitational and buoyant forces are the dominant factors, and surface tension is relatively unimportant; the reverse, however, is true for small waves.

The major causative agent with regard to wave formation is wind, with boats and biotic organisms as lesser contributing elements of minor importance. In deep water (large, deep lakes, inland seas, open ocean), the height and period of a wave are determined by the velocity of the

FIGURE 4–3 Forces acting on a wave, tending to establish equilibrium and dissipate the wave.

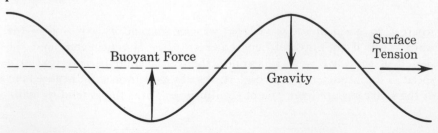

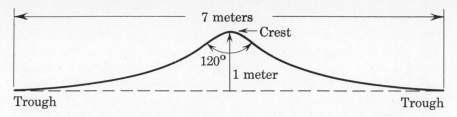

FIGURE 4–4 Maximum height of a wave. Wavelength and wave height cannot exceed a ratio of 7 to 1 or a crest angle of less than 120° without breaking.

wind, the duration of the wind, and **fetch** (the distance wind blows over a water surface). The greater each one of these factors becomes, the higher the waves. Wave height is limited by wavelength, however, because, as shown in Figure 4–4, the proportion of wave height to wavelength cannot exceed a ratio of 1 to 7. The highest known oceanic wave was 34.1 meters (112 feet) from trough to crest and was known as the Ramapo Wave. The wave was observed from the bridge of the U.S.S.

FIGURE 4–5 Formation of waves and their spread from a storm center (low pressure area). *C* represents the crests of waves; *T* represents the troughs of the waves. As waves spread out, their wave energy will also spread out and eventually dissipate in the absence of a disruptive force.

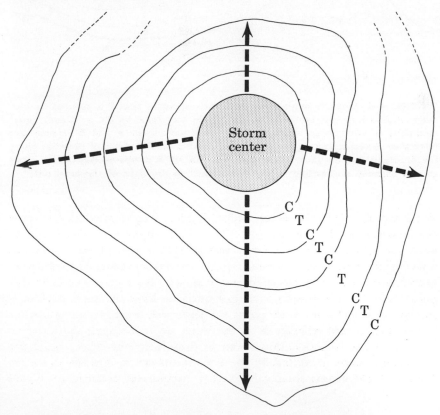

Ramapo, a Navy tanker, while on the open sea in the Pacific in 1933. The observer on the bridge, looking toward the stern of the tanker, noted that the crow's nest of the ship was in the line of sight with the crest of the wave. By simple geometric calculation, he was able to determine the height of the wave.

As waves move shoreward, wave height decreases as a result of the **spreading factor** (the intrinsic energy is dissipated over a greater distance parallel to the shoreline, Figure 4–5). As a wave reaches shallower water, its velocity is reduced, as shown in Figure 4–6, so that provided the submerged shoreline has a relatively even topography, waves will

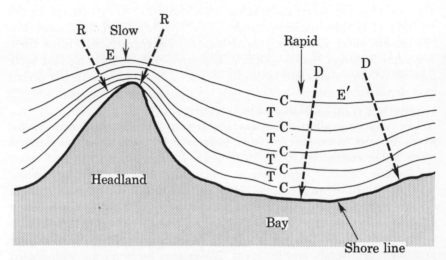

FIGURE 4–6 As waves move shoreward, their speed or period is reduced as they enter shallow water, as indicated at the left in the region of the headland. Equal quantities of wave energy represented by equal wave fronts *E* and *E'* demonstrate refraction (*R*) concentrating the wave energy over a small distance of shoreline along the headland, but the same amount of wave energy is dissipated (*D*) over a much greater distance of shoreline in the bay located to the right of the headland.

break parallel with the water's edge as wave height gradually exceeds one seventh of the wavelength. Wave form changes as the depth of water decreases; this occurs when water depth is half of the horizontal wavelength. Thus a wave measuring 25 meters from one crest to the next would begin changing shape in water about 12½ meters deep. At this point, wave height usually increases until we have the ratio of 1 to 7 (height to length), at which point the wave will break, forming smaller waves that in turn will break as the water depth becomes shallower as they approach the shore. Waves can be quite destructive because of the hydrostatic pressure exerted by these masses of water. A wave 13 meters high and 150 meters long can exert a hydrostatic pressure of 67,980 pounds per square meter. Such pressures can cause considerable damage, moving heavy objects (boats, piers, cottages) considerable distances. A boulder weighing 167,640 pounds and located 6 meters above sea level was moved 22 meters across rough rocks by wave action over a period of several months.

The movement of water particles is reduced 1/2 at 1/9 the depth of the wavelength, as compared with movement at the surface of a wave. In actuality, individual water particles do not move any great distance, but energy is transported onward to adjacent particles. Although movement of water particles is reduced drastically as distances increase from the surface of a wave, wave erosion occurs in ponds, lakes, and oceanic areas or wherever waves materialize. Wave erosion causes a change in the position of bottom sediments and is more intense in shallow areas, but the erosive effect is always proportional to wavelength, which, in turn, is greater in larger bodies of water. In most ponds or lakes we find wave erosion is seldom effective beyond a depth of 10 to 12 meters, but occurs at a depth of 40 meters in the English Channel, 50 meters in the Mediterranean Sea, and 200 meters in the open ocean.

The biota are affected by wave action in the intertidal and littoral zones, for the hydrostatic pressure generated by these masses of water is often great enough to crush or remove limpets, barnacles, and other crustaceans and tear freshwater or marine algae loose from the bottom. Waves will have an abrasive effect on the flora and fauna, keeping certain rock surfaces free of flora and fauna by the continual washing of sand and pebbles over these surfaces. For this reason, wave-beaten sandy or rocky beaches are generally more barren than are sheltered areas of lakes, ponds, and sea areas. Waves may be beneficial with regard to living matter; we find that *Balanus balanoides* (a barnacle) grows more rapidly along wave-splashed beaches than it does along sheltered areas because waves bring in considerable quantities of food. Movement of water (waves) will also aid in mixing atmospheric gases with the aquatic medium, thus promoting gas exchange. Waves will also modify the littoral or intertidal zone by adding an additional "splash zone" in the supralittoral or supratidal zone; this often widens the living zone, depending upon the wave intensity and the biota involved.

Currents. Currents are mass movements of large quantities of water from one point to another in streams (brooks, creeks, rivers), some ponds and lakes, and in oceanic bodies of water. Currents move more slowly but more uniformly than waves. The strength of any current is proportional to the amount of water passing any point over a unit period of time. In freshwater areas, currents are typically stronger after thaws or after periods of greater seasonal precipitation. Currents will transport solid objects considerable distances. A current of 20.6 cm./sec. (0.4 knot) will shift sand along the bottom; a current of 51.5 cm./sec.

TABLE 4–4. *Displacement of Sediments by Currents Relative to Soil and Organic Materials of Varying Diameter**

SEDIMENT TYPE	PARTICLE DIAMETER IN MM.	SETTLING VELOCITY CM./SEC.	TIME FOR SETTLING DEPTH 100 M.	DISPLACEMENT IN KM., CURRENT 10 CM./SEC.	DISPLACEMENT IN KM., CURRENT 1 M./SEC.
Coarse sand	2.0	25.0	7 minutes	0.042 km.	0.50 km.
Fine sand	0.1	0.8	3 hours	1.0 km.	10.0 km.
Silt	0.06	0.35	8 hours	3.0 km.	30.0 km.
Coarse clay	0.005	0.002	2 months	500.0 km.	5,000.0 km.
Fine clay	0.0005	0.00002	14 years	50,000.0 km.	500,000.0 km.
Radiolaria	0.50	0.4	7 hours	2.5 km.	25.0 km.
Foraminifera (large)	0.50	6.0	30 minutes	170.0 km.	1.5 km.
Diatoms	0.04	0.15	1 day	8.0 km.	80.0 km.
Foraminifera (small)	0.02	0.05	3 days	25.0 km.	250.0 km.

* Modified from P. H. Kuenan, *Marine Geology* (New York: John Wiley & Sons, Inc., 1950), pp. i–x, 1–568. Used by permission.

(1.0 knot) will shift fine gravel; and a current of 180.3 cm./sec. (3.5 knots) will shift angular stones as large as 3.8 cm. in diameter (see Table 4–4). Currents are always swiftest in surface waters at midstream, but become slower as they approach the bottom or the banks of a stream because of the frictional factor as is represented in Figure 4–7 (water against the surface of a substrate). Strong currents, particularly if erosion and flooding are occurring near the source of a stream, may carry considerable quantities of suspended material such as organic debris, fine particles of clay or silt long distances downstream. This makes for a more turbid body of water, reducing the illumination and hence photosynthesis of many aquatic plants. The reduction in photosynthesis may in turn profoundly affect the floral and faunal populations over a great expanse of the aquatic community. Shifting sediments and the consequent abrasive action of swift currents will also cause adverse results. Currents are beneficial in that they transport various organisms, particularly planktonic life, considerable distances and thus increase the geographic distribution of different species. These constantly moving bodies of water will also transport nutrients, gases, minerals, and other essential substances into areas requiring such materials. Oceanic currents carry tremendous quantities of water long distances.

There are a variety of different currents in any marine environment. Coastal, submerged, bottom, tidal, and Coriolis currents tend to com-

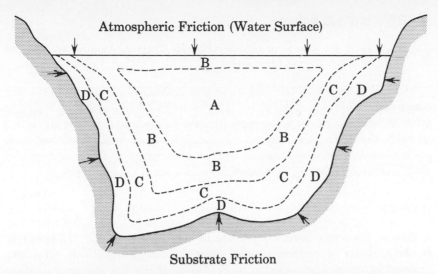

Atmospheric Friction (Water Surface)

Substrate Friction

FIGURE 4–7 The cross section of a stream showing decreasing current rate as a result of atmospheric and substrate friction in various regions of the section. Area *A* represents the most rapid current, *B* is somewhat slower, *C* is slower and *D* is the area where the current is slowest because of friction imposed by the submerged banks and stream bed.

pound the situation, making the study of currents and their effects an intricate and important part of oceanographic study. The Coriolis current, caused by the Coriolis effect, or a tendency for objects to drift to the right in the Northern Hemisphere and to the left in the Southern Hemisphere as a result of the earth's rotation, is an important factor in the movement of oceanic waters. In most cases the Coriolis force is so weak that it may be discounted because other factors exert forces of a far greater magnitude. In atmospheric and oceanic areas, however, the normally weak Coriolis force becomes highly significant because other factors are small in comparison. The ocean surface is not perfectly level because winds shift the surface waters, thus giving the surface an uneven contour. This shifting, in turn, leads to movement of water from regions of high level to areas of lower level. The moving water, however, is displaced to the right in the Northern Hemisphere by this Coriolis current that is established. Internal eddy stresses and surface winds will modify the Coriolis currents. Maritime regions of terrestrial environments are definitely altered by climatic conditions produced by major currents bordering these areas. The Gulf Stream off the eastern coast of North America and the Humboldt Current off the west coast of South America warm and cool these continental areas, respectively. Because of the complexity of oceanic currents and of the fact that gross tidal movement of water is restricted to oceanic areas these subjects will be discussed in Chapter XII (Marine Areas) that deals solely with marine ecology.

CHEMICAL PROPERTIES OF WATER

Water is commonly referred to as the universal solvent, for no other single fluid compares with water relative to its ability to dissolve a great array of solutes. Many substances dissolved in water can pass in or out through the living membranes of plants and animals. Chemical compounds ionize readily in water and provide many radicals and considerable versatility in the rearrangement of chemical substances.

OXYGEN

One of the most critical chemical factors in an aquatic environment is the amount of oxygen in the water because most living organisms (excepting anaerobic forms) require this vital gas for respiration. Since atmospheric oxygen is twenty to twenty-five times more abundant than is the content of oxygen in water, it does not attain the same degree of importance nor become a limiting factor relative to survival in a terrestrial area, as it sometimes does in freshwater or marine environments. As is evident in the accompanying table (Table 4–5), temperature and salinity govern the saturation concentration of oxygen, but thermal values are more effective than salinity in controlling the degree of saturation. Quite obviously, the lower the temperature, the greater the oxygen-retaining capacity of the water, whether it is freshwater or sea water.

In freshwater areas of any depth and in the salt water habitat, there are three recognizable zones with regard to oxygen concentration. A surface stratum, where the oxygen tends to be in equilibrium with the atmosphere above—that is, it will be near the concentration point for the existing thermal and saline conditions. Below this surface stratum of variable depth (generally a few centimeters to a half meter or more) is an intermediate stratum where oxygen values fluctuate in accordance with existing factors. Respiration, decomposition of organic materials

TABLE 4–5. *Comparison of the Saturation Concentration of Oxygen in Freshwater and Salt Water Environments with Varying Temperatures*

	TEMPERATURE, C.	SATURATION POINT IN MILLILITER PER LITER
Freshwater	0	10.27
Salt water*	0	8.08
Freshwater	30	5.57
Salt water	30	4.52

* Salinity of salt water is 34.33 parts per thousand.

(stagnant ponds), and stream pollution—all tend to reduce the amount of available oxygen, while photosynthetic activity will often balance or more than balance oxygen loss. At times, because of optimal photosynthetic conditions or rapid warming of water, this stratum may become supersaturated with oxygen; values of 300 per cent in some ponds and 180 per cent in marine areas have been recorded in the past. Finally, the deepest layers of water will usually have a very low oxygen concentration in the deeper lakes and oceanic areas because the continual decomposition of organic debris, the respiration of organisms inhabiting these deeper waters, and the complete absence of photosynthetic activity in these lower strata will tend to deplete the oxygen concentration. This deep stratum is entirely dependent upon the slow transport of oxygen from the overlying intermediate layer.

Oxygen concentration fluctuates in shallow marine and freshwater areas within a twenty-four-hour period. This fluctuation, which is particularly noticeable in ponds, in shallow lakes, and in intertidal areas, is called an **oxygen pulse.** Photosynthetic activity during the day results in a maximal oxygen concentration before dusk, but in the course of the nocturnal interval, constant respiratory activity reduces the available oxygen to a minimum before dawn. The following day, oxygen gradually increases, becoming supersaturated in regions where plant life is abundant, causing a bubbling of the gas from plant surfaces during periods of most intense illumination. Oxygen may be transported to different strata by turbulence (wave action). This is effective if water is shallow, but is unsatisfactory where deep bodies of water are involved. **Eddy transfer,** as shown in Figure 4–8, is a rapid and very effective means of supplying both upper and lower strata with oxygen, provided that an

FIGURE 4–8 Eddy transfer occurring along the upper and lower surface of an intermediate current in either a stream or lake (pond).

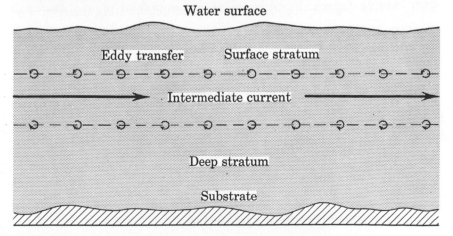

Water surface

Eddy transfer   Surface stratum

Intermediate current

Deep stratum

Substrate

intermediate current contains a sufficient supply of this vital gas. Mass sinking of large volumes of water during the spring and fall overturn brought about by temperature-density differences (discussed in the section entitled Stratification and Zonation in Chapter II, p. 32) is a means of circulating various gases within large bodies of freshwater. This mass sinking of water occurring twice a year (spring and fall overturn) will carry large quantities of oxygen into the deeper strata of ponds and lakes and is the most common means of transport in such areas. In the open ocean, oxygen is delivered to lower strata by complex currents. A polar current originating in arctic and antarctic seas will move from the surface with an average value of about 8.0 ml. of oxygen per liter of water. This water moves slowly, gradually sinking and carrying oxygen to great depths, arriving at the equator with about 3.0 ml. of oxygen per liter of water, then reaches the surface and begins its return to the poles. Water rarely lacks oxygen, but in the Black Sea below 150 meters and in certain restricted areas off the coast of southern California, oxygen is absent.

Some organisms are independent of the oxygen concentration in water because they move to the surface and obtain atmospheric oxygen. This is true of aquatic mammals and reptiles (whales, seals, porpoises, alligators, and others) as well as mature insects (aquatic beetles, true bugs), freshwater snails, and some larval insects (mosquitoes, fly larvae). Ingenious devices such as air tubes or the ability to trap air bubbles in surface hairs or under wing covers are utilized by some of these forms to insure submersion for an interval of time. Some bacteria and a few animals can live anaerobically by breaking down food substances such as glucose, glycogen, and other carbohydrates and obtaining oxygen from this source. *Toredo*, the shipworm, can live anaerobically, for half of the dry weight of its body is glycogen! The mussel, *Mytilus edulis*, often lives in polluted waters, where the oxygen concentration is low owing to decomposition. This organism can live without oxygen for several weeks, but during this time it remains relatively inactive. The Japanese oyster, *Ostrea gigas*, according to Ishida (1935) showed little change in respiratory rate until the oxygen concentration was reduced to 1.5 ml. of oxygen per liter of water. Moore (1942) found that freshwater fish tolerated lower oxygen concentration values when exposed to winter temperatures than when exposed to summer temperatures. In general, plants have a lower oxygen requirement than do animals of equal weight. Where competition for available oxygen occurs between plants and animals, animals usually succumb first.

CARBON DIOXIDE

The decomposition of organic matter and the respiratory activity of plants and animals produce carbon dioxide. This gas is one of the essential raw materials necessary for photosynthetic activity by green plants. Carbon dioxide combines chemically with water to produce carbonic acid (H_2CO_3), which influences the hydrogen ion concentration (pH) of water. Carbonic acid dissociates to produce hydrogen (H^+) and bicarbonate (HCO_3^-) ions. The bicarbonate radical may undergo further dissociation forming more hydrogen (H^+) and carbonate (CO_3^{--}). The amount of free carbon dioxide in water is about 0.5 ml. of carbon dioxide per liter of water, but much more carbon dioxide is present in ionized form as bicarbonate (HCO_3^-) and carbonate (CO_3^{--}) radicals. Sea water with a salinity of 35 parts per thousand contains about 46.8 ml. of carbon dioxide per liter, much of which is in combined (ionized) form as CO_3^{--} or HCO_3^-. Free (uncombined) carbon dioxide will exist as carbon dioxide (CO_2) or carbonic acid (H_2CO_3), which remains in equilibrium with the combined forms.

When carbonic acid dissociates, it releases hydronium ions (H_3O), which alters the pH of water ($H_2CO_3 \rightarrow H^+ + HCO_3^-$; the H^+ released combines with water to produce the hydronium ion, $H^+ + H_2O \rightarrow H_3O$). At low pH values (acidic water), most carbon dioxide is present in free form, but at neutrality (or close to neutrality) most carbon dioxide exists as HCO_3^-, and at high pH values most carbon dioxide will be present as CO_3^{--}. As you can see, the anions HCO_3^- and CO_3^{--} plus the anions of other weak acids increase as conditions become more alkaline, tending to resist hydrogen ion changes. This is called **buffer action, or buffering**. Buffering effectively reduces hydrogen ion variability in bodies of water. Sea water and hard freshwater have high quantities of these anions, yielding a highly buffered medium. Surface waters of the open ocean will have pH values of 8.0 to 8.4, but deeper water will be closer to neutrality (pH 7.4 to 7.9). There is often a wider range of pH values in shallow marine waters, estuaries, and tide pools. Hydrogen ion values in freshwater areas may vary from 2.0 to 12.0, but most bodies of freshwater have a pH ranging between 6.0 and 9.0. In poorly buffered ponds and lakes (soft water areas), the photosynthetic activity of plants reduces the amount of carbon dioxide during the daylight period, but at night the respiratory activity of plants and animals leads to an increase in the quantity of the gas. These changes in carbon dioxide content lead to changes in pH, causing a pH pulse (Figure 4–9), which is brought about by the dissociative changes described. This same pH pulse would be obvious in hard freshwater and oceanic areas if there were no buffering action; however, buffering reduces pH variation to a minimum.

The amount of free or uncombined carbon dioxide in water is of ecological importance; it governs the precipitation of calcium in the form of calcium carbonate ($CaCO_3$). Calcium precipitates when temperatures and salinity are high and the amount of uncombined carbon dioxide is low; this means more carbonate (CO_3^-) is present to combine with the calcium cation (Ca^{++}). These conditions exist in shallow tropi-

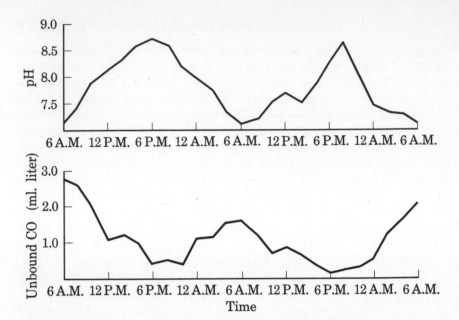

FIGURE 4–9 Changes in the hydrogen ion concentration of surface water in a freshwater pond over a two-day period during late summer in the upper graph. The lower graph indicates the changes in carbon dioxide concentration which increases during the dark portion of the forty-eight-hour interval owing to an interruption of photosynthetic activity.

cal waters, where evaporation is high. This raises the salinity and the photosynthetic activity of plants and reduces the quantity of free carbon dioxide in the water. The precipitation of calcium carbonate in tropical areas such as the Bahamas explains the preponderance of thick calcareous shells of shallow water tropical mollusks, plankton, and algae. In deep oceanic waters, temperatures are low and there are no photosynthetic plants; consequently, the carbon dioxide content of the water is high. Deep water fauna (mollusks, crustaceans) possess very fragile skeletons because the precipitation of calcium carbonate is minimal.

HYDROGEN SULFIDE

The deeper strata of many bodies of water, including ponds, lakes, and some estuaries, may contain significant amounts of the toxic gas, hydrogen sulfide. The discharge of this gas is always associated with a substrate that is rich in decaying organic matter. If concentrations of the gas build up, all life but anaerobic bacteria are excluded from the area. Thus we find that in the deeper strata of the Black Sea there is no life exclusive of bacteria because the oxygen concentration drops to zero below 180 to 200 meters, and the hydrogen sulfide concentration is about 0.75 per cent of saturation just below the 200-meter level in most parts of this sea. The accumulation of this toxic gas in the deeper waters of the Black Sea is caused by the Bosphorus Ridge, located only 40 meters from the surface waters, which prevents an effective circulation of water from the Mediterranean Sea. The incoming water tends to float on the surface of the Black Sea, so that only the upper 180 to 200 meters are aerated while the lower 1900 meters retain their hydrogen sulfide concentration. The organic mucks and oozes of many lagoons, estuaries, and lakes may contain a high concentration of hydrogen sulfide, but the organisms associated with this type of substrate (polychaets, lamellibranchs, and others) depend on the overlying bodies of water for sufficient amounts of oxygen to sustain the vital processes.

HYDROGEN ION CONCENTRATION (pH)

Hydrogen ion concentration (relative acidity or alkalinity) has been previously mentioned in this chapter. Early ecological investigators overemphasized the importance of pH to such an extent that it became the source of many jokes about ecological work. A later psychological reaction tempted some ecologists to ignore completely the hydrogen ion concentration. At present, most ecologists are agreed that pH values are very real factors, but probably limited in effect, that cause variable reactions on the part of living organisms.

In freshwater habitats such as acid bogs, swamps, and drainage streams carrying water from these areas, it is not uncommon to record pH values as low as 1.4. Despite the high acidity, rich populations of acidophilic flora and fauna thrive under such conditions. On the other hand, certain lake waters may be quite alkaline, particularly in limestone areas, where the pH may range from 10 to 12. Basophilic plants and animals are found in these areas. In a vast majority of freshwater localities, hydrogen ion values range between 5.5 and 8.5, though a large majority of organisms can tolerate a considerable range of pH values. The speckled trout, for example, can tolerate a pH range of 3.3 to 10.7 without apparent harm, but it is normally found in waters with pH values ranging from 4.1 to 8.5. Welch (1952) has stated that the hydrogen ion concentration is unlikely to be a limiting factor for many freshwater organisms, though a few of them are stenoecious. *Stentor coeruleus*, a protozoan, is restricted to areas with a pH range of 7.7 to 8.0.

Oceanic areas exhibit little change in pH values over vast areas because of the effective buffering action discussed above in the section "Carbon Dioxide." Shallow water areas have a far more extensive pH range brought about by reduced salinity and increased photosynthetic activity. In some tide pools the diurnal range of pH values may be great. Atkins (1922) noted that the marine alga *Ulva* raised the pH as high as 10.0 during midday when photosynthetic activity was progressing at a maximal rate. After dark, values of 5.8 or lower are not uncommon in these shallow bodies of water. Many marine organisms are euryoecious with respect to hydrogen ion values. The wood-boring isopod *Limnoria lignorum* is unaffected by values ranging from 4.5 to 9.6. The intertidal gastropod *Littorina obtusata* displays normal reactions when exposed to an environment where the pH fluctuates between 5.8 and 8.2, but when placed in a more acidic medium (3.8 to 5.8) the gastropod is active, but its behavior is abnormal. It has been found that this same mollusk can tolerate a pH as low as 2.2 for eight hours. Marine diatoms are able to grow where pH values range from 6.5 to 9.0. Algologists have found that some marine algae have intracellular pH values that are extremely acid; *Desmarestia latissima,* a brown alga, has an intracellular pH of 0.78!

Selected References

Atkins, W. R. G. 1922. The influence upon algal cells of an alteration in the hydrogen ion concentration of sea water. Jour. Mar. Biol. Assoc. United Kingdom, 12:789–791.

Bevelander, G. 1952. Calcification in molluscs. Biol. Bull., 102:9–15.

Birge, E. A., and C. Juday. 1911. The inland lakes of Wisconsin. The dissolved gases of the water and their biological significance. Wisc. Geol. Nat. Hist. Surv. Bull., 22:1–259.

Boyce, S. G. 1954. The salt spray community. Ecol. Monogr., 24:29–67.

Brown, H. W., and Minna E. Jewell. 1926. Further studies on the fishes of an acid lake. Trans. Amer. Microsc. Soc., 45:20–34.

Edwards, G. A., and L. Irvin. 1943. The influence of temperature and season upon the oxygen consumption of the sand crab, *Emerita talpoida* Say. Jour. Cell. Comp. Physiol., 21:169–182.

Ishida, S. 1935. On the oxygen consumption in the oyster, *Ostrea gigas* Thurberg under various conditions. Sci. Repts. Tohoku Imp. Univ., 10:619–638.

Krogh, A. *Osmotic Regulation in Aquatic Animals* (New York: Cambridge Univ. Press, 1939), pp. 1–242.

Kuenan, P. H. 1937. On the total amount of sedimentation in the deep sea. Amer. Jour. Sci., 34:457–468.

———. *Marine Geology* (New York: John Wiley, 1959), pp. i–x, 1–568.

Moore, H. B. *Marine Ecology* (New York: John Wiley, 1958), pp. i–xi, 1–493.

Moore, W. G. 1942. Field studies on the oxygen requirements of certain freshwater fishes. Ecology, 23:319–329.

Pearse, A. S. *The Emigrations of Animals from the Sea* (Dryden, N.Y.: Sherwood Press, 1950), pp. i–xii, 1–210.

Russell, F. S. 1927. The vertical distribution of plankton in the sea. Biol. Rev., 2:213–262.

Sparks, R. 1936. On the relation between metabolism and temperature in some marine lamellibranchs and its zoogeographical significance. Kgl. Danske Videnskab. Selskab; Biol. Medd., 13:1–27.

Stauber, L. A. 1950. The problem of physiological species with special reference to oysters and oyster drills. Ecology, 31:109–118.

Twenhofel, W. H. *Principles of Sedimentation* (New York: McGraw-Hill, 1939), pp. i–x, 1–610.

Welch, P. S. *Limnology* (New York: McGraw-Hill, 1952), pp. i–xi, 1–538.

Wilson, D. P. *Life of the Shore and Shallow Sea* (London: Nicholson & Watson, 1951), pp. i–xvii, 1 213.

Yonge, C. M. *The Sea Shore* (London: Collins, 1949), pp. i–xvi, 1–310.

V. Climatology

A consideration of the environment and its effect on animal and plant life must take into account the climatic conditions prevailing in the immediate area. Often there is confusion between the two terms, *weather* and *climate*. Both refer to meteorological elements prevalent in a particular locality, but the time unit varies. Weather refers to relatively short-term conditions in any area—generally, hourly, daily, or weekly changes. The climate, in contrast, entails long-term periods—months, seasons, or years. In this chapter we shall endeavor to examine only the climatic conditions that are of prime importance to the plant or animal.

Climatic factors of considerable importance to the organism are temperature, precipitation, humidity (vaporized moisture), solar radiation, wind, and barometric pressure. In the following account climatic factors will be discussed individually, but it must be emphasized that there is such considerable interaction between meteorological factors that recording a single factor seldom gives a true picture of the environment or explains an organism's success or failure in a particular area. Thus, even though the temperature may be ideal for a population of plants, if the precipitation is too great or scant, the plant will fail to survive. Similarly, although temperature and precipitation are within reasonable limits for an animal, if the humidity varies too greatly the organism must locate itself in a different environment or die.

TEMPERATURE

Thermal ranges on earth vary considerably, with the lowest recorded temperature of −126.9° F., a reading taken on August 24, 1960, at the Soviet plateau station of Vastok in Antarctica. The highest temperature, 136.4° F. in the shade, has been recorded in the Sahara Desert (Azizia, Libya). These are thermal extremes recorded from widely separated points on our planet. In any one area, we find that ranges of temperatures are far more restrictive, but temperatures in any one locality, whether we are concerned with an extensive area or a small segment of a microenvironment, will demonstrate some variability from time to time. It is not uncommon for temperatures to rise or fall 10 degrees within a period of an hour in terrestrial areas. Temperatures vary with latitude throughout the world. In general, though exceptions exist, higher temperatures prevail in the equatorial areas, and cooler temperatures in the polar areas, with the south pole having the lower thermal values. As for life, many plants and animals thrive under conditions of thermal fluctuation, for very often different stages of a life cycle require or show improvement with differences in temperature. Generally, larval or embryonic stages are more sensitive to thermal variability and often cannot tolerate the changes that would not endanger more mature organisms. In the past, there has been a tendency to emphasize temperature in the environment, perhaps because it is a factor that is easy to measure and the equipment is easily installed and records are readily interpreted. Actually thermal variability may be of little importance in many cases, particularly in mature aggregations of plants and animals because many are eurythermal.

Thermal averages or means for any area are of very limited value to the ecologist; they render only rough indications of the true conditions transpiring in any locality. U.S. Weather Bureau Stations situated throughout the United States often report average or mean temperatures, such as the monthly maximal mean temperature and the monthly minimal mean temperature, which are practically of no value to the ecologist for two reasons. First, such temperature records cover an extremely long time period from the ecologist's standpoint. Very often ecological problems are of such a nature that hourly or daily thermal values or ranges are of considerable importance and may explain such activities as migration, hibernation, and other related events. Second, the weather station recording such data may be situated a short distance or a very great distance from the area under investigation. At any rate the climatic situation will vary. Weather Bureau data, therefore, are not indicative of the living conditions to which the organism is exposed (Wolfe, 1951; Wolfe, *et al.*, 1949). We find that maximal and minimal temperatures recorded in the immediate area for a unit period of a day or a week are

FIGURE 5–1 Maximum-minimum thermometer with metallic index can be reset at any time to measure the maximum and minimum temperature transpiring for any unit period of time in any locality. The scale at the right registers maximal temperatures. The black indices have recorded a minimal temperature of 10° F. and a maximal temperature in excess of 130° F.

FIGURE 5–2 An electrically powered barometer with a revolving drum for tracing the hourly and daily changes in barometric pressure. The drum makes one complete revolution per week.

of far greater value to the ecologist. For example, for the month of June an area might have a mean temperature of 22.0° C. (about 70° F.), yet maximum temperatures might approach 35.0° C. (about 90° F.) and minimum temperatures 9.0° C. (about 48° F.). This is a temperature range that might be intolerable to a species with an optimal thermal requirement of 22.0° C. Another area might have the same mean temperature, but the thermal range could be far more restrictive, with maximal values of 26.5° C. (about 80° F.) and a minimum of 15.0° C. (about 60° F.). A maximum-minimum thermometer (Figure 5-1) is an inexpensive instrument generally used to record the highest and lowest temperatures that have occurred in a particular area. Temperatures in small, restricted spaces may be recorded by small thermister probes (Figure 5-3).

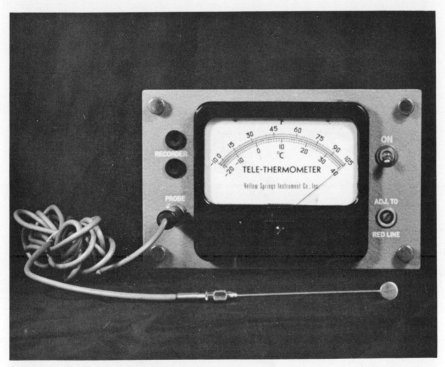

FIGURE 5-3 A thermister unit with a banjo-type probe used to record the micro-environmental temperatures instantaneously or for a unit period of time.

Frost, representing condensed surface moisture that has frozen on objects, is an indication of freezing temperatures (0° C., or 32° F.) in the immediate area. It must be realized, however, that in order for frost to appear, the humidity must be sufficiently high to allow surface deposition of moisture on objects. Consequently, freezing temperatures may occur without frost if the humidity is sufficiently low. Freezing temperatures damage or kill some forms of life, because annual plants and the exposed parts of many perennials die after exposure. Woody stems, roots, rhizomes, seeds, and spores survive the freezing temperatures and renew their growth and reproductive activity with the return of higher temperatures. Invertebrates die, except a few that migrate to warmer climes; vertebrates likewise hibernate or migrate if freezing temperatures become too severe. The length of the frost-free period in any area is important, for it will dictate the types of organisms that exist in the locality. It is during this portion of the year that plants and animals exhibit greatest activity, undergo most rapid growth, and carry on the vital reproductive activities necessary for the propagation of the species. In tropical and semitropical areas there is seldom any frost, but plants and animals subjected to freezing temperatures in these areas may be damaged or destroyed in large numbers because many of them have no means of protection or of avoiding such harsh environmental conditions.

PRECIPITATION

The amount of moisture falling on an area, regardless of the physical form—that is, whether it is in liquid, vaporous, or frozen form—is designated as precipitation. The type of precipitation depends upon the season and meteorological factors such as wind, air pressure, and temperature. Rainfall is the most common type of precipitation in temperate and tropical areas. The manner in which the rain falls is of considerable importance ecologically because it may vary from a light drizzle to torrential downpours. Light drizzle is often of little importance; relatively little water is deposited over long periods of time and very little moisture actually penetrates the soil because much of it evaporates rapidly. In marked contrast, a gentle, steady rain is most effective because much of it penetrates the soil, replenishing the soil water necessary for the continued existence of soil plants and animals. Torrential rains, so common in tropical areas and during localized thunderstorms, can often be most disastrous because sustained rainfall of this type may lead to extensive soil erosion and flooding. Flooding and erosion are the result of extensive quantities of runoff water. Rain falls so rapidly that not all of it can penetrate the soil, and over an extensive area the surface runoff may build up into considerable amounts and take the path of least resistance, causing gullying or channeling and carrying soil particles with it (erosion).

Hail, sleet, and snow are forms of frozen rain. Hail is formed by the rapid and repeated ascent of water through areas of supercooled (cooled below 0° C., or 32° F., but not present in frozen form) water droplets

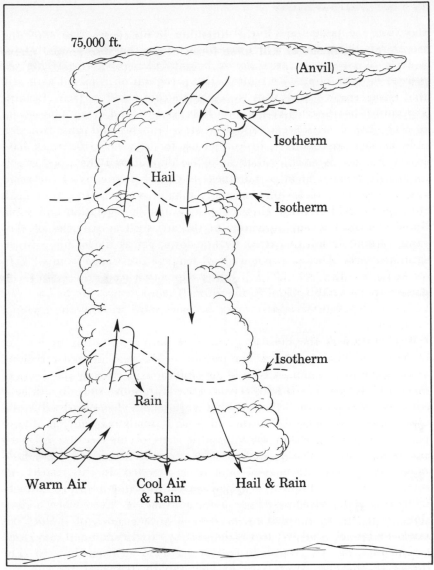

75,000 ft.

(Anvil)

Isotherm

Hail

Isotherm

Isotherm

Rain

Warm Air

Cool Air
& Rain

Hail & Rain

FIGURE 5–4   A thunderhead, indicating the direction of air flow through the storm cloud and the repeated ascent and descent of water involved in the formation of hail. Dotted lines represent isotherms or lines of equal temperature through the cloud.

in cloud masses into cooler temperature zones, freezing the water. Concentric layers of supercooled water accumulate on the surface and freeze as the ice pellets pass through the middle and upper regions of the thunderhead (Figure 5–4). These chunks, or balls, of frozen moisture may be of considerable size and weight. Since hail is formed during the warm growing season, it may cause considerable damage in agricultural areas. Sleet (ice pellets) and snow are formed during cooler portions of the year. Ice pellets are fine transparent beads of ice that represent frozen rain. Sleet occurs when rain falls from a warm air mass through a layer of air that is freezing or below freezing before striking the ground or some object. Very often such precipitation is mixed with rain that is supercooled and turns to ice on touching cold surfaces, forming a beautiful but destructive glaze on trees, shrubs, and grass. The weight of such glaze is often great enough to snap branches and cause considerable damage, particularly in coniferous forests where the trees have leaves that act as additional areas of ice deposit and the wood is soft and easily broken. Food procurement is difficult for many of the vertebrates (especially birds) that normally inhabit northern forests or fields through the winter when glaze encrusts available vegetation and seeds. Snow is formed when impurities in the air, such as particles of clay, sand, carbon, or ash in extremely fine form, act as nuclei for a supersaturated mass of water vapor if cloud temperatures range from $-20°$ C. ($-4°$ F.) to $-12.2°$ C. ($10°$ F.). Water vapor that comes in contact with these nuclei crystallizes and forms snow. If temperatures are below $-39°$ C. ($-38°$ F.), supersaturated vapor becomes snow without the presence of nuclei.

Just as rain is the most frequent type of precipitation in warmer climates and during the warmer portion of the year in cooler regions, snow is the most common type of precipitation in circumpolar areas of the world during the coldest periods of the year. Snow, since it is in flake form, is not as compact as water—that is, 10 inches of snowfall will equal about 1 inch of rainfall. Plants and some animals may not be able to convert snow into usable water until a thaw occurs because in many plants and animals this crystallized water must be converted into a fluid before it can pass across root hairs or be ingested. In this respect, we may say that a condition of **physiological drought** prevails, though, ironically, water in a crystalline phase is plentiful. Even when a thaw does occur, the snow often melts so rapidly that much of it does not percolate into the soil but leaves the area by rapid runoff and may cause serious flooding and erosion in regions far removed from the area. The degree of thawing depends upon how rapidly temperatures rise, the maximum temperatures attained, and how long these temperatures remain above the freezing point. Mist and fog are two supplementary forms of precipitation; the water is in exceedingly fine droplets and evenly dispersed throughout the atmosphere, so that it falls very slowly, if at all. A sudden drop in temperature can cause condensation and rain.

The measurement of precipitation is accomplished by means of rain gauges, which will measure all types of precipitation. The simplest type of rain gauge is represented in Figure 5-5, but a more complex and expensive one is the tipping bucket rain gauge. The bucket receiving the precipitation is divided and balanced so that one side fills, tips water into a reservoir, and then allows the other side to fill. This device

(A)   (B)

FIGURE 5–5   A cylindrical rain gauge (A) with a dipstick to measure the precipitation in any area; a wedge type rain gauge (B) with etched divisions allows measurement of rainfall to the nearest one-hundredth inch.

is delicately balanced and will tip after 1/100 of an inch of rainfall
enters the bucket. A remote control device may be installed so that an
electric signal is relayed to a recording device every time the bucket
tips. Another type of recording device weighs the precipitation and
records the weight directly on a graph in milliliters or inches of rainfall.
The ecologist usually measures precipitation in the metric system (milliliters), but the U.S. Weather Bureau uses the British system (inches).

The distribution of precipitation varies considerably from area to area as a result of prevailing winds, temperature differences, and movement of frontal systems. U.S. Weather Bureau statistics are valuable to the ecologist only in that they will yield information relative to the general trend in precipitation. Any ecologist must realize that the amount of precipitation will vary, even within the limits of a habitat, depending on vegetation density and the general topography. The distribution of rainfall throughout the year is as important as the total quantity of precipitation within a unit period of time. The mere fact that two areas receive 40 inches of rainfall per year does not necessarily mean that they will have the same type of vegetation or animals. Forty inches may fall within a brief span of time (desert biome) or may be evenly distributed throughout the year (deciduous forest biome). In general, forest and grassland areas require an even distribution of rainfall if the flora and fauna are to be maintained without showing signs of adverse climatic conditions. In desert areas there is an uneven distribution of rain, which occurs once or twice a year, so that many plants must germinate, grow, and reproduce (flower and produce seed) within a brief period of time—a few days or weeks.

Since animals depend on the vegetation for food and shelter, and the vegetation is directly dependent upon the quantity and distribution of precipitation in terrestrial areas, all of the living components of the environment depend on precipitation either directly or indirectly. The amount of rainfall throughout the year for a desert type of environment ranges from 0 to 10 inches; 10 to 20 inches will support a grassland type of environment (short grass prairies); 20 to 30 inches, a long grass prairie or savanna (open woodland); 30 to 50 inches, a "dry deciduous or coniferous forest"; and over 50 inches of rainfall per year will allow for the establishment of a wet temperate forest (coniferous or deciduous type) and tropical rain forests. A comparison of maps in Figure 5–6 showing the annual precipitation throughout the forty-eight states of the continental United States and the type of vegetation naturally occurring in these areas indicates the dependency of vegetation on annual precipitation.

VAPORIZED MOISTURE

Heat caused by solar radiation evaporates millions of tons of water vapor into the atmosphere, daily, from open bodies of water (lakes, rivers, swamps, and oceans) moist earth, and transpiring leaf surfaces; it is not uncommon for a small tree to lose 2,000 gallons of water from its leaf surfaces during the course of its growing season. As moist air rises, it cools in the upper atmosphere, causing some condensation as the saturation point (100% relative humidity) is reached, forming clouds of various

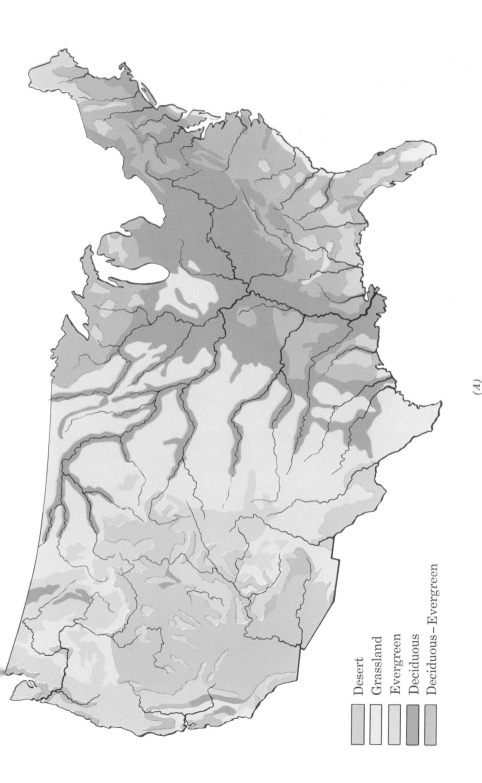

Desert
Grassland
Evergreen
Deciduous
Deciduous – Evergreen

(A)

FIGURE 5-6 Comparison of vegetation (Map A) and precipitation zones (Map B) in the United States. Note how deciduous forest vegetation follows stream systems in the Midwest.

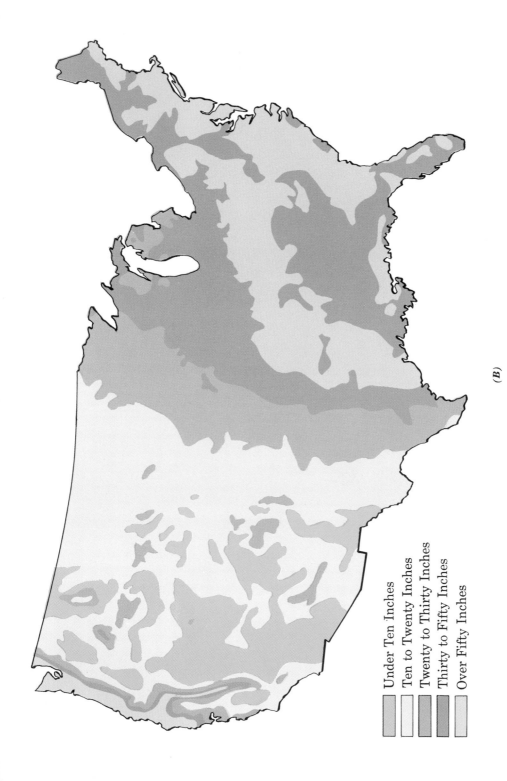

Under Ten Inches
Ten to Twenty Inches
Twenty to Thirty Inches
Thirty to Fifty Inches
Over Fifty Inches

(B)

FIGURE 5-6 Comparison of vegetation (Map A) and precipitation zones (Map B) in the United States. Note how deciduous forest vegetation follows stream systems in the Midwest.

types. Everyone has seen cloud formation in miniature. A tea kettle emitting steam from a spout is an example: as the hot water vapor cools below its saturation point in the surrounding air, a cloud is formed. Warm air exhaled on a cold day by an animal forms a small cloud of supersaturated moist air before it disperses into the surrounding drier atmosphere. In nature, clouds are formed by moist air rising from warm ground surfaces into the air; there is an **adiabatic cooling** (about 3° C., or 5½° F. for every 1,000 feet of elevation). Clouds are also formed when warm ocean or lake air passes over cooler land surfaces, particularly when air is forced to rise to clear hills or a mountain range. Clouds are classified according to their method of formation. Clouds formed by rising air currents tend to appear puffy and piled; they are referred to as **cumulus type.** Clouds that are formed when a layer of air is cooled below the saturation level without gross vertical movement appear as flat sheets; they are called **stratus** clouds.

Clouds, according to an international system of classification, may be placed into four families. The high cloud family consists of clouds that are located about 20,000 feet above the earth's surface (at the base); the middle clouds may have a base at about 10,000 feet; and low clouds may have a base at ground level (fog), but rarely extend above 6,500 feet. A fourth family, clouds of vertical development, include the **cumulonimbus** (thunderhead) clouds (Figure 5–7) that exhibit violent updrafts and have the greatest vertical dimension of any single cloud type. The base of such a cloud may be close to ground level, but the anvil head may be located at 75,000 feet or higher. **Nimbostratus** clouds, the layered, dark, rain clouds, and the cumulonimbus clouds complete the water cycle that is so important to life on earth. Such a cycle includes the following events: evaporation, cooling, condensation, precipitation, absorption (by plants, animals, and soil) or runoff into bodies of water—followed by evaporation.

Water in a much more finely dispersed form than the obvious clouds fills the atmosphere in varying amounts from place to place and from one time unit to the next. Often this invisible atmospheric moisture is termed *humidity,* which is the amount (mass) of water vapor present in a certain volume of air. The higher the temperature of the air, the greater the mass of moisture that particular volume of air can retain; thus at 0° C. (32° F.), the atmosphere can retain a maximum of 4.85 grams of water vapor per cubic meter; at 16° C. (61° F.), 13.65 grams of moisture per cubic meter; and at 30° C. (86° F.), a maximum of 30.4 grams of water vapor per cubic meter. **Absolute humidity,** a term seldom used because of its limited value, refers to the amount of water vapor present in the air, such as the number of grams per cubic meter. **Relative humidity,** the term most often used or implied, is the percentage of moisture present in the air under existing conditions of temperature and pressure as compared to the condition of saturation (100% relative

(A)

(B)

(C)

(D)

FIGURE 5–7 Cloud types: photo *A*, cirrus (high clouds); photo *B*, cirro-cumulus (mackerel sky); photo *C*, cumulus (fair-weather clouds); photo *D*, nimbo-stratus (rain clouds); photo *E*, cumulo-nimbus (thunderhead). Photos *A–D*, courtesy of the U.S. Dept. of Commerce, the U.S. Weather Bureau; photo *E*, courtesy of the U.S. Air Force.

(E)

humidity) under the same conditions. If the temperature of the air changes, relative humidity also changes, although the moisture content of the atmosphere may remain the same. Thus air with a relative humidity of 75% at 20° C. will contain less moisture than will air with a relative humidity of 75% at 25° C. If air is heated, the relative humidity drops because the air can retain a greater percentage (mass) of moisture per unit volume; but if the temperature drops, the relative humidity also drops. Contrary to popular belief, dew does not fall; it is water vapor that has reached the saturation point (100% relative humidity) by coming in contact with a solid surface that is cool enough to cause the condensation of moisture. Examples are the surface of blades of

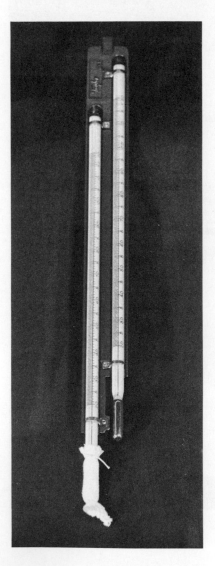

FIGURE 5–8 A sling-type psychrometer with a dry bulb thermometer (right) and a wet bulb thermometer with a wick wrapped around the bulb (left) for determining the relative humidity.

grass after dusk that cool rapidly after the sun has set, or the cool surface of a container of ice water on a humid (muggy) day in summer.

The relative humidity in a localized environmental area may be measured by several instruments. In confined spaces it is most convenient to make a colorimetric comparison between standard color discs and paper impregnated with cobalt thiocyanate. After a certain time (about two hours) the paper changes color, which is then checked against the standard that will give the relative humidity. The only drawback in using this technique is the amount of time necessary for color change. For less restricted spaces, a regular **psychrometer** may be used. Such an instrument is simple to make. Two thermometers, a dry bulb thermometer and a wet bulb thermometer, are mounted side by side on a flat board (Figure 5–8). Wrapped around the bulb of the wet bulb thermometer is a muslin or nylon wick that is moistened with distilled water prior to operation. The board is swung through the air in a rotary fashion, which will cause evaporation from the surface of the wick; this in turn lowers the temperature of the wet bulb thermometer. The drier the air (the lower the relative humidity), the greater the evaporation and the lower the temperature recorded on the wet bulb thermometer.

FIGURE 5–9 A revolving disc hygrothermograph with a clock wind mechanism for recording the humidity and temperature simultaneously.

A difference in temperatures between these two thermometers for a particular barometric pressure will give the relative humidity. The relative humidity is ascertained from a table prepared by C. F. Marvin (1941) for the U.S. Department of Commerce. An electrical resistance apparatus employing a film of lithium chloride that changes electrical resistance with small changes in relative humidity has also been used in recent years. **Hygrographs** are instruments used for recording humidity conditions for longer periods of time. Usually a revolving drum or a circular disk equipped with a calibrated sheet of paper (Figure 5–9) will give a continuous record of humidity changes for a day or week. The sensitive element consists of a bundle of blonde human hair that changes length with changes in humidity. The change in length is recorded by movement of an inked stylus over a sheet of recording paper, giving a continuous record of humidity fluctuation. Another instrument, the **hygrothermograph,** records the temperature and humidity simultaneously on the same chart.

Vapor pressure deficit (V.P.D.), a term often used by ecologists, is an indication of the evaporation tension that exists in the immediate area. In other words, the evaporation rate is proportional to the vapor pressure deficit, not the relative humidity. Vapor pressure deficit represents the difference between the partial pressure of water at saturation and the prevailing vapor pressure of the air. Thus it is the "deficit," or the amount of water vapor necessary under existing conditions to saturate a particular volume of air. Evaporation, or the loss of water from a moist surface or a body of water, will vary in rate, depending upon the climatic conditions present in the immediate area. An increase in temperature, which will raise the moisture-retaining capacity of the air, will also increase the rate of evaporation. Thus on a hot summer day, evaporation occurs at a maximal rate. This moist air rises rapidly and cools as it rises vertically, often forming the familiar cumulonimbus cloud (thunderhead). An increase in wind movement over a moist surface (up to a certain value) will also increase the rate of evaporation because the moisture (moist air) that is evaporating will be moved away and replaced by a drier air that in turn has a greater water-retaining capacity. Evaporation rate decreases with increases in atmospheric pressure and water vapor. The rate of evaporation is controlled by a number of structural adaptations in living organisms. Plants may reduce their rate of evaporation (transpiration) by having a thicker bark on exposed limbs, shorter stems, or fewer and smaller leaves. The number of openings (stomata) on the leaf surface may be reduced in order to conserve more moisture. These structural adaptations are particularly vital in desert or semidesert environments where water is a precious commodity and must be retained between infrequent, irregular, or sparse amounts of precipitation. As a consequence, we find many variations and combinations of the above-mentioned structural features in plants living in regions where precipitation or physiological drought are important factors in the struggle for survival. Animals inhabiting these areas reduce the rate of moisture loss by having fewer sweat glands or none at all, a thick pelt, thick skin, or a body surface covered by scales (reptiles) or an exoskeleton (insects).

Although water balance is important in all organisms, animals inhabiting desert areas are more drastically affected by water balance than are terrestrial animals in other types of environments. Replenishment of lost water is more difficult in arid areas, yet water loss is continuously occurring. Water is lost from the body by sweat glands in the skin, water in the feces, water in urine, and water vapor in expired air. These losses must be balanced by water gains brought about by drinking water, water in food, or oxidation water. During the course of evolution, various physiological adaptations have enabled desert animals to live in an area where effective control of water loss is necessary for survival. Water holes yielding a continuous supply of drinking water for the desert fauna are not always available, particularly where periods between measurable amounts of precipitation are in intervals of years rather than of months. Many desert animals either depend on vegetation or other animal life containing appreciable quantities of water or on dry plant food such as seeds that contain relatively little free water. Many of the animals living on dry foods possess as much water in their tissues as do nondesert forms of life because they are able to convert some of the ingested food into water by oxidation. This involves oxidizing the food to produce carbon dioxide and water, as shown in the following equation:

$$C_6H_{12}O_6 \text{ (glucose)} + O_2 \rightarrow 6CO_2 + 6H_2O.$$

Fats are most efficient in yielding water through oxidation because the greater proportionate amount of hydrogen yields 1.1 grams of water per gram of fat metabolized, but a gram of carbohydrate and fat release 0.6 gram and 0.3 gram of water, respectively.

Water loss in desert animals is reduced by the production of a concentrated urine containing higher concentrations of salts and urea than are found in nonxeric forms. Man releases a urine with a salt content of 2.2 per cent and a urea concentration of 6 per cent; the kangaroo rat (*Dipodomys*) releases a urine with a salt content of 7 per cent and a urea concentration of 23 per cent. Other vertebrates and some invertebrates—birds, reptiles, insects, and some mollusks—conserve water by producing large quantities of uric acid. Uric acid is relatively insoluble in water; it crystallizes from solution, thus allowing for the reabsorption of water in the excretory organ. Some types of animal life inhabiting deserts have an outer covering (scales of reptilian representatives and the exoskeleton of arthropods) that impedes the passage of moisture from the internal tissues of the body. Finally the behavioral pattern of activity of many desert forms, particularly mammals, has evolved as a favorable factor in prevention of water loss. Many of the mammals are active only during periods of darkness, when the evaporation rate of the surrounding atmosphere is low. During the diurnal period they seek shelters such as burrows or caves, where the humidity is higher, temperatures are lower, and the loss of water is decreased to a great extent.

The rate of evaporation can be measured by several rather simple instruments. A device used at many weather stations is the **evaporimeter**, which consists of a container with an exposed surface of water. The rate of water loss from the surface can be recorded in milliliters of water loss per square centimeter per day or any other convenient system of measurement may be used by recording the amount of water that must be added over a certain period of time to bring the water level back to the zero line or its original level. For a number of years, ecologists have used a simple device recommended and manufactured by Livingston

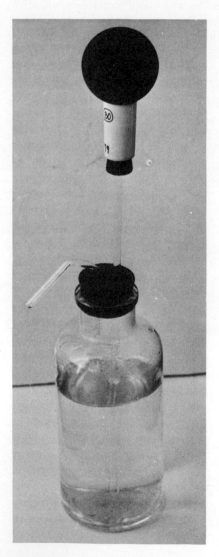

FIGURE 5–10 A Livingston black bulb atmometer mounted above a glass reservoir. When used in conjunction with a white bulb it may be used in calculating the radiant energy as well as the rate of evaporation for a particular area.

(1908). This instrument, called an **atmometer** (Figure 5–10), consists of a porous hollow porcelain bulb filled with distilled water and connected to a reservoir with a zero line. Water evaporates from the surface of the sphere in direct proportion to the vapor pressure deficit in the environment. The amount of water loss (volume) may be measured each time by filling the reservoir to the zero line after a unit period of time and recording the volume of distilled water added. Rain, dew, mist, or fog will not affect the readings if a glass wool-mercury rain trap is placed in the glass tube running from the reservoir to the bulb. Limitations of the instruments used to measure evaporation rate (evaporimeter and atmometer) are the danger of contamination and the fact that they cannot be used in freezing weather. Any foreign particles contaminating the surface of an evaporimeter or atmometer, such as fungi, algae, insects, dust, and other debris, will affect the rate of evaporation. Ecologists have attempted to nullify this factor by adding minute amounts of fungicides to the distilled water in the reservoir. Though the amounts are minute, the evaporation rate will be altered. It is perhaps open to argument as to whether or not it is best to contend with the contamination or to subject one's figures to some distortion by the addition of anticontaminants. At any rate, the atmometer bulbs must be carefully cleaned periodically to remove surface debris that accumulates over the course of time. After cleaning, they must be calibrated against a laboratory atmometer that has been standardized for this purpose.

A precipitation-evaporation ratio (often expressed as P/E ratio) is the amount of precipitation (volume) for a unit period of time in a certain unit area in comparison to the rate of evaporation (volume) for the same time period and unit area. This ratio is more indicative of the vegetation and hence animal populations that will be found in an area than is either measurement (precipitation or evaporation) considered independently. Thus we may find that two areas may have nearly identical rates of precipitation and the same pattern of distribution, but the evaporation rate in each area may be quite different owing to differences in prevailing winds, consistent differences in barometric pressure, and temperature variability. Similar precipitation rates but different rates of evaporation, or similar rates of evaporation but variations in the amount of precipitation can make the difference between grassland and forest type communities, which will harbor radically diverse plant and animal communities.

SOLAR RADIATION

Radiation received from the sun makes photosynthesis possible and furnishes the planet with the heat energy necessary to warm and maintain temperatures in various areas. The intensity of solar radiation will vary, depending on a number of factors. Within a twenty-four-hour period, the intensity of variation is often acute because when the sun is directly overhead at noon, the angle of incidence of the sun's rays with respect to the earth's surface is approximately 90° (greatest angle of incidence), so that one square meter of sunlight measured at ten meters above the earth's surface will heat about one square meter of the soil, water, or vegetation very intensely (Figure 5–11). However, the same surface area (one square meter) at the same height above the earth's surface (ten meters) will cover a far greater area before or after the noon period because of the reduced angle of incidence. Thus the sun's rays would illuminate and heat a larger area with the same total intensity. One way to demonstrate this fact is to hold a flashlight vertically over a white sheet of paper several inches from the surface in a darkened room. Mark the area illuminated, then tip the flashlight 45° from the vertical and again mark the zone illuminated. As you can see, a far larger zone is illuminated when the source of light is suspended at an angle, but with far less intensity. To return to the natural situation, a certain quantity of heat and light energy is concentrated within an area of one square meter at noon, but the same amount of radiant energy may be dissipated over two square meters during a certain interval before and

FIGURE 5–11 Diagrammatic representation of area illuminated with changes in the angle of incidence (greatest angle of incidence, Diagram *A*; reduced angle of incidence, Diagram *B*). The angle of incidence is inversely proportional to the size of the area illuminated, but directly proportional to the intensity of illumination.

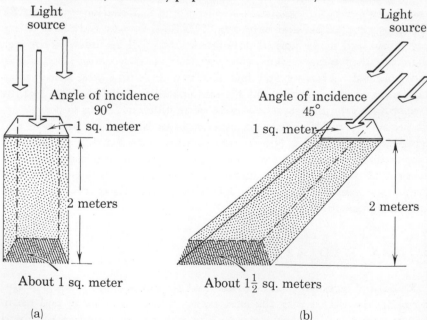

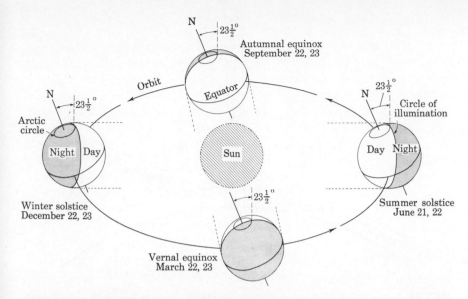

FIGURE 5–12 Orientation of the earth's axis remains fixed in space as the earth revolves about the sun, producing the seasons. From *The Earth Sciences* by Arthur N. Strahler (Harper & Row, Publishers, 1963).

after noon. There is always a **temperature lag** because it will take some time for the convection of heat from the earth's surface to warm the atmosphere above. Maximum temperatures generally occur at about three o'clock in the afternoon in temperate areas.

The season of the year (seasonal aspect) will also cause a variation in intensity of solar radiation because the axis on which the earth rotates may slant a maximum of 23½ degrees from its plane of orbit twice during the year. When the Northern Hemisphere is tipped toward the sun at its greatest angle, this part of the world will experience summer. This is called the **summer solstice;** it occurs on or about June 22. The sun at this time is directly over the Tropic of Cancer (north of the equator). The days are longer and the nights are proportionately shorter the farther north one goes, until in the polar area (Arctic Circle) the day is twenty-four hours long (Land of the Midnight Sun) for a brief interval of time (Figure 5–12). The Northern Hemisphere is warmer for three reasons: the days are longer (about 15 hours in Washington, D.C.); the sun is more nearly overhead, giving a greater angle of incidence; and the sun's rays will pass through less atmosphere (less energy will be diffused by the atmosphere) and a greater amount of radiant energy will reach the earth (Figure 5–13). On or about December 22 the Northern Hemisphere experiences the **winter solstice.** The sun is directly over the Tropic of Capricorn (south of the equator), the Southern Hemisphere is now enjoying the summer weather, and the daylight period is twenty-four hours long in the antarctic area. The arctic region is now sunless, receiving no direct sunlight at all. On or about March 21 and September

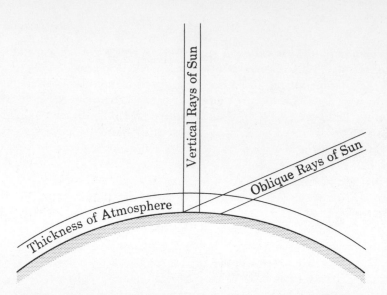

FIGURE 5–13 When the sun is directly overhead, vertical rays strike the earth's surface, releasing more radiant energy than is true of oblique rays which must pass through more atmosphere, dissipating some of the energy. Changes in the angle of the sun occur daily and seasonally. From *Weather and Climate* by Clarence E. Koeppe and George C. De Long. Copyright 1958. McGraw-Hill Book Company. Used by permission.

23 the periods of the **spring** and **fall equinoxes,** respectively, occur. During these periods, the sun is directly over the equator, and day and night are of equal duration over all parts of the globe. The greatest amount of radiant energy received on earth will be in the vicinity of the equator. Polar areas in both hemispheres receive the least amount of solar radiation, as they are never exposed to the direct rays of the sun but always receive varying degrees of oblique radiation.

The intensity of radiation will affect living organisms at different latitudes and seasons of the year. The rate of photosynthesis will increase in direct proportion to the intensity of illumination, to a certain optimum. The optimal values will vary with the age of the plant and the species, so that these figures may range from a hundred foot-candles to several thousand foot-candles for most species. Supraoptimal values may severely limit photosynthesis because the thermal factor associated with light intensity increases transpiration and consequently removes one of the important raw materials (water) for food manufacture. Animals are variously affected indirectly by differences in solar intensity. They will depend on photosynthetic rates of plants, whether the animals are herbivorous or carnivorous (see the section entitled "Food Relationships Among Organisms" in Chapter VII). They are more directly affected by the thermal factor accompanying varying light intensities. Poikilothermous (cold-blooded) organisms often become more active as environmental temperatures increase. Some organisms **estivate** or **hibernate** as

118 |

the solar radiation increases or decreases, in keeping with their thermal requirements. Hibernation is associated with decreased environmental and body temperatures and a lowered rate of metabolism. As the winter season approaches, these organisms seek refuge in caves, dens, burrows, or other shelters and begin a long inactive period interrupted by some to seek and eat stored food. Most hibernating animals depend on stored body fat to maintain a basal metabolic rate during this relatively inactive period. Estivation, on the other hand, is a period of minimal activity during the warmer and often drier part of the year, induced by high temperatures and a lack of moisture or lowered environmental humidity. Snails estivate by secreting a tough, mucoid membrane, known as an epiphragm, across the aperture of the shell.

Some animals with little or no pigment may be severely damaged or killed by exposure to ultraviolet radiation, as this type of solar radiation can cause damage or destroy unprotected tissues. The increased ultraviolet radiation does not penetrate the deeper tissues of larger plants and animals; injury is confined to the more superficial layers of cells. However, unicellular organisms, including bacteria, algae, protozoa, and eggs of different vertebrates and invertebrates, are killed by exposure to ultraviolet radiation with wavelengths shorter than 3100 A. Division of cells can be arrested or impeded and mutations brought about by irreversible alterations in nucleic acids imposed by exposure to this type of radiation. Cell division is arrested by the inhibition of DNA synthesis within the nucleus of the cell, while more concentrated doses of ultraviolet radiation halt RNA synthesis and protein production in the surrounding cytoplasm. It has been found that tissues or cells damaged by ultraviolet radiation may partially recover upon exposure to visible light; such exposure is called **photoreversal,** or **photoreactivation.** Full recovery is never accomplished; the damaged cells or tissues react as though they had received a smaller dose of radiation than that actually administered. This reaction is referred to as the dose-reduction principle.

Photoperiodism, or the length of the daylight period in proportion to the period of darkness, will have its effect on living organisms. The photoperiod varies continuously, but slightly, in the natural environment, in keeping with the season of the year. A longer photoperiod will insure a greater amount of photosynthesis (and subsequent growth) by a plant, for generally there will be a greater net receipt of solar energy. A longer photoperiod also means an increase in temperature, which will often increase the metabolic activities of the plant. The reproductive activities of some plants are or can be controlled by variable lengths of the photoperiod, while those of other plants (day-length independent plants) are not directly affected by this environmental factor. Some plants require a short photoperiod, a daylight period of less than twelve hours to carry on reproductive activity—that is, blossom formation, flowering, and seed production. These plants will bloom in the spring or fall when the photoperiod is shortest, yet thermal conditions are adequate for reproductive activity. Other species require a long photoperiod (greater than twelve hours) and will bloom and produce seed sometime during the interval of the summer solstice.

Many animals are directly affected by changes in the photoperiod. The most obvious activity directly associated with photoperiodism is the increased reproductive activity (observed in certain groups of animals) that accompanies such changes. The breeding cycles of many mammals and birds are governed by the differential rate of hormonal production which, in turn, is controlled by the photoperiod. Such reproductive cycles usually correlate to optimal thermal conditions for the survival of the young, and an increased food supply. Migrations of birds, mammals, and insects are thought to be triggered by the photoperiod. The general condition of the pelt or plumage has been correlated with changes in the photoperiod. In recent years, there has been an indication and some experimental work to support the thesis that in some diverse groups of plants and animals the length and the number of dark periods occurring over a unit period of time are more important than the length of the daylight period. It is believed that the periods of darkness have a more profound effect on hormonal productivity.

FIGURE 5–14 Exposure meter with the target element (left) recording the amount of light energy, in foot-candles, striking the surface of the target element.

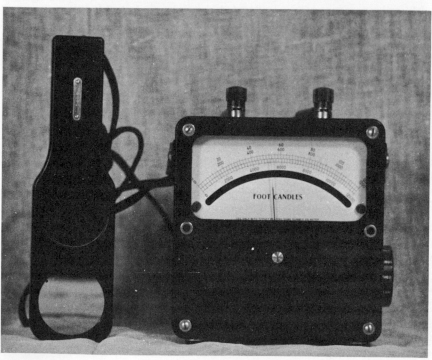

The intensity of solar radiation may be measured in any given environment by recording the incident light with a photographic exposure meter (Figure 5–14). The more expensive apparatus will include target elements that allow direct reading in any part of the environment, which will be recorded in foot-candles of light intensity. There are certain difficulties involved in such measurements. Obviously, inexpensive meters are not accurately calibrated. Photoelectric cells in exposure meters are not sensitive to varying wavelengths of visible light and are relatively insensitive to infrared radiation. Differences in the angle of incident light with respect to the earth's atmosphere will yield much redder light in the Northern Hemisphere during the winter than during the summer. For the same reason light is redder in the early morning and late afternoon than it is during the midday period.

WIND

To fully appreciate the importance of wind in the environmental picture, it will be beneficial to examine briefly the invisible blanket of gases surrounding our planet—the atmosphere. The **troposphere** is the layer of the atmosphere closest to the earth's surface; it is in this layer of air that nearly all of the clouds are located, and most of the turbulent changes in air masses will transpire. Just above the troposphere is a thin zone of air, the **tropopause,** some 20,000 to 40,000 or more feet above the earth's surface. This layer serves as a boundary between the turbulent troposphere and the quiet, weatherless stratosphere. Although it was once believed that the tropopause was a single, unbroken sheet of air extending from the poles to the equator, we now know that it is comprised of three main overlapping sheets of atmosphere—called the arctic, extratropical, and tropical zones—extending from the polar to the equatorial region (Figure 5–15). Between these overlapping layers of the tropopause are high-speed winds, known as **jet streams.** The largest current of air is situated between the arctic and extratropical layers. These masses of high-speed air were first discovered by B-29 pilots during World War II while flying from the Mariana Islands to Japan. Recently, jet streams have attracted widespread attention from ecologists and meteorological personnel because of their far-reaching effects on weather over large areas of the world. Shifts in these high-speed currents of air have been responsible for the severe winters experienced in 1962–63 in Japan, in North America, and in Europe, causing record-breaking snowfall and below-normal temperatures, with widespread loss or damage to plant and animal life. A typical jet stream may be 300 miles or more in width and 2 to 5 miles high, with greatest wind speeds at the core (250 miles per hour or more) and gradually diminishing toward the periphery. Wind speed tends to be higher during the winter than during warmer

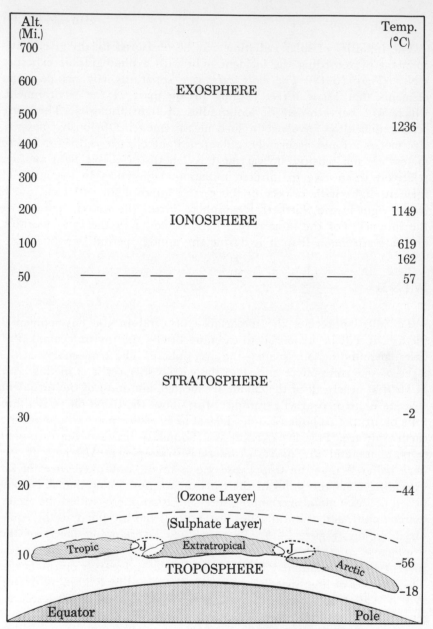

FIGURE 5–15 Diagrammatic representation of layers of the atmosphere with the inclusion of layered parts of the tropopause and location of two important jet streams. Thickness of layers is variable, but an arbitrary scale in miles is included along the right border of the diagram.

weather; hence the core of a jet stream may have winds of only 50 miles per hour in the summer. The number of jet streams and their position change continuously, although three main currents of air during the winter have been noted, with some degree of frequency, over the Northern Hemisphere. One is located over northern Canada, one over the United States, and one over the subtropics. Jet streams travel in a predominantly easterly direction over the earth's surface.

Above the tropopause is the relatively calm **stratosphere,** extending from about 7 to 17 miles above the earth's surface. Temperature is relatively uniform in the stratosphere, according to balloon-recorded data; it varies from approximately −58° C. to about −42° C. Above the stratosphere is the stratopause, a transitional zone below the **mesophere.** The mesosphere is located between 20 and 52 miles above the earth's surface. Rocket-grenade experiments have indicated that there is a gradual increase in temperature in the mesosphere, rising from about −42° C. at its lower limit to about 0° C., followed by a thermal reversal, at higher altitudes, bringing about a gradual drop in values so that the temperature is about −102° C. at the upper limit of the mesosphere.

The outermost limit of the atmosphere is the **exosphere,** where air particles are continuously bombarded by cosmic radiation and exist only in atomic rather than molecular form. Thermal ranges are extreme in this area, ranging from about absolute zero −238° C. (−460° F.) during the interval of darkness to 2,482° C. (4,500° F.) during exposure to solar radiation.

To return to our more immediate atmospheric environment, the troposphere, wind is caused by an uneven heating of air in contact with the earth's surface. Air is heated by convection currents caused by a warming of the earth's surface by solar radiation. As the air is heated, it becomes lighter and rises; this lighter, warmer air (low pressure) is replaced by cooler, heavier air (high pressure). The horizontal movement of this cold body of air replacing a mass of warmer air is wind. Though winds may enter any region from any direction, we usually find that there is a tendency for them to move from one predominant direction most of the time. Such movements of air are called **prevailing winds.** We find that such wind patterns are often established in maritime localities or along large lakes or bodies of water. Cool air moves from the water surface toward the land surface, where the air is warmer owing to the more rapid heating and subsequent convection of heat from the land surface. This warmer, lighter air is replaced by the cooler, heavier air moving off the water, thus establishing prevailing breezes. If a mountain range is located a short distance from the coast (as is true in California), these moisture-laden cooler air masses must rise to clear the mountain ranges. In rising, the air cools and cannot retain its moisture, which then falls as snow or rain on the ocean side of the range, yielding a very lush or wet forest vegetation. The air mass crossing the mountain range will be relatively dry and leave a "rain shadow" on the inland side of the mountain, which produces an arid or semiarid vegetational community.

A wind moving at right angles to isobars (an isobar is a line drawn on a chart or diagram connecting places of the earth's surface having equal barometric pressures during a specified time or period) is following a pressure gradient—moving from a region of high pressure to a region of low pressure. Such a movement of air is called **antipriptic wind.** Surface winds or air masses that are within 50 feet of the ground or water surface are slowed by frictional resistance, which is a force that always opposes the movement of an air mass, regardless of its direction. The greater the speed of the wind and the rougher the surface, the greater is the frictional resistance. The speed of wind moving over a relatively smooth surface such as water or bare, level ground will be cut some 20 to 30 per cent, but its speed may be reduced 60 per cent or more when the wind is moving over forests or rough terrain. Wind direction will be displaced by the Coriolis effect, increasing with distances from the equator and increases in wind velocity.

In the past, it was believed that the circulation of air on a global scale followed the pattern formulated by the Englishman, George Hadley, during the eighteenth century. According to Hadley's theory, air warmed in the equatorial regions of the world would rise and move poleward at a considerable altitude. As the air moved poleward, it gradually cooled, became heavier, and moved earthward, then gradually moved toward the equator to complete the cycle according to Diagram A in Figure 5–16. Prevailing easterly and westerly winds located in the Northern and Southern Hemispheres were caused by the rotation of the earth and the resultant deflection. Wind energy, it was assumed, originated from kinetic energy produced by the cyclic overturn of the atmosphere.

FIGURE 5–16 A vertical sectional representation of the classical (Diagram *a*) and the actual (Diagram *b*) circulation of air masses over the Northern Hemisphere. In Diagram *A*, air masses are shown rising in the equatorial region, moving poleward and dropping as they cool. In the actual pattern of circulation, air revolves in the equatorial cycle (*E*) and polar cycles (*P*) and moves opposite to the classical pattern in the intermediate area (*I*).

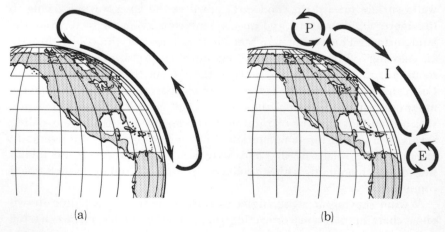

(a)   (b)

Recently, with the advent of weather satellites, delicate electronic equipment, and increased numbers of recording stations that are widely distributed, it has been possible to develop a different interpretation of global circulation. Small cycles in the region of the equator and polar areas follow the classical pattern: warm air rising and cooler air dropping, as shown in Diagram B in Figure 5–16. In the intervening zone covering a much broader latitudinal area, atmospheric currents appear to move opposite to the expected gravitational course, with cool air rising in the subpolar region and warm air dropping in the subtropical zone. This antigravitational movement of air requires the expenditure of kinetic energy. It has been hypothesized that this energy is generated by high pressure air cells that are detached from the polar air masses and swirl in a clockwise, or anticyclonic, direction southward and from low pressure air cells that break away from warm, equatorial currents and moving northward in an anticlockwise, or cyclonic direction. These high and low pressure cells, assisted by the Coriolis effect, power the **prevailing westerly winds** that exist from 30° North or South latitude to 60° latitude. The westerly winds are strongest at about 35° latitude and at an altitude of approximately seven miles, although the latitude and altitude vary slightly with the season and the general weather conditions.

Coriolis effect explains how low and high pressure cells are maintained for considerable periods and generate the energy necessary for the prevailing westerlies and the antigravitational circulation that apparently occur in the middle latitudes. Without this displacement of pressure cells, winds would travel along pressure gradients from high pressure to low pressure areas, and no strong high or low pressure cells would prevail. North or south of the equator, the Coriolis effect, which acts at right angles to the direction of movement, becomes increasingly stronger, shifting pressure cells to the right in the Northern Hemisphere, allowing for the buildup of cyclonic and anticyclonic regions that lend variability to the weather. The magnitude of the Coriolis force is governed by the speed of the air cell and latitude because it is directly proportional to the linear speed and the sine of the latitude, so that it becomes stronger at higher speeds and with increased latitude from the equator to the poles. The shift of these wind masses to the right (Northern Hemisphere) establishes the westerly winds and the prevalent circumpolar cyclone (counterclockwise whirl). The tropical easterlies develop as a result of the barometric pressure gradient established between subtropical areas of high pressure and the equatorial low pressure zone. The movement of air in this region flows westward or from the east; it is referred to as the **tropical easterlies.** These easterly winds (trade winds) are strongest at about 15° North or South latitude and at an altitude of one or two miles.

Windstorms of a localized nature are of ecological importance at times because such winds may transport living organisms such as pollen, light seeds, and even small animals (insects) considerable distances, far removed from their former habitat. Thus wind has carried such organisms over mountain ranges, across rivers, and across other formidable geographical barriers, allowing colonization of widely dispersed areas, provided the surrounding ecological conditions satisfied the minimal requirements of the organism. Winds of all types will also control the rate of evaporation and the distribution and duration of rain or snow in different areas. The more violent windstorms will be discussed in the following section, "Barometric Pressure," as changes and movement of such pressure cells is an important factor in the establishment of such storm centers.

Wind direction is determined by means of a rotating wind vane; wind speed may be calculated by means of an **anemometer.** The open cup anemometer has three open cups that will catch a wind from any direction and cause the cups to rotate. Through the rotation of the cups and a series of moving parts the wind speed is recorded either for direct reading or on a graph for a unit period of time. Although a number of types of anemometers are available for determining wind velocity, one of the most widely used instruments is the open cup anemometer, a standard piece of equipment at U.S. Weather Bureau stations throughout the nation. Winds are classified on the basis of their speed: breezes vary from 4 (slight breeze) to 31 (strong breeze) miles per hour, and gales from 32 (moderate gale) to 63 (whole gale) miles per hour. Storm-classified winds will have speeds ranging from 64 to 72 miles per hour. Any wind with a greater velocity is classified as a hurricane.

BAROMETRIC PRESSURE

Gravitational forces attract molecules of air, concentrating these molecules or increasing their density with increased proximity to the earth's surface. Any surface exposed to the atmosphere, regardless of altitude, is exposed to a force equal to the weight of the atmospheric gases above that point. Since such pressure is usually measured with a barometer of some type, it is often called **barometric pressure.** Air pressure is greatest at sea level because of the thickness of the atmospheric envelope; in fact, the air pressure is great enough to force a column of mercury 760 mm. (or 29.2 inches) in an evacuated tube at sea level. As altitude increases above sea level (upland terrain, mountain tops), the air pressure becomes proportionately less because the remaining mass of air located above the object is reduced in thickness (and weight).

Although mercurial barometers are standard instruments for measuring barometric pressure, the anaeroid barometer, which is portable, is used when the instrument must be moved or exposed to frequent handling. This instrument contains a flexible diaphragm that covers a partially evacuated chamber and moves in response to changes in pressure. A series of levers magnifies the movement of the diaphragm and

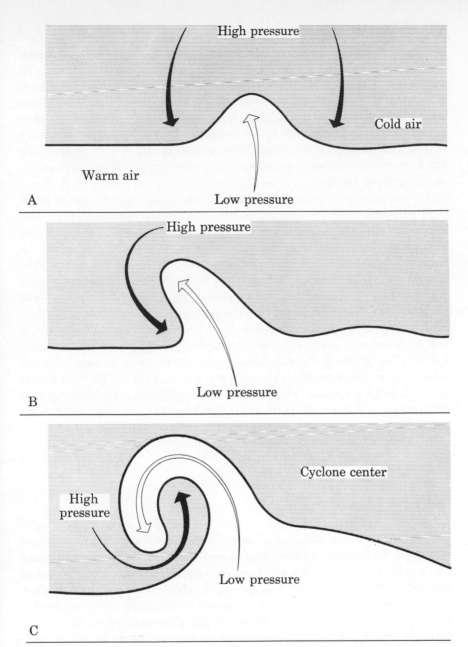

FIGURE 5–17 Three stages in the formation of a cyclone. A warm air mass from the south (low pressure cell) becomes lodged between two high pressure cells, forming a wave that gradually begins to circulate in a counterclockwise direction in the Northern Hemisphere.

records the movement by means of an indicator that moves across a calibrated scale. Atmospheric pressure is often expressed as mass per unit volume, so that it may be expressed as grams per cubic meter. Air pressure or atmospheric density at sea level is 1,300 grams per cubic meter; it decreases to 100 grams per cubic meter at 12 miles altitude (above sea level) and to only 1/1,000,000 of a gram per cubic meter at 105 miles altitude. Meteorological maps depicting air pressure over geographical areas record air pressure as force per unit area. **Millibars** are the units used; 1,013.2 millibars is equivalent to atmospheric pressure at sea level. A millibar is one thousandth of a bar. A bar is a force of one million dynes per square centimeter of surface (a dyne is the force required to move one gram at an acceleration of one centimeter per second per second).

Air pressure also varies with air movement in limited areas. Local high pressure areas develop where air cools and drops earthward. This is particularly true in the horse latitudes and polar areas. High pressure air masses have whirling clockwise motion (counterclockwise in the Southern Hemisphere) within the pressure cell, called an **anticyclonic** movement. High pressure, indicated by rising barometric pressure, generally means fair weather, light winds, and thermal stability. Low pressure cells are often formed by the heating and expansion of air that creates an area of relatively low pressure. They may also develop between two high pressure areas of different temperatures (Figure 5–17), forming a wave that gradually develops into a counterclockwise movement of air (clockwise in the Southern Hemisphere). Air moving in this direction is referred to as a **cyclone.** Such movement may initiate the development of a major storm center. The approach of a low pressure cell can be predicted by falling barometric pressure, overcast skies accompanied by rain or snow, and strong winds. Temperatures may change abruptly during the passage of a low pressure cell.

WINDSTORMS

The more violent and destructive storms caused by a combination of wind and air pressure differences may not only destroy animal and plant life but have a long-lasting effect on the communities by severely changing the entire environmental situation. Tornadoes are the most violent of such storms, with a diameter of about 198 meters (660 feet) and a forward speed of 20 to 40 miles per hour. The destructive force of a tornado lies in the fact that the counterclockwise winds in the funnel-shaped cloud often exceed a speed of 300 miles per hour. Added to this destructive wind force is the reduced atmospheric pressure near the vortex that can cause houses and barns to explode because of a pressure differential (low pressure outside the building and normal pressure inside). The 100 to 200 mile per hour updraft within the funnel can carry trees, animals, and other objects upward hundreds of feet and then drop them some distance away. Frogs and fish have been carried from bodies of water and dropped some distance away. Tornado funnels that travel across bodies of water will carry some water as well as aquatic

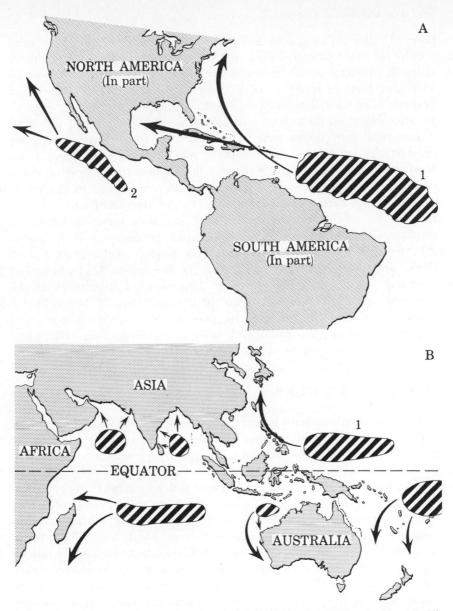

FIGURE 5-18 World hurricane belts of the Western Hemisphere in Map *A*. Diagonally lined areas represent regions of origin in the Atlantic (1) and Pacific (2) with arrows showing the alternate routes followed by the majority of hurricanes. Map *B* indicates the hurricane zones of the western Pacific and Indian Oceans. The area of origin, numbered 1, that develops between the Marshall Islands and Philippines is the most prolific origin of hurricanes (typhoons).

organisms of various types into the destructive funnel; these water-laden masses of swirling wind are called **water spouts**.

Hurricanes develop in tropical areas over open ocean water in areas of uniform temperature and devoid of frontal systems. Winds are greater than 78 miles per hour and may exceed 150 miles per hour. The storm area is far more extensive than that of the tornado, often 400 or more miles in diameter. Furthermore, a hurricane is distinctive owing to its very slow forward speed, usually 15 to 30 miles per hour. Hurricanes develop in regions of contrasting winds; a low pressure cell develops in an area where northeast and southeast trade winds converge, called an **intertropical convergence zone.** The earth's rotational force is necessary to start the spiraling action of these wind fronts. Since there is no rotational force present at the equator, hurricanes always develop north or south of the equator. Hurricanes are more numerous in the southwestern North Pacific, originating between the Marshall Islands and the Philippines, moving toward the China Coast, then traveling northeastward over the Philippines, Korea, and Japan. In that part of the world, they are called **typhoons.** Hurricanes also develop in the South Indian Ocean and sweep westward, causing severe damage on Madagascar and southeast Africa. Ranking third in frequency of hurricanes is the southern part of the North Atlantic off the west coast of Africa. Hurricanes spawned here move westward, over the West Indies, Mexico, and Central America or northwestward, skirting and sometimes striking the coasts of the southeastern or northeastern United States (Figure 5–18).

MICROCLIMATES

The **microenvironment** is an intangible term referring to areas of variable extent, depending upon the individual's interpretation of the spacial limits of such an area. Even ecologists are not in total agreement in this respect, but an investigator confining his work to a region within six feet of the ground is said to be concerned with a microenvironment. Many areas of ecological investigation are considerably more restrictive, for the investigation may be concerned with the environment within animal droppings, a fallen log, the surface of a leaf, litter of the forest floor, and so on. The wind, rate of evaporation, humidity, and temperature that prevail in these areas of limited size make up the **microclimate.** The measurement of conditions within this microclimate, where a distance of a centimeter or a few millimeters may result in an entirely different set of conditions, has necessitated the development of specially designed instruments. This field of investigation has developed rapidly within the last score of years and the array of instruments now available has increased proportionately.

GRAPHIC REPRESENTATION OF CLIMATES

Climatic conditions may be graphically represented by transferring recorded data to a graph over a period of time, generally a twelve-month period, though the time interval will vary, depending upon the investigation. A chart of this type is called a **climograph.** It may be used to compare the environmental conditions in several areas because it enables one to make a very rapid comparison between two localities (Figure 5–19). Temperature, precipitation, vapor pressure deficit, or some other climatic factor may be plotted along one axis, and time or another

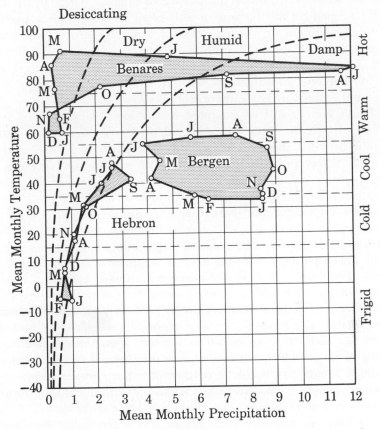

FIGURE 5–19 A climograph (hytherograph) of monthly temperature and precipitation in three areas—Benares, India, Bergen, Norway, and Hebron, Labrador. Climatic comparison is possible at a glance: Benares is hot and generally dry; Bergen is cool and humid; Hebron is mostly cold and very dry. Letters indicate months of the year. From *Weather and Climate* by Clarence E. Koeppe and George C. De Long. Copyright 1958. McGraw-Hill Book Company. Used by permission.

factor along the other axis. The **hytherograph,** a specialized type of climograph, always records temperature and precipitation. The amount of precipitation is plotted along the horizontal axis (abscissa) and thermal values are plotted along the vertical axis (ordinate). In a graph of this type it is possible to place a number of hytherographs on one graph for as many geographical localities.

INTERACTION OF CLIMATIC FACTORS

In conclusion, it must be emphasized that consideration of a single climatic factor while ignoring others is as inexcusable as using climatic norms and means obtained from weather bureau data to discuss microclimatic variability in a distinctly different environmental situation. The interaction of a number of climatic or microclimatic factors is most important ecologically because it will often indicate why a particular organism is present or absent. After all, it is the entire environmental complex that affects the organism and may well modify its behavior. Only if an individual climatic condition acts as a true limiting factor (see section on "Limiting Factors" in Chapter II), would it assume major importance in any environmental situation.

Climatic factors will be modified in any locality by the presence or absence of aquatic areas, the size and extent of such areas, and the distance between the nearest aquatic appendage and the locality in question. Water has a high latent heat of evaporation, meaning that large quantities of heat will be absorbed without causing a rapid rise in temperature of the water. Heat will also be lost from the surface of water at a far slower rate than from surrounding terrestrial areas. The slower heating and cooling of water will have an ameliorating effect on temperatures in land areas bordering large bodies of water. Such regions would not experience the extremes of temperature that inland areas would. Thus we find that a **continental climate** prevails in regions divorced from large lakes or oceanic areas. Such regions will experience more severe extremes of temperature in summer and winter. **Marine** or **lake climates** will have a narrower range of temperatures, both from day to day and season to season as a result of the slower heating and cooling of water, which tends to modify the thermal factor in neighboring areas. Finally it should be pointed out that climatic conditions, as we have discussed them, affect the terrestrial environment most radically, but there is also an indirect effect on the aquatic environment. Climatic changes may increase the turbidity of the water, cause flooding and extend the size of the aquatic area temporarily, transport minerals and salts elsewhere, and cause the inevitable thermal changes that will transpire during the course of time.

The sea level is rising, resulting in a loss of land along the shores of the United States. Along the eastern seaboard and the Gulf Coast, the sea level has risen more rapidly than it has along the Pacific. The rate of increase along all coasts has slowed since 1940. A general warming trend in the climate, causing some of the earth's ice cover to melt and changes in amounts of rainfall are apparently responsible. Annual global temperatures increased about 1° F., and annual global winter temperatures rose about 2° F. from 1880 to 1940. This winter warming was even more pronounced, nearly 3° F., in far northern latitudes. In the last twenty years, there has been a reversal of this warming trend, nullifying about one third of the earlier thermal increases. This rise in sea level along our coasts since the turn of the century has contributed to the heavy damage suffered where storms surge along the eastern seacoasts.

Selected References

Bedford, Franklin T. *Climates in Miniature* (New York: Philosophical Library, 1955).

Blumenstock, D. I., and C. W. Thornthwaite. "Climate and the World Pattern," *Climate and Man* 1941 Yearbook of Agriculture. (Washington, D.C.: Government Printing Office, 1941), pp. 98–127.

Brooks, C. E. P. *Climate Through the Ages* (London: E. Benn, 1949), pp. 1–395.

Byers, H. R. *General Meteorology* (New York: McGraw-Hill, 1944), pp. i–x, 1–645.

Cantlon, J. E. 1953. Vegetation and microclimates on north and south slopes of Cushetunk Mountain, New Jersey. Ecol. Monogr., 23:241–270.

Geiger, R. *The Climate Near the Ground* Revised by M. N. Stewart. (Cambridge, Mass.: Harvard Univ. Press, 1957), pp. 1–494.

Huntington, E. *Civilization and Climate* (New Haven, Conn.: Yale Univ. Press, 1924), pp. i–xix, 1–453.

Kendrew, W. G. *The Climates of the Continents* (London: Oxford Univ. Press, 1937), pp. i–xii, 1–473.

Kincer, J. B. "Climate and Weather Data for the United States," *Climate and Man* 1941 Yearbook of Agriculture. (Washington, D.C.: Government Printing Office), pp. 685–747.

Livingston, B. E. 1908. A simple atmometer. Science, 28:319–320.

Longstreth, T. M. *Understanding the Weather* (New York: Macmillan, 1953), pp. i–viii, 1–118.

Marvin, C. F. 1941. Psychrometric tables for obtaining the vapor pressure, relative humidity, and temperature of the dew point. U.S. Weather Bureau Publ. 235:1–85.

Stickel, Lucille F. 1948. Observations on the effect of flood on animals. Ecology, 29:505–507.

Tannehill, I. R. *Hurricanes* (Princeton, N.J.: Princeton Univ. Press, 1938), pp. i–x, 1–257.

Uvarov, B. P. 1931. Insects and climate. Trans. Ent. Soc. London, 79:1–247.

Wolfe, J. N. 1951. The possible role of microclimate. Ohio Jour. Sci., 51:134–138.

Wolfe, J. N., R. T. Wareham, and H. T. Scofield. 1949. Microclimates and macroclimates of Neotoma, a small valley in central Ohio. Ohio Biol. Surv. Bull. No. 41, 8:1–267.

VI. Biotic Factors

RELATIONSHIPS AMONG ORGANISMS

It might be said that no organism under natural conditions is divorced from all other living things. Generally a number of different species will exert either a direct or indirect effect on a particular individual because the vital processes of growth, nutrition, and reproduction depend upon the interaction of other members within the species (intraspecific interactions) or between members of heterogeneous groups (interspecific interactions). Close associations among homogeneous and heterogeneous aggregations may be beneficial, harmful, or have no apparent effect on either individual. We shall first consider some of the beneficial relationships that may arise in interspecific associations because they will often exert a considerable effect on population growth and community structure in a natural environment.

Commensalism is a relation existing between members of different species in which one organism definitely benefits from the association, but the other individual is not benefited or adversely affected under normal conditions. Examples of such interactions are numerous in the literature. Many small organisms are known to live within the protective covering or body of a larger individual. Commensal crabs are common within some oysters, and usually within the protective U-shaped tube of

Chaetopterus. Sponges (Figure 6–1) will also harbor a rich fauna within the spongocoel, protected by the living cells of the sponge and undisturbed by the environmental conditions within the cavity (spongocoel). Anyone who examines the endemic fauna of a spongocoel for the first time is amazed by the diversity of life within this tiny microenvironment;

FIGURE 6–1 A marine sponge (*Ircinia*). Photograph was taken in its natural habitat. Sponges may contain a diverse fauna within the spongocoel (main cavity) of the organism. Photograph by courtesy of John Storr, State University of New York at Buffalo.

even small fish are found within this confined area. Remora fish, or large shark suckers (*Echeneis naucrates*), have an ovoid sucking disc developed from the anterior dorsal fin as shown in Figure 6–2. This pad, which is equipped with muscular flaps that can open and create a suction, enables the remora to attach itself to the outer surface of a shark, although remoras have been found attached to other fishes such as drums, swordfish, marlins, and others. In some instances this warm water fish of moderate length (usually about two feet) will attach itself to large sea turtles or even skin divers! Sharks transport this fish to a feeding area. The remora swims around, feeding on the scraps of food left behind by the shark and then reattaches itself to the surface of a shark to be trans-

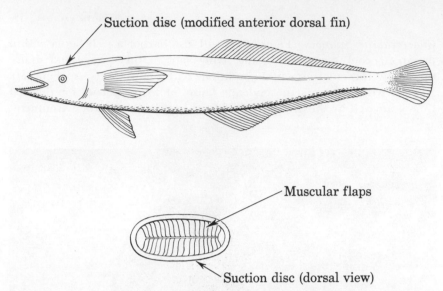

Suction disc (modified anterior dorsal fin)

Muscular flaps

Suction disc (dorsal view)

FIGURE 6–2 The remora fish and its attachment disc, a modified fin, located on the dorsal surface of the head, enables an attachment to other larger fish (usually sharks). Upon reaching a feeding area, the remora fish detaches itself and feeds on the small fragments of food left behind by the sharks.

ported to another area. Epiphytes, such as Spanish moss (*Tillandsia usneoides*), which live on the branches of trees can be considered commensals because they depend upon the tree for aerial support and the proper environmental conditions that exist at this level. But the tree neither suffers nor benefits from such association.

Another type of heterogeneous association is known as **protocooperation.** In this type, a relation exists between two organisms in which each benefits from the other, but neither individual must remain associated with the other in order to survive. Some authors refer to this type of association as **nonobligatory mutualism.** Several marine crabs use living coelenterates, sponges, and other invertebrates as a form of camouflage to cover the dorsal surface of the exoskeleton. The crab avoids detection while the invertebrate benefits by being transported to areas containing greater quantities of food and oxygen. *Pagurus,* the familiar hermit crab, lives in the empty shell of some marine snail (as shown in Figure 6–3) which it carries around with it; as the crab grows it will leave the smaller shell and acquire a larger one. In many instances, however, the shell may be covered with hydroid coelenterate (*Hydractinia echinata*). This organism not only serves as a camouflage for the crab but will frequently enlarge the shell by building up the free edge, thus saving the crab the need for exchanging shells at some time in the future. The spider crab (*Libinia*) often covers the dorsum of the carapace with hydroids, algae and worm tubes, allowing both groups of organisms to benefit from this common association. Certain species of green algae (the zoochlorellae)

FIGURE 6–3 A snail shell occupied by a hermit crab, with attached fauna including barnacles and worm tubes located on the external surface of the valve.

are located in the gastrodermis of some coelenterates. In this relationship the coelenterate benefits from the production of food by the photosynthetic algae, and the algae are protected and exposed to a comparatively homogeneous environment.

A more radical relation existing between two organisms is known as **mutualism, or obligatory mutualism.** In this kind of relation, the two organisms must remain together in order to survive. The algal-fungal association, or lichens, which are so common in nature, are startling examples of mutualism. Photographs of the three basic types of lichens found in nature are shown in Figure 6–4. The alga depends upon the fungus for water and protection and the fungus, in turn, receives food produced photosynthetically by the alga. Flagellate protozoans of the order Hypermastigida, such as *Kofoidia loriculata* that lives in the intestine of the termite *Kalotermes simplicornis,* or *Joenia annectens* that lives within *K. flavicollis,* depend upon environmental conditions and nourishment provided within this microenvironment. The termite is also dependent upon this gut fauna, for without the conversion of cellulose into absorbable materials (acetic acid) the termite would surely starve to death. C. C. Adams made the comment at one time that nature seldom drew a sharp, definite line, so that one could clearly distinguish, without exception, one phase or activity from another; but the demarcation, if we can call it that, was nearly always fuzzy, with one concept or principle commonly merging with another. Many organisms have an active fauna and flora living within the confines of the digestive tract, so at first thought it would appear superficially that we could draw a rough parallel with the intestinal fauna of termites and cite many cases of mutualism. But such is not the case. Some intestinal flora and fauna can and will survive in areas other than the gut cavity. Others cannot; they depend on the intestine for protection, proper temperature, humidity, and a continued food source. The animal possessing this heterogeneous community of microorganisms may derive some small amount

(A)

(B)

(C)

FIGURE 6–4 Photographs of the three basic types of lichens: crustose type on granite (A), fruticose type (B), and foliose type (C). Photograph C shows the predominant large, flattened foliose type of lichen found on a boulder surface in Superior National Forest, Minnesota. Photograph C, courtesy of the U.S. Forest Service.

138

of benefit from its presence, but it does not depend upon these organisms for survival. Thus we have associations in nature that are not clear-cut examples of commensalism, protocooperation, or mutualism, but rather varying degrees of each.

The various relations that occur among organisms, previously cited, are interspecific cases. But beneficial intraspecific associations occur in nature as well. Colonial life is exhibited in many different phyla of plants and animals. A group of organisms living together in colonies may demonstrate intraspecific signs of commensalism, protocooperation, or mutualism because they may afford one another protection from enemies and from adverse temperature conditions and other environmental factors, collective efforts in gathering food, and the greater chance of fertilization during the reproductive phase of life. All of these activities are of a beneficial nature and often increase the propagation of the species. Solitary organisms, not being able to cope with these problems, would succumb, and the species would eventually become extinct, as has happened in many cases during the course of evolution. Varying degrees of colonial or social life may be observed in different groups of animals. Maternal or paternal care is observed among certain species, such as the female earwig (Order: Dermaptera), the male stickleback (Family Gasterosteidae), and many of the reptiles, birds, and mammals. The parental care lavished upon the offspring varies in respect to the period of time for which such attention lasts and the degree of care and protection that is afforded the colony or social group of young individuals. The female earwig merely protects her brood chamber from occasional predators, but in the Class Aves, the male and female feed the young, fend off enemies, teach the young to fly, and lead an independent life.

In some lepidopteran groups (particularly moths), there is a social life that will endure throughout the larval period. The common tent caterpillar (*Malacosoma*) makes a webbed tent in the fork of a tree, usually a choke-cherry (*Padus virginiana*), by utilizing the efforts of several hundred larvae. These organisms leave the tent during the day to forage, returning at night to their common abode. Toward the end of their larval period they leave this common webbed chamber and pupate as solitary individuals. Among the wood cockroaches (*Cryptocercus*) family, groups live together in rotting logs and ingest wood, which is in turn digested by protozoans located in the digestive tract—an example of mutualism. When the young nymphs molt, the digestive tract is emptied, with a complete loss of these mutualistic protozoans. The nymph must ingest some of the fresh excrement from other members of the colony or starve to death—so that in this case, colonial life is necessary for survival.

More highly evolved examples of colonial life or social development are apparent among insect groups such as the termites, ants, social wasps, and some of the bees. Although social habits have arisen independently in these groups, there is a striking parallelism, hence a strong temptation to compare these insect colonies with our own human establishments. Within these highly evolved groups, social development has progressed to such an extent that castes, or social orders each comprised of individuals structurally and functionally different from those in the other castes, have become established. A colony consists of a primary reproductive caste, with the basic task of establishing a colony and reproducing the individuals that will make up the other social groups. A worker caste, which is generally sterile, produces the food and feeds the rest of the colony as well as enlarges the colony or improves existing chambers. A soldier caste, typically equipped with large protective mandibles (jaws) and/or repellent substances, guards the entrances to the colony and protects the other castes. In some groups there is a secondary reproductive caste (often wingless) that will become functional if the primary reproductive individuals (the king and queen) should be injured, die, or be killed. Different castes of ants belonging to the species *Pheidole instabilis* are represented in Figure 6–5.

Social groups, such as flocks, herds, and packs of vertebrates may be ephemeral, disbanding after the completion of a migratory movement to another area. Herds or packs of animals may occur periodically as a result of decreased amounts of food or the presence of immature organisms in the group. Quail (*Colinus virginianus*) coveys disband in the spring, prior to the mating period, into breeding pairs, and the covey organization is not resumed until late summer, after the maturation of young chicks that have been hatched that same spring.

Some groups of animals have evolved a pack or herd instinct over the course of time that has become a permanent mode of life. The herd or pack has evolved as a logical means of survival, for a solitary animal may be attacked and killed by a predator species with little difficulty, but a pack or herd immediately imposes a numerical factor that must be reckoned with. Most predators will patiently follow packs or herds for days, waiting for a weaker member of the group to straggle or watching for an indolent individual to stray from the group so that it may be attacked with comparative ease. A wolf pack (*Canis lupus*) is an example of a gregarious group that remains together throughout life. As is true of many social groups in nature, the pack has a leader to whom all of the members of the pack are submissive because his position has been attained by endurance, strength, and often by winning over others engaged in conflicts within the group. Although his position may be contested occasionally by members of the pack, the leader remains the dominant and governing force of the entity. This obedience to a leader has been cleverly used by man in domesticating wolves and gradually developing breeds of dogs over many thousands of years. Man has replaced the leader of the pack in terms of devotion and obedience. A domesticated dog that has evolved from wolf stock—the chow, the

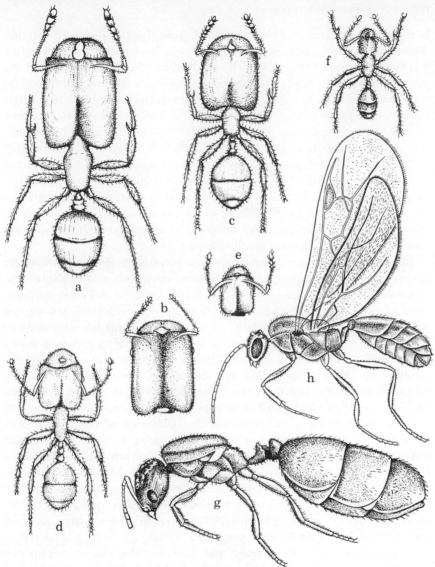

FIGURE 6–5   Different castes of ants: *a* is a soldier; *b-e* are intermediate workers; *f* is a typical worker; *g* is a dealated female; and *h* is a male. The species represented is *Pheidole instabilis*. From *Ants: Their Structure, Development and Behavior* by W. M. Wheeler (Columbia University Press, 1910).

husky, the setter, the spaniel—knows but one master and will remain devoted to him for life. There are many cases on record where the death of a master or his induction into military service is felt so keenly by his pet dog that the animal refuses food and will often die. This devotion to a single individual, man or woman, begins at about four or five months of age and lasts for a lifetime.

Other breeds of domestic dogs (collies, German shepherd, terriers, hounds, and beagles) may have evolved from the jackal (*Canis aureus*). The origin of the domestic breeds of dogs is certainly open to argument; it has not been definitely established that the wolf-jackal hypothesis is a more likely explanation than other theories proposed by vertebrate evolutionists. Jackals are not unconditionally loyal to a single leader, perhaps because they are not exposed to the severe, harsh conditions encountered in the tundra and northern boreal forests, where the wolf is the common inhabitant. Jackals inhabit an environment that is beset with fewer dangers; as a consequence the pack or community is often dispersed, certainly not as intimate in terms of day-to-day contact as is the wolf pack. Jackals will change leaders frequently. For this reason, dogs that might possibly have evolved from jackal stock may shift any bit of allegiance they may be capable of demonstrating from one master to another without much difficulty.

The leader of any group of animals is usually the undisputed, dominating force of any aggregation. Continual environmental pressures and at times adverse conditions have tested the alertness, courage, and tenacity of this dominant organism. Owing to this selective process, an individual organism upon whom the rest of the group becomes dependent emerges from the aggregation. In some of the avian groups a flock's behavior is governed to a great extent by a hierarchical order that determines the priority accorded certain members with regard to food, water, roosting site, and even the choice of copulatory partners. In such an avian group, a single bird dominates all the others, but another bird (though subordinate to the first) dominates the rest of the flock, and so on down to the last bird in the hierarchy, who is subordinate to all other members of the flock. In some groups, the stability of the hierarchy is such, according to Allee (1931), that removal of the bird from a flock followed by reintroduction does not necessitate a reassertion of its hierarchical position within the aggregation. The leader never deserts the group because he has been instinctively placed in a hierarchical position requiring at least primitive responsibility.

Often it is the leader's courage and initiative that insures group survival. Despite the dangers involved, a leader must often stand, fight, and sometimes die to save other members of the aggregation; this responsibility evidently takes precedence over any instinct for personal safety. African hunters have often encountered a dead leopard surrounded by carcasses of male baboons. It is evident that among these dead primates there was invariably a leader of the troop, who, along with other males in the same troop, stood and fought this traditional enemy to give the females, younger males, and infant baboons a chance to escape and survive. Very shortly, it has been noted, a leader appears from among the survivors of the attack who will wield the same authority and evidence the same sense of responsibility for the group that had been exhibited by past leaders. Flocks of countless species of birds, schools of fish, and a large number of mammals are dominated by the leadership principle because evolution of such behavior has made it abundantly clear that these organisms are more likely to cope with the environment and survive than would be true under solitary circumstances. Dependency on leadership among gregarious groups of animals continues even after they are placed in a zoo or comparable states of captivity and no longer have problems with regard to predators, food, competition, and so on. If these organisms are not separated but are placed in company with others of the same species, a leader soon emerges. This self-appointed but unopposed ruler will reign supreme, dominating the activities of the aggregate even under these conditions of complete servitude when there is no further need for the leadership principle that is necessary for survival in the natural state.

So far, we have discussed the beneficial advantages of interspecific and intraspecific coexistence. Negative or disoperative reactions, however, occur in every ecosystem. But even though these reactions will have a detrimental effect on an individual organism, there are long-term benefits involved, for they tend to limit population growth and prevent disastrous overpopulation of an environmental area. One of the most widespread and obvious means of limiting population size is by predation. Most animals in any ecosystem will have one or more enemies that will hold populations in check. In fact, if predation continues unchecked, it may completely depopulate an area of a particular species. Aggregations of animals operate on the basis of careful checks and balances; if the prey increases in number in a particular area, the predator species undergoes a corresponding increase, as shown in Figure 6–6, and the prey population is kept within tolerable limits. As the prey species is gradu-

FIGURE 6–6 Hypothetical representation of predator-prey relationships regarding population numbers (N). N_1 is the prey population and N_2 is the predator population plotted against time in Diagram A and plotted against number of prey versus predators in Diagram B. Reprinted from *Distribution and Abundance of Animals* by H. G. Andrewartha and L. C. Birch by permission of The University of Chicago Press, 1954.

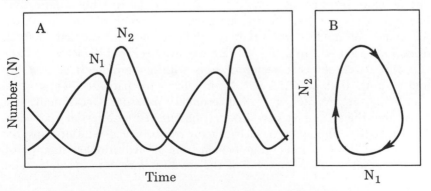

ally killed off, predators decrease in numbers as a result of starvation or migration to other areas. Although an ecosystem may maintain a tremendous number of species, all held in check by alternating periods of growth, predation and regrowth, a disoperative reaction may be caused by man who, out of greed or ignorance, kills off certain species or alters the environment in such a way that predators or prey are killed in large numbers. Such activities may upset the natural balance that had formerly existed in the area.

An extremely disoperative reaction that affects a larger segment of the community because there are no major groups of plants or animals that escape is **parasitism.** This adverse activity requires a highly specialized organism possessing structures and a physiology that will enable it to extract successfully essential materials from a host plant or animal. Fortunately, parasitic organisms, both plant and animal, in the course of evolution have lost the primitive structures and evolved highly specialized organs, and often a complex life cycle, requiring several hosts. Such characteristics and conditions will often prevent parasitic organisms from reaching any particular stage of its life cycle, despite a tremendous reproductive potential. As a result of such natural safeguards, parasitism seldom reaches the disastrous proportions possible in cases of uncontrolled predation. If an individual parasite extracts too much nutrient material from the host, it may lead to a premature death of the host and parasite. Very often the most recently introduced parasites will cause a more severe and sometimes disastrous effect on an ecosystem than do parasites that have existed in the area for some time. The recent invasion of the Great Lakes area by lampreys parasitic on the fish population is a dramatic example of uncontrolled parasitism and its destructive effect on the endemic fauna. One by one the fishing interests in the various lakes has suffered from the parasitic attack on freshwater fish.

In many cases, parasitism has modified population growth because invasion of a host organism will eventually shorten its life cycle, weaken the plant or animal, and drastically inhibit the reproductive activities and in some instances cause sterility. Because many parasites will require one or more intermediate hosts as well as a definitive host, more than one species may be harmed by one particular species of parasite. A tremendous reproductive potential, coupling sexual and asexual methods of reproduction within a single life cycle, insures rapid dispersal of parasites and attack of vast host populations within the immediate area. We find at times that parasites will be infested with parasites. These parasites living on parasites are called **secondary parasites.** Occasionally it is found that the secondary parasites may be infested with **tertiary parasites.**

Competition, though a negative factor in ecological relationships, has undoubtedly been of long-range benefit from an evolutionary standpoint, for it has insured the survival of the hardiest members of the species.

The most adaptive ecological members of a trivial group and those with the hardiest genetic makeup are destined to maintain the species. Competition implies that several species or members of a species are engaged in a common attempt to obtain some substance or environmental factor. Competition among plants for increased amounts of sunlight necessary for sufficient photosynthetic activity, adequate amounts of minerals, and water are common. But keen contests will materialize in intraspecific groups of animals for food, shelter, mates, breeding sites, and countless other factors. As a factor or condition becomes scarce or not as readily available in the ecosystem, the competitive effort becomes more intense and may evolve into a death struggle, with the ultimate death of weaker or less adaptive individuals. Usually, competition may begin as a more or less passive operation, gradually becoming more keen with the passage of time. Among plants, this disoperative activity will usually require a considerable amount of time before reaching a decisive conclusion, but among animals it may be a rather short-lived affair.

Finally, an association that is solely of an interspecific type is **neutralism**. As the term clearly implies, two different species are not affected either adversely or beneficially by rather close association. As a matter of fact, the two organisms (plants or animals) may live in extremely confined quarters (a microhabitat) and may often come into intimate contact with one another, but their breeding behavior, nutrition, and other vital processes are generally so different that from the standpoint of relationship the other organism does not exist. Neutralism exists when abundant supplies of food and shelter are available to the inhabitants. But neutralistic behavior may change when environmental conditions change. A catastrophic event or a radical environmental change can so alter the food or shelter available that two species may be forced to substitute other foods (found in limited quantity) or find alternate shelters, which may lead to sharp competition between two formerly neutralistic species.

Often one of the forementioned activities may last for only a brief period of time. The period of parasitism for many of the Hymenoptera lasts only as long as the larval period, after which the organism is a free-living individual. The Ichneumonidae, a family of parasitic wasps, parasitizes other insects (particularly moths and butterflies) so extensively that this group of insects is one of the most important natural checks to many serious enemies of forests and agricultural crops. The family is a large one, with over 10,000 species, many of them most abundant in forested stands. The female ichneumon fly of a number of species moves over the bark of trees. Suddenly, she thrusts the sharp, steel-like ovipositor into the wood (Figure 6–7) and with unerring accuracy places her eggs in a grub or caterpillar below the bark—a host that she literally never sees. The victim is paralyzed by a poison released at the time of ovi-

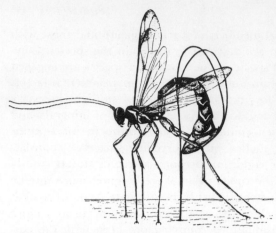

FIGURE 6–7 A female ichneumon fly with ovipositor inserted into a plant stem so that eggs may be laid in an insect host located within the plant tissues. Reprinted from *Insect Enemies of Eastern Forests*, U.S. Department of Agriculture, Misc. Publ. No. *657*:1-679.

position, which prevents it from putrefying prior to the time the eggs of the wasp hatch. After hatching, the larval wasp parasitizes the host so extensively that its death is inevitable.

At times parasitic behavior and mutualism may be combined during the life cycle. The yucca moth, a member of the Family Prodoxidae, flies to flowering *Yucca* (Spanish bayonet), scrapes pollen from the anther, and kneads it into a ball. She flies to another bloom and places this ball of pollen on the female organ (the pistil), thus effectively pollinating the female flower. She oviposits in this flower, which, as a result of pollination, will produce seed, some of which are parasitized by the developing caterpillars. The relationship in this case is mutualistic, because otherwise the *Yucca* would not be pollinated. The seed and future generations of *Yucca* would not be insured without this species of moth. At the same time the moth relies on this single species of plant to provide shelter and protection for her eggs, which, upon hatching, have a readily available supply of food for early development. The larval stage is parasitic because it lives on part of the plant's living tissues. One interesting point might be noted in this respect: Not all of the seeds are parasitized by the developing caterpillars; some are left unharmed to insure the appearance of future generations of *Yucca* (and yucca moths).

HOME RANGES AND TERRITORIALITY

Among animals, portions of a habitat or several contiguous environmental areas will constitute the region over which an organism moves while engaged in routine daily activities. Such an area is called the **home range.** In many observed groups, this area, in terms of size, is quite constant for a given species. At the present time little is known about the home range among aquatic vertebrates and most of the invertebrates (terrestrial and aquatic). Indeed we are not even sure that such areas are established for some of these groups. Considerable information is currently available on the home ranges of birds, many reptiles, and mammals in terrestrial areas. In fact, many of us have observed domestic dogs and cats in suburban developments, wandering over a particular number of blocks, often following established trails or routes, then returning home. The home range of necessity will always include the burrow, nest, den, or roosting place of the animal. This restricted region within the home range is called the **homesite.** Often the homesite is located close to the center of the home range. However, it may be eccentric in position. For example, shore birds that nest along the water's edge feed on the aquatic fauna; hence the lake or a small peripheral part of an ocean would constitute the home range. In this instance, the homesite would be truly eccentric in position.

A home range is usually established first, followed by the construction of a homesite. From investigation of a number of groups, it has been observed that the limits and extent of the home range of most of these groups will remain constant, but the homesite may be abandoned and a new position established because of a disturbance, such as flooding, fire, some other catastrophic event, or raids by other animals, or simply because of an opportunity to move closer to a feeding area. Some animals will establish an alternate homesite (see Figure 6–8) within their home

FIGURE 6–8 The limits of the home range traversed by an organism during its most active period of the year is represented by the solid line. At other times, when activity is curtailed by environmental conditions, the home range may be limited to the area bounded by the dotted line. The primary homesite is shown at *A;* the alternate, or secondary, homesite is located at *B.*

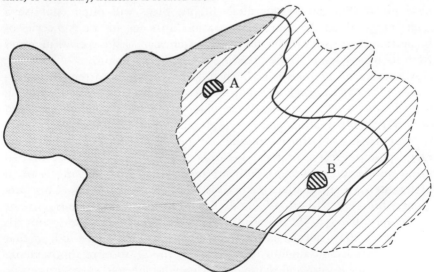

range; if something causes the individual to leave the primary home-site, he will establish himself in the previously constructed alternate area. Home ranges will vary in size for different animals; in general, the larger, more mobile mammals and birds will have an extensive home range, often a number of square miles. Wolves, for example, often have a home range of five or more square miles, while field mice may customarily travel over an area less than a square acre in size. Male members of a species generally have larger home ranges than do females, but the extent of such areas will vary with the stage of the reproductive cycle, the season of the year, and availability of food. In general, the presence of young at the homesite, a plentiful food supply (often correlated with the season of the year), or a season preceding estivation or hibernation will tend to restrict the size of the home range. Undoubtedly, many organisms have home ranges, but because of limited information and observation we know of very few. Some organisms such as the caribou (*Rangifer arcticus*) and many marine fish are truly nomadic, continuously moving from one region to another, never remaining in one area long enough to establish a home range. Although these animals are categorized as nomads, they may remain in an area for several days or even a week. The period of time an organism must remain in one locale in order for that region to be considered a home range is arbitrary and should be considered from the standpoint of the species and its habits. Evans and Holdenreid (1943) chose a month for the California ground squirrel (*Citellus beecheyi*). But every investigator must make his own decision as to how long an organism must remain in one geographic locale in order for that area to be considered an established home range. Perhaps as our research continues in this field, a more precise temporal unit for each major group of animals will be established. Ornithologists have noted that during migratory flights, birds will often establish a home range along the route of migration. In some instances a series of home ranges are set up and used year after year as the species migrates from its winter home to the breeding site and back again.

A number of methods have been used by ecologists in the past to determine the extent of a home range. For organisms that are active during daylight or twilight periods, direct observation from some camouflaged or secretive observation point is preferable, provided the home range is not extensive. Nocturnal animals or species that have a sizable home range pose a greater problem because direct observation is of limited value or worthless. A more indirect method such as tracking is often preferable. An alternative method is that of setting traps. This procedure, however, will often force an organism to alter the home range or altogether abandon the homesite and home range. Trap-shy animals will restrict their normal movements during a trapping period, so that the true extent and amount of movement, the position of the homesite in relation to the size and shape of the home range, and so on, cannot be determined. The trapping method involves a considerable amount of time and labor. The area is divided into quadrats of a certain size, and traps are placed in the center of each quadrat. The home range, as diagrammatically represented in Figure 6–9, would extend to the outside corners of the outermost quadrat in which the organism is captured. Trap areas must be checked frequently to prevent injury or killing of

FIGURE 6–9 An area divided into quadrats (squares in diagram) had a trap set in the center so that the home range of a small mammal could be determined on the basis of quadrats that were occupied. The dotted line represents the boundary of the home range, and the number within the quadrat represents the number of times the animal was caught in a particular trap.

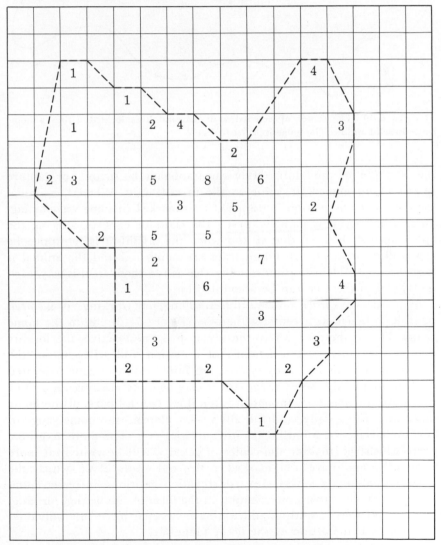

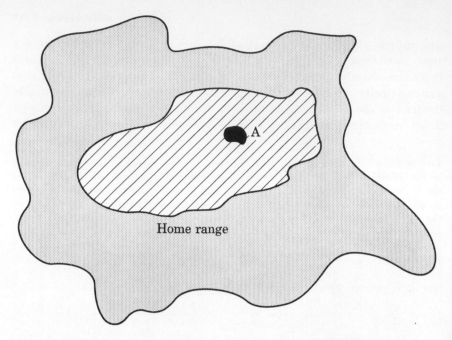

FIGURE 6–10 The center of activity, with diagonal lines located within a home range in solid outline. The homesite is located at *A*.

the organism by predators. Often the traps may be sprung, or capture species of no immediate value to the investigation. When the animal that is under observation is trapped, he is marked in some way—by tagging, using harmless paint, clipping the claws or ears, or altering the appearance slightly—so that if and when the organism is retrapped he can readily be identified. Often traps are numbered and the animal is tagged with an identification number that is recorded. In this way, each individual in the area can be accounted for.

By means of direct observation, trapping, or tracking, it is often possible to designate a **center of activity** (Figure 6–10) within the home range. This is the area where the organism is most active—the locality that receives the greatest amount of attention and will contain the feeding area. Center of activity does not imply that this zone is located in the center of the home range, for it may be quite eccentric, nor must it contain the homesite, though it often does. Not all parts of the home range are visited daily, and for this reason plotting the home range of any animal may be a long and rather tedious task. The more accessible areas, which will include the center of activity, will be visited far more frequently, and have well-marked paths and trails along which the organism habitually moves. Adverse climatic conditions, increased numbers of predators, man's intervention in the form of lumbering, farming, construction work, hunting, and fishing may often force the individual to abandon that portion of the home range.

TERRITORIES

It is common knowledge that dogs bark, growl, snap at, and sometimes attack strangers who enter the owner's yards. Even more annoying is the utter disregard displayed by such domestic creatures for legal boundaries separating yards or public sidewalks. Such overt display of aggression is a very primitive drive, called territoriality by the ecologist. A **territory is the defended portion of a home range under natural conditions.** Some breeds of dogs have retained this behavior pattern. They consider the master's yard and often adjacent yards, streets, and sidewalks as a territory to be defended in the event of invasion by strangers. The breed of dog (its innate genetic aggressiveness) and prior training will determine the amount of tenacity with which he or she will defend the territory. In nature, a territory is defended against invasion by individuals of the same species, but not always against other species. The fact that territories are frequently monospecific areas is important in the community economy, for it does not prevent other species from searching for food, locating homesites, home ranges or establishing territories of

FIGURE 6–11 Diagram *A* represents a continuous territory with a geographic continuity between feeding and breeding territories. In Diagram *B*, the species establishes feeding and breeding areas which are separated by an undefended segment of land. *H* designates the homesite in each case.

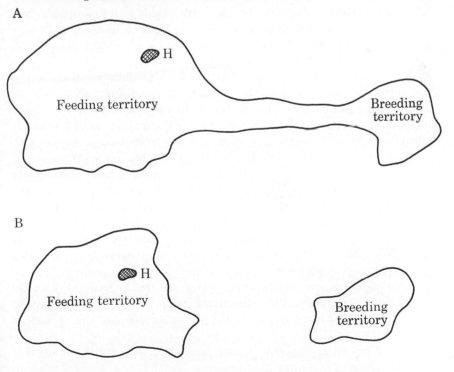

A

Feeding territory

H

Breeding territory

B

Feeding territory

H

Breeding territory

their own. It must be emphasized that territorial behavior is not universal among animal species. Many never show any indication of this behavior. The extent of any territory, as is true of home ranges, will be dictated by a number of environmental variables. Some species defend their entire home range—in this case the home range and territory are one and the same—while other species defend only a small segment of the home range. The time of year, breeding seasons, sex, and age of the organism (females and immature members of a species will often establish smaller territories)—all will account for variability in territorial extent. H. E. Howard (1920) was one of the first biologists to report on territorial behavior among avian groups. At the present time more is probably known regarding territorial behavior among birds than any other group of animals.

Different types of territories may be established within a home range. Territories may be established in a small area in the vicinity of the nest or homesite (one of the most common types of territories). Other territorial areas are known to exist in feeding areas, in breeding areas, and around mates, colonies, or aggregations of animals. Some species establish only one type of territory—that is, a breeding, a feeding, or a homesite territory. In other cases, several types of territory may be established and defended. If several types of territories exist, they may be continuous or discontinuous as represented in diagrams A and B of Figure 6–11. That is, there may be interconnecting passages that are defended (a continuous territory); or, as is the case with highly mobile animals such as birds and certain mammals, these areas are reached by trails or flyways that are not protected (discontinuous territories).

Variance in Behavior. Male songbirds will warn other members of the same species by plumage display behavior or continuous song that he has established a territory. One of the main functions of the male song is this warning. Another function it serves is the attraction of a mate. It indicates that the male is receptive and ready in many instances to initiate breeding activity. W. C. Dilger (1956) has reported that one of the means by which several thrushes—the wood thrush (*Hylocichla mustelina*), the olive-backed thrush (*Catharus ustulatus*), the hermit thrush (*C. guttatus*), and the veery (*C. fuscescens*)—identify one another with respect to species is by the song of the male. It so happens that all of these species are reproductively active at about the same time and often inhabit the same general locality. Males of migratory species will arrive first and set up a territory; several days later the female will arrive and often choose a nest site. In some groups, the female will aid the male in defending a territory. With the termination of the breeding season, the male abandons the territory and joins other birds of the species to form flocks.

Marine birds often establish nesting territories. It is easily understood why this behavioral pattern evolved. Often, nesting sites are at a premium. Also, they are vital for survival. By vigorously defending the territory, not only does the organism itself but also the species stand a better chance of survival. The progeny or future progeny are protected against danger of extinction by trampling of the young or of the eggs, or by theft of the eggs or of the offspring by other members of the rookery. Often these territories are extremely small—only a few square inches or so in size—along cliffs where nesting sites are extremely crowded in order to conserve as much room as possible for nests. Feeding areas among these groups are seldom defended. Similarly, birds with colonial habits will defend small territories in the vicinity of the nest site to conserve as much room as possible for other nests. American or yellow-billed cuckoos (*Coccyzus americanus*) and black-headed gulls (*Larus ridibundus*) in England have been observed in this regard. Crows (*Corvus brachyrhynchos*) often band together at a communal roosting site, with no display of territorial aggressiveness, but during the diurnal period they separate and establish feeding territories.

Territorial and breeding behavior of the green heron (*Butorides virescens*) that nests along the Gulf Coast, the islands of the Caribbean, and the northern coast of South America during the fall and winter have been observed in considerable detail. During the winter, the birds have drab yellow-green plumage and legs, but after they complete the migration, coloration changes take place that transform the male, and to a lesser extent the female, into a more striking-looking bird. The yellowish-green legs become a yellow-orange, and a patch of skin anterior to the eyes turns from green to blue-black. Breeding grounds are located in an area north of the Gulf Coast into southern Canada. Males become very aggressive after arrival in the breeding area; they establish rather large territories and allow no member of the species, male or female, to enter the boundaries. Female herons usually spend a number of days or weeks at feeding grounds along the edges of rivers, streams, ponds, lakes, or tidal estuaries, never approaching the territorial areas of the male birds during this period.

Males begin flying around the margins of their territories, emitting harsh *scaws* whenever they perch on a boundary tree or post to warn other males of the species of his territory. Any errant male approaching or entering the territory is at first warned by a ruffling of the back feathers by the resident male. If this is not sufficient warning, a more hostile display—opening the bill and rasping at the invader—generally sends even the boldest male fleeing. If these warnings are not heeded, the male attacks the vagrant, driving him from the territory; the resident male rarely loses such a battle. It should be noted, in terms of behavior, that physical contact is the last resort, occurring only after repeated threats. This is the usual pattern of defense in territorial behavior in many groups of animals. The continuous harsh scawing of the male eventually attracts the female to the territory, but the male chases a female from the territory just as he would any male intruder. Only after some period of time (usually several days) is the female allowed to stand on a boundary of the territory.

The male then begins to establish a nest site or repair a nesting area that had been used the year before. After the initial nest building activity, the female heron is permitted to enter the territory but is not allowed to approach the nest site. As these activities progress in definite sequence, it is apparent, the area of the territory becomes progressively smaller, for the male no longer defends the outer margins of his former territory. A flight well within the original boundaries of the original

FIGURE 6–12 The green heron (*Butorides virescens*), showing the stretch display that is an integral part of mating behavior in this species.

territory, followed by a return to the nest site after each flight, is repeated a number of times by the male. Soon afterward, the male and female engage in similar mutual flights, with the female gradually being allowed to alight on the nest tree. Signs of eventual mating are then initiated by a stretch display on the part of the male (Figure 6–12), which consists essentially of stretching the neck, with the bill held erect, and a ruffling of the head and neck feathers and a side-to-side rocking or swaying of the entire body. Eventually the female enters the nest alongside the male; both may stand side by side for hours. Finally, there is a mutual caressing of heads, bills, and nibbling of feathers, followed by a stretch display by the female. Such overt activity on her part (she has been a somewhat passive participant until this time) is a significant sign that she is prepared for copulation, which follows. At this stage in territorial behavior, we find that only the nest site and its immediate area are defended. In other words, the territory has become smaller as the breeding period has continued. After copulation, the nest site is defended by both mates. The aggressive behavior of the male green heron is not peculiar to this species, but is common among many territorial organisms. During the early stages of breeding behavior, even the female is threatened, for at this time she represents a species intruder of his territory. Later, the male gradually becomes less aggressive towards the female; he must restrain the female's tendency to flee by indicating his gradual willingness to engage in reproductive activities.

David Lack, the British ornithologist, has noted territorial behavior demonstrated by caged male robins (*Erithacus nubecula*). After caging a male bird and placing him in an area considered to be his territory, Lack observed that if another bird of the same species was enticed into the area, the caged bird exhibited considerable activity comparable to the aggressive behavior of uncaged birds of the same species. The bird fluttered around within the cage, sang, and carried on various phases of aggressive display. If the same caged bird was removed from its territory to another area, it then became silent and submissive, very often huddling in a corner of the cage, not exhibiting any of the overt behavior previously displayed within its own territory.

Mammalian territories are, in general, less well defined. Squirrels and chipmunks, however, exhibit territorial aggressiveness, the males being more combative than females. Generally, the homesite is defended more strenuously than are other areas, but if the food supply becomes critical, feeding areas become territorial zones. Larger mammals such as deer will establish home ranges that will vary with the season and sex. The male will procure a harem and a highly mobile territory—that is, the territory is not established on any set plot of ground, but will vary in position in relation to the location of the hinds (females) of his harem. Male fur seals (*Callorhinus ursinus*) and sealions (*Zalophus californianus, Eumetopias jubata*) organize territories on isolated islands to which they return every year. The Pribilof Islands in the northern Pacific is a well-known breeding area for fur seals. After spending the winter and early spring in fishing and feeding in the Sea of Japan, the bulls arrive first—in late April and early May—followed by the females several weeks later. Prior to the arrival of the females (about the middle of June), all territorial rights have been established. Bull seals have fought among themselves for territories; usually, the original occupant maintains his position within his small plot of land. The row closest to the beach is prized territory and is retained by the larger, stronger bulls. Behind the beach property are territories established by smaller, weaker bulls. Each territory is valued in proportion to its distance from the beach for several reasons: (1) The beach owners will have first choice with regard to selection of the pregnant cows upon their arrival from the coastal waters of California. (2) The location of territories at some distance from the beach necessitates running the gauntlet of enraged bulls. Each member of an inland harem makes his way to or from the water by way of the intervening harems. The male, often weighing five hundred pounds or more, competes for females (usually weighing no more than eighty pounds) as they arrive, establishing a harem, with the stronger and larger, more aggressive males possessing the largest harems, of as many as thirty or more females. Figure 6–13 is a photograph showing several harems guarded by jealous bull seals on one of the Pribilof Islands. Competition for females involves considerable aggressive behavior, including vocal warnings and physical combat, because younger bulls are continually attempting to lure cows away from an established harem. Birth occurs two or three days following the arrival of the female. The bull takes no interest in the pup, but copulates with the females of his harem, thus insuring the subsequent birth of pups some twelve months later.

The harem bulls leave the island in mid-August to seek food, for their former bulk has been reduced to a mere three hundred pounds during the months they have defended and maintained their harems. They swim to fishing grounds and feed many miles away before they return to the islands. The only enemy, other than man, that the seal encounters in its aquatic habitat are killer whales (*Orcinus*) that often decimate entire herds of seals, especially during the periods in which the male is replenishing his food supply during late summer. After the young have been suckled and raised to the point when they are able to care for themselves, the island is deserted by the young pups and cows for an aquatic existence. They leave in October for the warmer California waters. The bulls will leave for their own fishing grounds in the western Pacific some months later (December).

In lower vertebrate groups, there is no well-established evidence that amphibians have territories. But reptiles (particularly lizards) do exhibit territorial behavior. Among fish groups, the male stickleback defends

FIGURE 6–13 Fur seals in large herds during the mating season on the Pribilof Islands of the North Pacific. Note the large dark males guarding their harems of smaller, lighter-colored females. Pups in the foreground are small and dark. Photograph by Victor Scheffer is of the Polovina Rookery. Courtesy of the Fish and Wildlife Service, U.S. Department of the Interior.

the nest site, which, in most cases, consists of a very small area. Different species of sunfishes (Family: Centrarchidae) will establish territories during the breeding season, but not at other times of the year. As is true in most instances, it is the male member of the species that actively defends the territory. Many of the invertebrates have received only limited attention with respect to home ranges and territories. Some of the arthropods do establish home ranges and territories. The fiddler crab (*Uca*) has a home range of one or two meters encircling the opening of the burrow. This home range area is also a territory and will be vigorously defended. Ants are one of the few groups of insects known to defend territories (Elton, 1932); homesites and feeding or foraging areas are protected by the soldier and worker castes. Dragonflies will establish a linear territory along a stream or in the vicinity of a body of water that they will patrol and defend against invasion by other members of their species.

Courtship behavior between species is varied and relies upon one or more stimuli offered in sequence, in combination, or singly. These stimuli may involve visual, olfactory, auditory, or tactile responses on the part of mating pairs. Visual and auditory responses have been most thoroughly investigated by ecologists up to the present time. No doubt this is owing, in part, to our own acute reception of such stimuli in contrast to those of olfaction and touch. Among most invertebrates, behavioral activity is often a means of species and sex recognition. Mixed swarms of fireflies are able to identify a particular species and sex by the frequency and duration of flashes. Male fiddler crabs (Figure 6–14) inhabiting tidal flats by the hundreds are often found in groups of mixed species. The female identifies a proper mate by the frequency and speed with which the one large claw is moved. Perhaps different colors on the appendages and body also aid in proper identification of the male member of the species.

Male crickets of the genus *Acheta* utilize sound stimuli to attract mates in the same way that birds use songs as a means of identifying sex, the location of a territory, and the readiness to engage in copulation. The male cricket attracts a female by stridulating, producing a sound by rubbing together rough surfaces of the forewings held at a 45-degree angle. After a female has approached the male, he produces an entirely different mating sound that activates the female to assume a copulatory stance while a spermatophore is transferred to her reproductive system. The male lashes the female with his antennae during the period of copulation, producing a continual tactile stimulus during the period of sperm transfer. Male spiders are often pounced on and eaten by the aggressive

FIGURE 6–14 Photograph of fiddler crabs (*Uca*), a common organism along the intertidal mud or sand flats of a marine environment. Male crabs have the large claw and are the larger organisms shown.

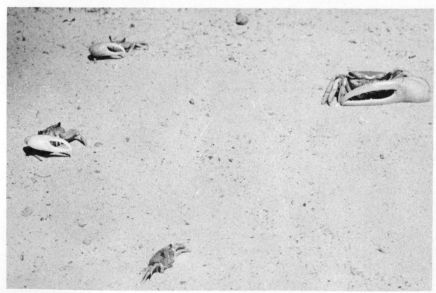

female if there is not a preliminary recognition signal made by the male such as a swaying of the body, movement of the appendages, or a significant tugging of certain strands of the female's web. In some species of flies of the family Empididae, the male presents a female with an insect (food) or silken balls produced by the male that may either contain food, or in the case of some species, may be completely empty. The food or silken ball distracts the female long enough for effective copulation without the danger of the male being eaten by the female member. In these cases, courtship behavior is a necessary procedure if the male wishes to remain alive.

Amphibians engage in courtship behavior that arouses the female primarily by tactile and chemical stimulation. These tactile stimuli are important for both sexes of the salamander because they undoubtedly aid in the release of a spermatophore by the male as well as insure a proper stance and pattern of behavior by the female. In many groups of salamanders the female will pick up the spermatophore by way of the cloacal vent. Tactile stimuli consist of rubbing the flanks or ventral surface of the female with the snout, tail, or entire body. It is believed that chemical substances are expelled into the water by the male and propelled toward the female by a repeated lashing of the tail. The male European wild rabbit (*Oryctolagus cuniculus*) elevates his tail, exposing the white underside to the female while walking away in stiff-legged fashion; then as he circles the female, he changes the position of his tail so that it is directed toward the female at all times. Such behavior is preliminary to actual copulation and undoubtedly serves as a sexual stimulus for the female, preparing her for the remainder of the sex act. Little is known about courtship and reproductive behavior in many groups of animals, but this phase of ecology promises to yield many interesting behavioral patterns and will eventually answer many of the complex problems dealing with **ethology** (animal behavior).

SIGNIFICANCE OF THE HOME RANGE AND TERRITORY

In so far as is known, no animal that organizes a home range or territory is consciously aware of such activity; it is the result of natural selection and genetic factors acting over a long period of time. The establishment of these areas is of considerable biological significance. They are often of prime importance as regards survival, because they make for better adaptation to the environment and aid in the fundamental biological activities such as mating, shelter, and food procurement. The value of a home range lies in the fact that by traversing an area almost daily, an animal establishes trails that lead into various parts of the home range. These trails and every landmark along its length become familiar to the animal and may spell the difference between existence and death when it is attempting to escape a predator

FIGURE 6–15 A well-established trail of a mammal within its home range. The trail runs through a dense stand of old field vegetation and veers to the left in the background.

within its home range. Predators or any intruders are at a marked disadvantage within a well-established home range because, being unfamiliar with the landmarks and trails, they become hopelessly lost, at least momentarily, within the vast maze of trails (Figure 6–15) and passages that often exist. The occupants have a definite superiority in that they are often able to escape into refuges or alternate homesites previously prepared for just such an eventuality.

The longer an organism remains within a particular home range, the greater the probability that it will attempt to improve the homesite and construct refuges and alternate homesites, along with additional avenues of escape. An organism driven from its home range into unfamiliar territory will experience the same loss of direction as would an intruder in the home range of the fleeing organism. This unfamiliarity with its surroundings will render the organism more vulnerable to attack. Since any natural refuges that might exist would in all probability be encountered by pure chance without any previous orientation with landmarks. In order to utilize a home range and take full advantage of the benefits derived from such a behavior pattern, it is essential that the organism have an associative memory. This would limit such behavior to higher groups of invertebrates and the vertebrates, as associative memory is dependent on a well-established nervous system capable of reacting and recalling various patterns or shapes within its immediate area.

Man, in the course of evolution, has experienced a regression with respect to some of the sensory receptors and a refinement of others, in contrast to other mammals. We are inclined to believe that the extent of home ranges and territories is recognized by the sense of sight and movement within these areas, but such is not the case in many instances. Man, though his sense of sight is keen, has lost much of the olfactory area possessed by many of the lower mammals. This reduction in size in the human organism should not be misinterpreted as proof or evidence that man's sense of smell has diminished, because there is no correlation between the size of the olfactory area and keenness of the olfactory sense. However, it is quite obvious that man's olfactory sense is not as acute as that of some of the other mammals. Consequently, we find that in spite of our own evolutionary shortcomings, other groups of vertebrates utilize this keen sense of smell to distinguish home ranges or territories of other members of a species. We find that bears urinate, roll in the urine, then rub themselves against "frontier trees" of their home range. Other bears of the species will seldom roam into such an area after picking up the scent of another's urine. Wild boars and bison rub themselves against trees, and the hippopotamus scatters feces with its tail throughout its home range. Some mammals possess scent glands that release secretions upon foliage, litter, soil, or the trunks and branches of trees. Examples are antelope and deer, with excretory glands situated near the eyes, and many of the ruminates that release secretions from between the toes. Thus a keen sense of smell is employed by many organisms in order to recognize territories and home ranges of other members of the species.

Significance of territorial behavior lies in the fact that an active defense of any geographic area will often insure to breeding pairs or solitary individuals the necessary essentials for life. Defensive behavior within certain areas will restrict the population density of the species for the region, thereby preserving the carrying capacity of the ecosystem (see "Quantitative Relationships of Food Material" in Chapter VII). This, in turn, will prevent serious damage of the habitat by overpopulation. In view of these facts, territoriality insures the survival of a certain percentage of the population and the subsequent and successful maturation of progeny, for it prevents the trampling of eggs, the young, the depletion of food supplies, and the usurping of homesites. Excessive fighting is eliminated because any one member of a population will come into contact with relatively few individuals of his own species in areas where territories are well established. This reduction of aggressive behavior during the breeding season is of definite survival value; less aggressiveness in the vicinity of the homesite reduces the possibility of injuring or destroying eggs and young. Parent organisms with an instinct to defend the homesite and feeding grounds against trespass by other species members are bound to stand a better chance of survival. This, in turn, favors natural selection of these organisms, with a tendency for such behavior patterns to become fixed in the progeny. In most all cases, the male actively defends the territory by song, display behavior, aggressive action, and bright colors.

Territorial defense tends to severely limit social activity that may at times be beneficial to the population. In species with strong territorial tendencies, the amount of cooperation, excepting between mates, is practically nonexistent during periods of defensive behavior. Certainly there is no common defense against predators, as is true of nonterritorial organisms that roam in herds or packs and are often dependent upon sheer numbers and common defense to guard against population losses from predation. If territorial activity is in effect when cooler or abnormally low temperatures prevail, the excessive loss of individuals can be avoided by collective use of body heat through huddling. At times, though rarely, territorial behavior and social cooperation are modified so that an organism may benefit from group action and at the same time take advantage of territorial qualities of merit. Some birds and monkeys establish a **social territory** often termed a **flock,** or **band territory.** Sticklebacks will often found colonies during the breeding period and establish property borders for individual nest sites, but in the event of severe disturbance the entire colony will rally to a common defense of the social territory.

MIGRATION

The movement of animals from one area to another, whether it concerns a vertical movement of a few millimeters from one soil level to another or the extensive flights such as those of the golden plover or the arctic tern, is known as **migration.** There is, perhaps, more information available about the migratory flights of birds than there is about other groups. It is known, however, that this reaction to various ecological conditions is not confined to birds alone. Mammals (bats, bison, deer, fur seals, and whales), reptiles (sea turtles), fishes (eels, salmon)—all are familiar groups of vertebrates known to follow particular migratory routes correlated with seasonal changes. Invertebrates will migrate, although, with the exception of insects, such migrations are of a limited distance. Several terms relative to migratory movements should be defined, because they appear often in the literature. **Migration** is a direct movement from one locality to another, with a periodic return to the original locality. **Emigration** is the egress of a species from some region with no intent to return to the area. The converse movement is **immigra-**

tion, an invasion of a locality by a species with no prospects of departure. **Remigration** is similar to migration in that individuals leave an area, and there is a return to the original area. It differs from migration, however, in that different members of the species return; in other words, a later generation makes the return flight. Remigration is common among invertebrates, especially insects (see, below, this section).

Interesting information has come to light as a result of intensive tagging procedures and recent laboratory work performed by many scientists. Several of the most interesting problems that have been given considerable attention in recent years are the causes or factors responsible for initiating the migration of a group of organisms and the way in which these organisms are able to navigate during this mass movement to their destination. The navigatory problem is all the more amazing in view of the fact that often such journeys are made despite the intervention of unsatisfactory climatological or oceanographic conditions. The green sea turtles (*Chelonia mydas*) that have been tagged and studied by Archie Carr (University of Florida) is a case in point. These turtles are known to nest on Ascension Island, a small spire of barren volcanic rock, 7.15 miles long and about 6.25 miles wide, approximately 1,400 miles from the Brazilian coast (Figure 6–16). It is truly a feat in navigation that the turtles reach such a seemingly inhospitable speck in the South Atlantic, considering not only its size and the distance that must be traversed, but also the difficulties of navigation. The turtles swim against the south equatorial current, a body of water that maintains a steady

FIGURE 6–16 The South Atlantic area showing Ascension Island, midway between the coasts of South America and Africa. The direction of surface currents is indicated by arrows. The main route followed by the green turtle in its annual migrations is marked by diagonal lines.

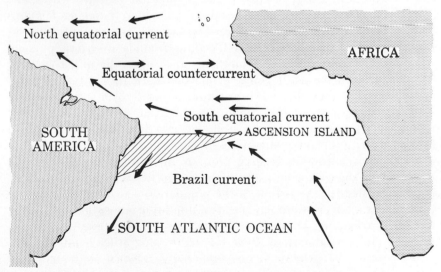

flow of nearly 4 knots (4.6 miles per hour) from the African coast toward the continent of South America. The course the turtles take must compensate for currents and waves because they travel at an angle to the major current. It is truly amazing that despite these difficulties they arrive at this exact pinpoint with such precision and regularity each April. Females lumber onto the beach to lay a hundred eggs or so every two weeks for about two months. Males copulate with the females to insure fertilization of eggs the following year. Copulation occurs in the pounding surf, with the male grasping the female with large nails on the front flippers and a horn on the tip of the tail. Generally, by mid-June the turtles return to the sea and appear off the South American coast for the rest of the year.

Migrations of butterflies in Ontario were described in a report by Beall (1941a, 1941b), based on seven years of field work in the area. Spring and summer populations contained many old, sexually mature individuals that gradually died with the advent of fall. Young, sexually immature monarch butterflies (*Danaus*) migrated southward, flying near the ground (within 20 feet of the surface) and often against the wind. Beall (1946), on the basis of measurements and a statistical analysis of the measurements, found that the returning migrants that arrived during the spring in Ontario were related to the fall emigrants, but were not the same individuals (an example of remigration). Another insect, (*Plusia gamma*) a moth, migrates every year from continental Europe to Britain in early spring (late April or May). Several generations of the moth have been reproduced in England. Of the several hundred species of butterflies throughout the world, about fifty are known to migrate.

One motivating force, aside from the reproductive factor (sea turtles) and environmental stimulus, to move to areas with a more favorable climate (butterflies and moths), is the population pressure within the animal's native habitat. The European lemming (*Lemmus lemmus*) leaves the mountains of southern Norway, Sweden, and the arctic tundra farther north at times when their breeding grounds are overpopulated. They often travel more than a hundred miles, generally under cover of darkness, toward the sea. Upon reaching the shore, they enter the water and swim until they die, leaving behind a small token population in their breeding areas. Other small mammals—mice, voles, hares, and rabbits—are known to emigrate from an area if the population level exceeds a critical value. Migrations of the African springbuck (*Antidorcas euchore*) from its feeding grounds in South Africa toward the west coast of the continent are believed to have been triggered by a high population density. A portion of the population remained in its native habitat, but a larger group left the area, migrating across bushman country, often trampling through native villages on their way to the sea. Hunters and predators took their toll of the migrating band; the survivors entered the Atlantic Ocean and finally drowned. Although some people strongly support the hypothesis that such movements are caused by increased density of the population, others argue that this is merely dispersal that happens to be more obvious if the populations are larger and therefore more individuals are dispersing. Just as logically, it may be some intrinsic environmental factor—paucity of food, shelter, increased tension among members of a species caused by overcrowding, or more subtle factors—that trigger a sudden migration of a large segment of the population.

The ability of animals to travel immense distances and return to the same homesite or the same patch of ground never ceases to amaze. The Pacific salmon (*Oncorhynchus* spp.) returns to the small stream from which it hatched, after swimming hundreds of miles through the ocean and making an additional long trip upstream, often over obstacles. Fur seals return to the Pribilof Islands, off the Alaskan coast, after traversing over 3,000 miles of ocean. A few authors seem inclined to believe that these animals have a mysterious sixth sense that enables them to guide themselves unerringly to their destination. Although it has never been disproven, most biologists, I believe, doubt the existence of any such sense within the body of any organism. For one thing, the ability to migrate is widespread among many groups of vertebrates and invertebrates. To suggest that such a diverse aggregate shares this sixth sense would seem highly improbable. It is assumed that the senses possessed and shared by a majority of these organisms are far more keenly receptive to certain stimuli than we can imagine. Even after animals have been living in a state of captivity for many years, as in museums, zoos, and circuses, the migratory urge is still strong: they are usually more restless and attempt to fly or leave their cages during the migration interval, even though there is no physiological or environmental need so far as basic requirements are concerned. From common knowledge or experience, we know that the visual receptors of a hawk, the olfactory receptors of many carnivores, and the thermoreceptors of reptiles are far more acute than our own. It is the utilization of these sensory receptors so highly attuned to the various environmental stimuli and/or the ability to orient with regard to celestial bodies (sun and stars) that enable these organisms to achieve their migratory destinations with unerring accuracy.

One more brief account of migratory accuracy among the flightless emperor penguins (*Aptenoides forsteri*) will reinforce the fact that animals may travel great distances and return to the precise spot without the need for recourse to any obvious landmarks. In the antarctic fall (late March), this penguin crosses hundreds of miles of barren ice and snow [only the Emperor and Adelie penguin (*Pygoscelis adeliae*) are restricted to the antarctic] to reach the breeding site that has been used in past years. Although these birds waddle in a clumsy fashion on land, they will also at times flop onto their bellies and propel themselves by means of their flippers and periodic shoves with their webbed feet. If the snow and ice are of the right physical consistency, they can travel faster in this toboggan-like fashion than a man can ski. The female lays a single egg in May (at the beginning of the long antarctic winter), leaving it with the male, who props it on top of his webbed flippers and covers it with a fold of abdominal skin. The female returns to the shore, which is farther from the breeding site because the ice sheets grow during the winter. Here she gorges herself with fish, shrimp, and squid. Then she returns over the ice shelf that has become even more extensive during the intervening weeks. Often such migratory trips are solitary, made over barren masses of ice and snow and through frequent blizzards that sweep the antarctic at this time of year. Upon arriving at the nesting site, she finds a hungry chick to feed if the egg or chick has not been preyed upon by sheath-bills or giant petrels in an unguarded moment. The male loses over 30 to 40 per cent of his original weight (dropping from 75 to 50 pounds) during his incubatory fast. He has to endure environmental conditions of the most severe type, for during June and July temperatures fall to 40° below zero (Fahrenheit) and winds often attain a speed of 100 miles per hour or more. The chick is fed by regurgitation, while the male heads for open water and food. If the female should miss the breeding site or fail to return for a few more days, both male and chick would starve to death.

Birds usually follow certain **flyways** or regular routes of migration in moving from summer breeding ranges to the winter home range and back again. Several main flyways are utilized by birds in the Western Hemisphere. The **Mississippi Flyway** accommodates more birds than do the rest of the routes collectively. This important flyway is broad and extensive, occupying the Mississippi Valley area and surrounding regions, and serves as a route of migration between the north central United States and Canada. The easternmost flyway spans a vast stretch of the North Atlantic and accommodates the passage of birds between Nova Scotia and parts of eastern Canada and eastern Venezuela. A coastal route of migration, accommodating large flights moving between New England and eastern Canada and various parts of Venezuela, bifurcates into a passage across the eastern Caribbean and another across Cuba into the western parts of Venezuela. West of the large Mississippi Flyway are two smaller inland routes of migration, the **Central Flyway** and the **Mountain Flyway.** The former extends from North Dakota across Texas and the Gulf to southern Mexico; the latter extends from central Canada and northern Montana and terminates in central and southern Mexico. The **Pacific Flyway** originates in northern Washington and follows the western coast of the United States to southern Mexico. The **Cross Country Flyway,** beginning at the southern end of Lake Winnipeg in central Canada, extends across the Great Lakes area and connects with the

FIGURE 6–17 Important flyways of North America. *P*, Pacific Flyway; *M₀*, Mountain Flyway; *C*, Central Flyway; *M*, Mississippi Flyway; *Cᵣ*, Cross Country Flyway; *A*, Atlantic Coast Flyway.

Atlantic Coast Flyway in the vicinity of Chesapeake Bay (Figure 6–17 and Table 6–1). These flyways, although they become well-developed and recognized routes of passage for migratory birds in the areas mentioned, have in actuality only vaguely defined origins and terminations, for different species will migrate from different areas scattered throughout the Northern and Southern Hemispheres. Table 6–1 indicates that different species will fly variable distances into northern breeding grounds and occupy different southern home ranges. A word of caution: Table 6–1 represents the farthest northern or southern average limit for the species indicated. It should be pointed out, however, that members of a species may occupy areas far south of the northern limit or far north of the southern limit.

TABLE 6-1. *Nesting Areas and Flyways Used by Some of the More Common Species of Migratory Birds*

COMMON NAME	SCIENTIFIC NAME	FLYWAY	SUMMER NESTING AREA	WINTER NESTING AREA
Arctic tern	*Sterna paradisaea*	Pacific Coast, Europe, and African coasts	Victoria Island	Antarctica and bordering islands
Belted kingfisher	*Ceryle alcyon*	Mississippi and Atlantic Coast	Northwest territories, central Quebec, and Labrador	Northern Brazil
Bobolink	*Dolichonyx orizivorus*	Atlantic Coast	Southern Alberta and Ontario, Eastern New Brunswick	Central Colombia
Canada goose	*Branta canadensis*	Cross country, Atlantic Coast	Northeastern Alaska	Northern Mexico
Golden plover	*Pluvialis apricaria*	Pacific Coast	Victoria Island	Marquesas Islands
Red-eyed vireo	*Vireo olivaceus*	Atlantic Coast Central	Great Slave Lake	Southern Colombia, Southern Brazil
Redstart	*Setophaga ruticilla*	Atlantic Coast Mountain	Northwest Territories	Venezuela
Ruby-throated hummingbird	*Archilochus colubris*	Mississippi	Southern Manitoba, Nova Scotia	Panama
Scarlet tanager	*Piranga olivacea*	Mississippi	Northern Nova Scotia, Southern Ontario	Central Peru
Western tanager	*Piranga ludoviciana*	Pacific	Northern British Columbia	Salvador
Yellow warbler	*Dendroica petechia*	Mississippi Central	Southern Quebec Central Alaska	Northern Brazil

These same flyways are used for the return migration, which is stimulated by photoperiodic changes and favorable thermal factors. Flights are
usually nocturnal and may carry the bird several hundred miles per
night; the daylight period is used for feeding and resting in preparation
for continuing the migration the following night. Though individuals
of a species may fly several hundred miles per night, the average route
of movement for the entire species is much reduced in terms of distance
traveled. Figures compiled from observations along the Mississippi Flyway are interesting: they show that the distance covered gradually
increases as the species moves farther northward (Table 6–2). Birds such
as robins (*Turdus migratorius*), kingbirds (*Tyrannus*), and swallows
(*Hirundo*) migrate during the day and feed during their migratory
flight. They stop in suitable communities periodically to feed on insects
and vegetation, then move on to other areas. Research in the past dealing with the reasons for migration make one point quite clear: migratory movement of birds is initiated by quite different intrinsic and
extrinsic changes among species. In other words, a factor that may be
quite important in initiating a migratory response in species A may
have no effect on species B.

T A B L E   6 – 2 . *Variable Distances Covered by Birds Migrating Northward
Along the Mississippi Flyway*

GEOGRAPHIC REGION	DISTANCE COVERED (DAILY AVERAGE)
Southern Louisiana to southern Minnesota	25 mi./day
Southern Minnesota to southern Manitoba	40 mi./day
Southern Manitoba to Lake Athabasca	72 mi./day
Lake Athabasca to Great Slave Lake	116 mi./day

Two birds that migrate considerable distances are the arctic tern
(*Sterna paradisaea*) and the golden plover (*Pluvialis apricaria*). Arctic
terns have been known to breed in areas only 7½ degrees from the North
Pole, though its breeding range may extend as far south as Great Slave
Lake and along the Atlantic coast to Massachusetts. After the young
develop, these birds migrate south, crossing the North Atlantic and following the western European and African coasts to Antarctica, a distance
of 11,000 miles. Terns breeding in western Canada and Alaska follow
the North American and South American coasts (Figure 6–18) to Antarctica. Golden plovers (eastern group) may often migrate 2,400 miles
without pause or rest (though they have been seen resting on the ocean
surface at times) and unlike most birds they fly day and night. Another

FIGURE 6–18 Migration routes of the arctic tern along the Pacific Coast and throughout the Atlantic Ocean. Symbols represented are keyed as follows: ● breeding areas; ★ winter nesting sites; ■ recovery points; ▲ migration records. Courtesy of the Fish and Wildlife Service, U.S. Department of the Interior, from a drawing by Robert Hines.

unusual aspect of the migratory flight of the eastern golden plovers is their use of different routes in migrating north and south. In their southern migration, made in September, they fly over the Atlantic, passing Bermuda and the Antilles, to the eastern coast of South America. Here they may rest briefly before making the overland flight to Argentina, their usual winter quarters. In March, they migrate north across the Gulf and up the Mississippi Flyway reaching their northern breeding grounds in the arctic tundra, in early June, by a completely different route. The golden plover is not the only bird known to use different routes of migration for its annual trips north and south. The Connecticut warbler (*Oporornis agilis*) begins its southern flight by flying from southern Canada to New England and thence by the Atlantic Coast Flyway to Florida. Its return trip is made by way of the Mississippi Flyway back into southern Canada. The bobolinks (*Dolichonyx orizivorus*) and other birds are gradually changing their migration routes as is evidenced by bird-banding technics used in recent years.

ECOLOGICAL NICHE

The functional role an organism plays within a community or ecosystem is called its **ecological niche**. Perhaps the choice of the term *niche* is an unfortunate one for the ecological vocabulary, because students often confuse the term with a place or location. It is easy to understand why there may be confusion when we consider the dictionary definition of *niche*: "a cavity, hollow or recess, within the thickness of a wall for a statue, bust or other erect ornament; any like place." The connotation of *niche,* then, is a particular place or location. At times the term *place niche* is used to designate some particular location, although the ecologist would generally use the term **habitat.** When the term *place niche* is used to designate a particular place or location, it is necessary to use the term *functional niche* (ecological niche) to designate the functional position of an organism in a community.

Examples of organisms occupying various ecological niches in different geographic areas are numerous. Charles Darwin, on his famous voyage aboard H.M.S. *Beagle,* became quite interested in the adaptive radiation of the finches living on the Galápagos Islands, which are a group of volcanic islands located on the equator about 600 miles west of Ecuador, South America. It is conceded by most geologists that these islands arose through volcanic activity over a million years ago and had never been connected to the mainland of South America, so that originally, all of the organisms had been transported in some fashion over a broad expanse of sea to this isolated group of islands. Of the fourteen species of finches, thirteen are located on the Galápagos Islands and one is endemic to Cocos Island, which is some 300 miles northeast of the Galápagos region. Ten species of these finches are found on one island. These birds are placed in the subfamily Geospizinae, including four genera. The ground finches belong to the genus *Geospiza,* the tree finches to the genus *Camarhynchus,* a single species of warbler-finch to the genus *Certhida,* and an isolated species on Cocos Island has been placed in the genus *Pinaroloxias.* One of the tree finches (*C. crassirostris*) has a parrot-like beak and is basically a vegetarian, living on a diet of buds and fruits. The rest of the tree finches are insect eaters; three of these species feed on insects of different sizes and vary in size of body as well as size of beak in keeping with dietary needs. Another species (*C. heliobates*) feeds on insects in mangrove swamps. The most interesting species is the wood-

(A)

(B)

(C)

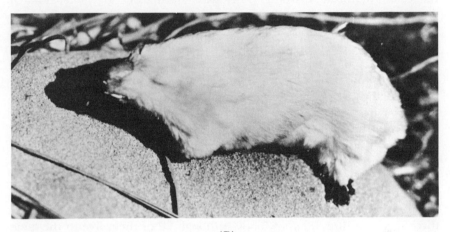

(D)

FIGURE 6–19 Several representative marsupial mammals of Australia that may be considered ecological equivalents of placental mammals in other parts of the world. Photograph *A* is the Tasmanian wolf, equivalent to the red wolf of North America. Photograph *B* is the rock wallaby, an equivalent of mountain goats or sheep in other areas. Photograph *C* shows several short-nosed bandicoots, equivalent to a woodchuck or groundhog of other regions. Photograph *D* is the marsupial mole (*Notoryctes typhlops*), equivalent to the placental moles on other continents. All photographs are by courtesy of the Australian News and Information Bureau, Department of the Interior, Canberra, Australia.

pecker-finch (*C. pallidus*). This woodpeckerlike bird climbs trees in search of insects in the cracks of bark. Although it has a woodpecker's beak, it lacks the long, extensile tongue of the woodpecker. It has solved this anatomical problem by carrying in its beak a cactus spine or small twig with which it dislodges the insects. This is one of the few recorded cases of tool utilization by animals other than the primates.

The ground finches have filled different niches normally occupied by other birds. Three species are seedeaters; they differ from one another in size of body and of beak. Another species (*Geospiza difficilis*) has a sharp beak rather than the parrotlike beak of the seedeater, for it feeds on prickly pear. Two other species (*G. conirostris* and *G. scandens*) live on the outlying islands; they differ in size, feeding on different types of seed and supplementing this diet with cactus. Thus we find that in the absence of other birds to occupy the niches available on the isolated Galápagos chain of islands, the finches have, in the course of time, radiated into various ecological niches, becoming modified anatomically and physiologically in keeping with their functional role (niche) in the community.

Other excellent examples of organisms occupying various ecological niches are found in Australia. This area—at one time a remote, isolated region—was inhabited by the marsupial mammals. These vertebrates evolved in terrestrial areas and gradually exhibited an adaptive radiation, filling the ecological niches normally occupied by placental mammals in other parts of the world. *Notoryctes,* the marsupial mole, *Thylacinus,* a marsupial wolf, *Petaurus,* the flying phalanger, and *Lagorchestes,* the hare wallaby—all resemble, to an amazing degree, the placental moles, wolves, flying squirrels, and jackrabbits (Figure 6–19) living in other areas while functionally filling the same ecological niche. There are a number of recorded instances of closely related species that occupy similar (or the same) place niches, but their physiological niche relative to their feeding habits and functional position in the community may be quite different. One example recorded by White (1951) are three species of weaver birds living in the vicinity of Lake Mweru, Africa. All three species utilize different foods, although all of them live in the same general area. Two of the species, *Ploceus melanocephalus* and *P. collaris,* even share the same nests. One species is insectivorous, the other feeds on seeds. Randle and Austing (1952) have observed that two owls, the saw-whet (*Aegolius aegolius*) and the long-eared owl (*Asio otus*), use the same roosting territory in the daytime (coniferous woodland). These nocturnal birds, however, hunt for prey in different areas and seek different genera of rodents: the saw-whet owl seeks out *Peromyscus* in wooded areas; the long-eared owl preys on *Microtus* and *Cryptotis* in open fields.

A number of areas of similar ecological makeup located in widely separated regions are inhabited by different species of organisms. These organisms, living under similar environmental conditions in different geographic regions are known as **ecological equivalents.** The mountain goat (*Oreamnos americanus*), found at high altitudes in montane areas of North America (British Columbia and northern parts of the Rocky Mountains within the United States), occupies the same niche, on the basis of its habits, food, and relationship to other organisms, as does the ibex (*Capra ibex*), which at one time was common in the Alps of

TABLE 6–3. *Ecologically Equivalent Organisms in Terms of Feeding Habits or Stratal Location Representing Several Geographic Areas of the World* *

TYPES OF ANIMALS	GEOGRAPHIC AREAS			
	EURASIA	AFRICA	NORTH AMERICA	SOUTH AMERICA
Class Mammalia:				
Herbivores	Red deer (*Cervus elaphus*)	Fallow deer (*Dama dama*)	Wapiti (*Cervus canadensis*)	Brocket deer (*Blastocerus* spp.)
Carnivores	Leopard cat (*Felis bengalensis*)	Golden-haired cat (*Felis rutila*)	Bobcat (*Lynx rufus*)	Jaguarondi (*Felis jaguarondi*)
Class Aves:				
Frugivores		African gray parrot (*Psittacus erithacus*)	Military macaw (*Ara militaris*)	Yellow-headed amazon (*Amazona ochrocephala*)
Carnivores	Griffon vulture (*Gyps fulvus*)	Milky eagle owl (*Bubo lacteus*)	Screech owl (*Otus asio*)	Harpy eagle (*Harpyhaliaetus coronatus*)
Class Reptilia:				
Subterranean snakes	Reed snake (*Calamaria*)	No common name (*Miodon*)	Worm snake (*Carpophis amoena*)	Spindle snake (*Atractus*)
Ground snakes	Common cobra (*Naja naja*)	Black-necked cobra (*Naja nigricollis*)	Prairie rattler (*Crotalus viridis*)	No common name (*Cyclagras gigas*)
Tree snakes	Golden tree snake (*Chrysopelea*)	Black tree snake (*Thrasops jacksoni*)	Rough green snake (*Opheodrys aestivus*)	Green tree boa (*Boa canina*)
Class Insecta:				
Locusts	Migratory locust (*Locusta migratoria*)	Desert locust (*Schistocerca gregaria*)	Rocky Mountain locust (*Melanopus spretus*)	South American locust (*Schistocerca paranensis*)

* Allee, W. C., A. E. Emerson, O. Park, T. Park, and K. P. Schmidt. *Principles of Animal Ecology* (Philadelphia, Pa.: W. B. Saunders Company, 1949), pp. i–xii, 1–837. Used by permission.

southern Europe (it is rarely found in these areas, except in protected regions). Another ibex, the Asian counterpart (*C. aegagrus*), is found in the montane regions of Asia Minor. Table 6–3 includes some of the common ecological equivalents found throughout the world.

Selected References

Allee, W. C. *Animal Aggregations* (Chicago: Univ. of Chicago Press, 1931), pp. i–ix, 1–431.

Baerends, G. P. 1959. Ethological studies of insect behavior. Ann. Rev. Entomol., 4:207–234.

Beall, G. 1941a. The monarch butterfly, *Danaus archippus* Fab. I. General observations in southern Ontario. Canad. Field Nat., 55:123–129.

———. 1941b. The monarch butterfly, *Danaus archippus* Fab. II. The movement in southern Ontario. Canad. Field Nat., 55:133–137.

———. 1946. Seasonal variation in sex proportion and wing length in the migrant butterfly, *Danaus plexippus* L. (Lep. Danaidae). Trans. Roy. Ent. Soc. London, 97:337–353.

Burt, W. H. 1940. Territorial behavior and populations of some small mammals in southern Michigan. Univ. Mich., Mus. Zool. Misc. Publ., 45:1–58.

———. 1943. Territoriality and home range concepts as applied to mammals. Jour. Mamm., 24:346–352.

Cagle, F. R. 1944. Home range, homing behavior and migration in turtles. Univ. Mich., Mus. Zool. Misc. Publ., 61:1–34.

Carthy, J. D. *Animal Navigation: How Animals Find Their Way About* (New York: Scribner, 1951), pp. 1–151.

Cloudsley-Thompson, J. L. *Animal Behavior* (New York: Macmillan, 1956), pp. 1–161.

Dilger, W. C. 1956. Adaptive modifications and ecological isolating mechanisms in the thrush genera Catharus and Hylocinchla. Wilson Bull., 68:171–199.

Elton, C. 1932. Territory among wood ants (*Formica rufa* L.) at Picket Hill. Jour. An. Ecol., 1:69–76.

Errington, P. L. 1937. What is the meaning of predation? Smithson. Rept., 1936, pp. 243–252.

Evans, F. C., and R. Holdenreid. 1943. A population study of the Beechey ground squirrel in central California. Jour. Mamm., 24:231–260.

Farner, D. S. 1950. The annual stimulus for migration. Condor., 52:104–122.

Gerking, S. D. 1953. Evidence for the concepts of home range and territory in stream fishes. Ecology, 34:347–365.

Graf, W. 1956. Territorialism in deer. Jour. Mamm., 37:165–170.

Heape, W. *Emigration, Migration and Nomadism* (London: W. Heffer, 1931), pp. i–xii, 1–369.

Hinde, R. A. 1956. The biological significance of the territories of birds. Ibis., 98:340–369.

Howard, H. E. *Territory in Bird Life* (London: J. Murray, 1920), pp. i–xii, 1–308.

Jacobs, M. E. 1955. Studies on territorialism and sexual selection in dragonflies. Ecology, **36**:566–586.

Kendeigh, S. C., G. C. West, and G. W. Cox. 1960. Annual stimulus for spring migration in birds. Anim. Behav., **8**:180–185.

Kluijver, H. N., and L. Tinbergen. 1953. Territory and the regulation of density in titmice. Arch Neerl. Zool., **10**:265–289.

Lack, D. *Darwin's Finches* (London: Cambridge Univ. Press, 1947), pp. i–x, 1–208.

Matthews, G. V. T. *Bird Navigation* (London: Cambridge Univ. Press, 1955), pp. i–vi, 1–140.

Nice, M. M. 1941. The role of territory in bird life. Amer. Midl. Nat., **26**:441–487.

Randle, W., and R. Austing. 1952. Ecological notes on the long-eared and saw-whet owls in southwestern Ohio. Ecology, **33**:422–426.

Russell, C. P. 1932. Seasonal migration of mule deer. Ecol. Monogr., **2**:1–46.

Smith, F. 1930. Records of spring migration of birds at Urbana, Illinois, 1903–1922. Bull. Ill. Nat. Hist. Surv., **19**:105–117.

Tinbergen, N. *Social Behaviour in Animals, with Special Reference to Vertebrates* (New York: John Wiley, 1953), pp. 1–150.

Urquhart, F. A. 1958. A discussion of the use of the word "migration" as it relates to a proposed classification for animal movements. Roy. Ont. Mus. Zool. and Paleo., Contrib., **50**:1–11.

White, C. M. N. 1951. Weaver birds at Lake Mweru. Ibis., **93**:626–627.

Williams, C. B. *Insect Migration* (New York: Macmillan, 1958), pp. i–xiii, 1–235.

Wolfson, A. 1945. The role of the pituitary, fat deposition and body weight in bird migration. Condor., **47**:95–127.

———. 1948. Bird migration and the concept of continental drift. Science, **108**:23–30.

VII. The Food Factor

If an organism is to survive for any period of time, it must either have the capability to manufacture its own food or seek an outside source of nutrients. A food may be defined as any material containing carbohydrates, fats, proteins, minerals, vitamins, and water that are utilized by the living organism to promote growth, repair vital tissues, or provide a source of energy. In order to accomplish even the simplest metabolic activity or maintain even a basic metabolic rate of activity during quiescent or semiquiescent periods such as during hibernation or estivation, an energy source is required. Foods are needed to form the essential components of vital chemical substances—the tremendous number of enzymes and hormones required by plants and animals—that insure normal function and body activity. Finally, we might mention the growth process: normal, orderly size increases—either in number of cells or in size of individual cells (or a combination of the two processes)—depend on a continual supply of food.

FOOD SOURCES

Plants, with few exceptions, are the ultimate source of organic food for all animals. The floristic part of the world environment produces food by means of photosynthesis, the basic elements of which are discussed in any general biology course. The empirical formula for photosynthetic activity, one which grossly oversimplifies this complex activity, is generally represented as follows: $6CO_2 + 6H_2O \rightarrow C_6H_{12}O_6 + 6O_2$. For a more detailed account of photosynthesis, see Whittingham and Hill (1955) and Meyer *et al.* (1960); for a brief, popular review of photophosphorylation and its significance, an account by Arnon (1960), which appeared in the *Scientific American,* is excellent. Two essential substances (not represented in the main part of the equation) are (1) chlorophyll, a green pigment necessary to carry on the essential combination of raw materials, and (2) a source of sunlight or artificial light with the proper spectral components, to supply the necessary energy. Figure 7–1 shows the relative efficiency of different wavelengths (visible spectrum) with respect to the rate of photosynthesis. Thus a natural environmental area depends upon an extraplanetary source of energy to satisfy the nutritional requirements of nearly every bit of life. Carbon dioxide

FIGURE 7–1 The rate of photosynthesis in terms of differences in wavelengths of the visible light spectrum represented in millimicrons from the violet end of the spectrum (400 millimicrons) to the red light (750 millimicrons). The graph has been produced as a result of data by W. H. Hoover, "The Dependence of Carbon Dioxide Assimilation in a Higher Plant on Wave Length of Radiation." Smithsonian Inst. Publ., Misc. Coll. 95: No. 21, 1937.

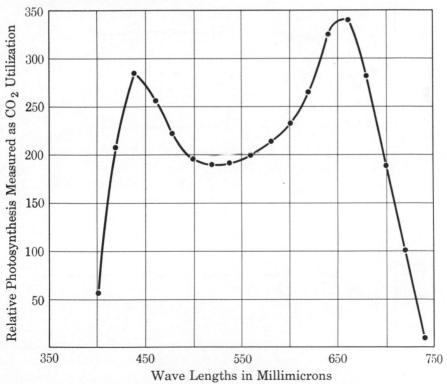

and water are the raw materials that are transformed within the green photosynthetic cell into a sugar (glucose), with the release of a vital gas (oxygen) as a by-product of the process. Even in a superficial discussion of this sort, it must not be forgotten that for photosynthesis to be accomplished many prerequisites must be satisfied. Needless to say, the raw materials, carbon dioxide and water, must be available in sufficient quantities. Carbon dioxide is often the limiting factor (see the section entitled "Limiting Factors" in Chapter II), because by increasing the carbon dioxide percentage of the air above the normal 0.03%, the rate of photosynthesis will increase if the rest of the environmental conditions remain stable. The amount of light must reach a certain critical level before photosynthesis can take place. This environmental factor is often a vital

FIGURE 7–2 The effect of increased light intensity represented in foot-candles on a shade tolerant plant (*Oxalis*) and a shade intolerant plant (bean). Note that the photosynthetic rate, which has been determined by the amount of carbon dioxide used over a unit period of time, levels off at about 2,000 foot-candles for the bean plant, but at only about one half of this light intensity for *Oxalis*. From R. H. Bohning and C. A. Burnside, "The Effect of Light Intensity on Rate of Apparent Photosynthesis in Leaves of Sun and Shade Plants," Am. Jour. of Botany, *43*:557–561, 1956. Used by permission.

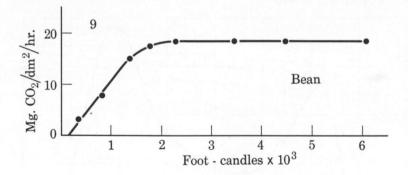

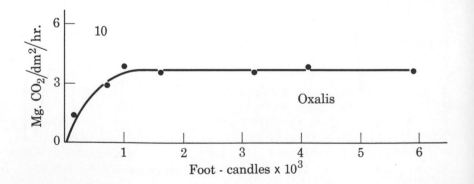

necessity for growth and development in aquatic environments and in forest communities. A typical curve of photosynthetic rate is shown in Figure 7–2, where the rate shows a steady increase from zero to about 2,000 foot-candles and then a leveling off despite further increases in light intensity.

Temperatures required for minimal photosynthetic activity vary with the species of plant. As temperatures rise, the rate of food manufacture also increases to a certain point. Beyond this point the rate undergoes a decrease until the plant dies from lethal temperatures. Certain micronutrients and macronutrients (potassium, nitrogen, sodium, and other trace elements) that are needed to form the vital chlorophyll molecule and to assist or take part in the formation of the countless enzymes and hormones required to carry on photosynthesis must be obtainable from the soil. A few animals—some of the Protozoa such as *Volvox* and *Euglena* —possess chlorophyll and can carry on photosynthesis under proper conditions of light and temperature. These organisms are a source of food for some aquatic animals. A few plants do not carry on photosynthesis but manufacture food by means of chemosynthesis. Such activity requires the breakdown of chemical compounds to release energy, which is then used to produce food for the organism (autotrophic bacteria). A few plants (the fungi) lack chlorophyll and must depend on other plants or animals for a source of readily available food. The heterotrophic plants will either parasitize other forms of life or obtain their nourishment saprophytically—by feeding on dead or decaying plants and animals.

Water is an important inorganic food for all organisms, for it makes up the greater percentage by weight of living cytoplasm. This compound is capable of forming solutions and consequently facilitating the passage of other foods and wastes across cell membranes and circulating materials through any area of the body. In aquatic, freshwater organisms special structures or modifications are necessary to remove excess quantities of water. In marine environments, the salt content of the water would cause a dehydration of living tissues in organisms that have cells with a lower salt content than that of the surrounding aquatic medium. In such organisms, chloride cells, salt glands, kidneys, and other types of organs secrete large quantities of salt to prevent water loss from internal tissues. In terrestrial areas, foods will furnish adequate quantities of water if the diet includes succulent vegetation or, in the case of predators, if adequate quantities of blood or tissue fluids are ingested. Some groups of organisms such as insects, reptiles, and birds excrete uric acid rather than urea. Uric acid is insoluble in water; consequently, it is not necessary to lose a quantity of water during excretion. Urea, on the other hand, is a waste product that must be dissolved in a quantity of water to prevent a concentration that would be toxic to the organism. Thus since organisms that release uric acid as a waste are able to conserve water, it is not necessary for them to have copious quantities of water in the diet.

FIGURE 7–3 A banner-tailed kangaroo rat, common inhabitant of arid regions of the southwestern United States. Courtesy of the Fish and Wildlife Service, U.S. Department of the Interior.

Metabolic water obtained from the oxidation of hydrogen in foodstuffs enables some organisms like flour beetles (*Tribolium*) to live on air-dry food. Kangaroo rats (*Dipodomys*) are able to live on seeds and other dry plant food and therefore eat little or no green or succulent food in their native environment. Figure 7–3 is a photograph of a banner-tailed Kangaroo rat. There are several ways this interesting organism obtains and conserves water in its native desert environment. The animal is able to oxidize 100 grams of barley and realize a transformation of this material into 54 grams of metabolic water. This small mammal has no sweat glands and is nocturnal in habit; it leaves its burrow on cool nights to search for food, thereby avoiding the intense heat and resultant water loss that would take place during the daylight period. Furthermore, the feces have a very low water content, and the kidneys release a very small volume of concentrated urea—a urea content of 23% and a salt content of 7% in contrast to a urea content of 6% and a salt content of 2.2% in man. Proteins will yield 70% of their dry weight in water; fats and carbohydrates may have 100% of their air-dry weight converted into water by oxidation of hydrogen. The ability to change wastes into uric acid and the metabolic conversion of dry foods into water enable desert organisms and individuals inhabiting regions of water scarcity to survive despite adverse conditions of water availability. Some of these facts have been presented in a previous chapter, but they bear repeating because of their important relation to feeding habits and environmental adaptability.

Aside from water, the basic food source in terrestrial areas are flowering plants. Grasses and grain crops represent a sizable segment of the earth's food supply. Fruits (reproductive structures produced by the flower of a plant) are utilized by diverse groups of organisms, from invertebrates to man. Leaves, stems, and roots of nearly every plant serve as food and in many cases provide shelter for many invertebrates. Flowering plants are the primary food source on land. Aquatic herbivores depend on nonflowering forms of vegetation for their food. Algae, diatoms, and bacteria are basic food sources in freshwater and salt water regions. Ironically, the giant kelps of oceanic areas are among the largest plants on earth, but they are situated in shallow waters and along ocean margins and are an unimportant segment of the food cycle.

FOOD RELATIONSHIPS
AMONG ORGANISMS

In the previous section, we discussed plants and a few animals capable of producing their own food by photosynthesis or chemosynthesis. These organisms that depend on the environment for raw materials and the proper environmental conditions for food production are **autotrophic** individuals. The **heterotrophic** biota, represented by very few plants and most animal life, are directly or indirectly dependent on this producer element for food because they lack the metabolic essentials to produce their own nutrients. **Herbivorous** organisms feed on plant life of some type (algae, bacteria, fungi, angiosperms) so that they are directly dependent upon this food-producing element of the food series. **Carnivores** are restricted to a diet of animal food and thus are indirectly dependent on the producer element. The carnivore that kills other animal life is a **predator** and the organism that is killed for food is the **prey**. **Omnivores,** as the name would imply from its Latin derivation, feed on plant and animal material generally, utilizing the type of foodstuff that is most readily available.

Parasitic organisms are types that are not confined to either the plant or the animal kingdom; both groups possess these unwelcome but highly specialized types of life. The **parasite** is dependent upon a living *host* for its food; it extracts from the host tissue fluids containing digested substances or materials that have been absorbed or ingested and have not yet been exposed to digestive action. Parasites may be highly specific (host specificity) and require one particular species of animal or plant during a portion of their life cycle in order to survive, or they may display an amazing degree of nonspecificity—that is, be able to live on a wide variety of hosts. **Saprophytic** and **saprozooic** individuals differ from parasites in that they extract their nutrients from dead plant or animal matter. It is at this point that I think terminology has become too specialized for the environmental situation. A saprophyte, which is a plant, feeds on dead organic matter; the saprozooic biota (animals) feed only on decaying plant or animal matter.

We have mentioned the autotrophic and heterotrophic organisms that exist in any environment and pointed out that autotrophs depend on

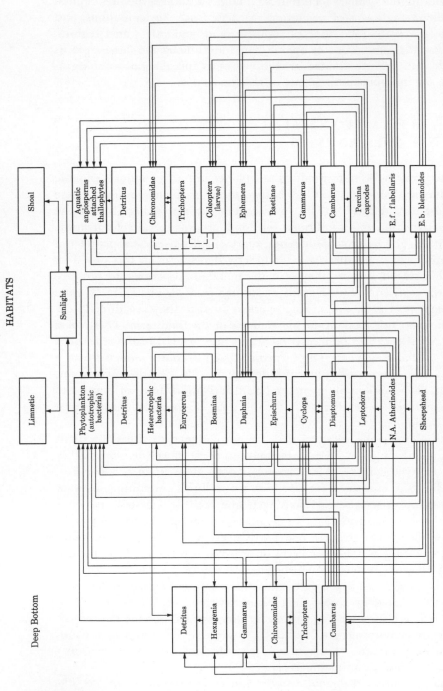

FIGURE 7–4 The food series of a freshwater drum (*Aplodinotus*), indicating the complexity and alternate foods utilized by members of the food series. From F. C. Daiber, "The Food and Feeding Relationships of the Freshwater Drum, *Aplodinotus grunniens* Rafinesque in Western Lake Erie," Ohio Jour. of Science, 52:35–46, 1952. Used by permission of *The Ohio Journal of Science* and the author.

raw materials available and that heterotrophic individuals depend on the autotrophs directly or indirectly. These relationships to the nutritional factor form a food series, called a food chain by some ecologists, in nature. The food series is not a closed circuit; there are many ramifications, and diverse routes of energy flow in any food series. Figure 7–4, from Daiber's article (1952) on the feeding relationships of the freshwater drum (*Aplodinotus*), shows only a portion of a typical freshwater food series and how very complex such interaction can become in nature. Food preferences will often vary within the life cycle of any one organism; thus in the larval stage, a lepidopteran (caterpillar) will ingest green leaf material, but as an adult this same insect is dependent on the nectar it can extract from a flower. Migrations and seasonal changes in the availability of certain foods will also add to the general complexity and ramifications of the food series. Figure 7–5 indicates the variation of food type ingested by a mammal in its native environment over a period of time.

Any food series consists of several trophic levels, with the **producer element,** the autotrophic biota, forming the solid base of the food series.

FIGURE 7–5 The seasonal shift in diet of the omnivorous raccoon in New York State. The diet shifts from apples, acorns, and so on, in the fall to earthworms, berries, and insects in the winter. From *Principles of Animal Ecology* by W. C. Allee, A. E. Emerson, T. Park, O. Park and K. Schmidt. Used by permission of W. B. Saunders Company, 1949, and the authors.

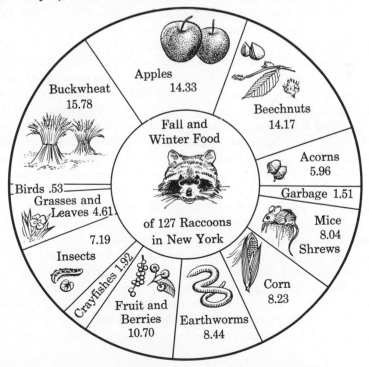

This group of photosynthetic organisms must exist if other levels of the food series are to be maintained. The second trophic level of the series includes the **consumer element,** a group of organisms with very diverse food habits and preferences because this level includes all of the herbivores, carnivores, omnivores, parasites, and scavengers. Any consumer that is dependent primarily on the producer element as a source of food is a **primary consumer.** A step above this level in the food series is the **secondary consumer,** an organism that is dependent on the primary consumer. In surveying the rest of the food series, it is possible for one to differentiate tertiary levels, and so on, depending upon the individual's position in the food chain. Much of the producer portion of any environmental situation escapes ingestion by the primary consumers; similarly, some of the consumers escape predation and meet a less violent death. The final consumer in any food series will eventually die as a result of climatic changes, disease, injury, poisoning, competition, or old age. In any case, all of these organisms—unconsumed producers, consumers, and feces and other waste products—will eventually be exposed to the final element of every food series, the **decomposers.** The decomposers, referred to as the reducer level by some authors, will transform the dead organic matter into raw materials that can be used again by the producer level of a food series.

In the past, the differences in total numbers of organisms situated in each trophic level, the biomass in these levels, and the total energy present were represented in pyramidal form. **Biomass** may be defined as the total quantity of living material (expressed in dry weight) present at a given time for a particular area. The pyramid of numbers and of biomass indicates that the producer element is ingested in large numbers by a smaller number of primary consumers; these primary consumers, in turn, are eaten by a still smaller number of secondary consumers, and so on, yielding a pyramid of numbers (Figure 7–6). The same situation becomes apparent when we compare the biomass in each trophic level; thus the total biomass of the producer element ingested by herbivores exceeds the total biomass of the herbivores. This stratum of the food series will exceed in biomass the carnivores, leading eventually to the final stage of the series (the apex of the pyramid). However, we find that in some cases certain levels of the pyramid may be inverted, because at times a large number of smaller organisms may feed on a relatively large producer, herbivore or carnivore, depending upon their position in the food series. For example, we find a large number of aphids (herbivores) may feed on a single plant (producer). The same is true for the biomass extant in each trophic level. The pyramid of energy is always of conventional shape because the transfer of energy from one trophic level to the next is rather inefficient, as some energy will always be lost. For example, of the total solar energy available only about 4/100

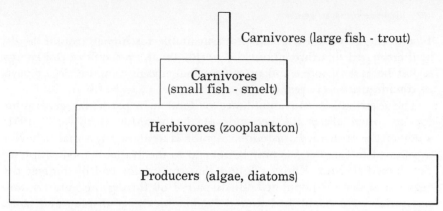

FIGURE 7–6 Diagrammatic representation of the pyramid of numbers in a fresh-water habitat. Though not always a true pyramid, producers usually form the broad base upon which other elements of the food series will rest. Theoretically, each step is capable of supporting fewer numbers of organisms.

of 1 per cent is utilized by plants in the production of food. Higher trophic strata are more efficient in energy utilization, but much heat energy is lost in transfer (Figure 7–7).

Plants form the broad base of the food chain. They transform the incoming solar energy into a food that can be utilized by higher trophic levels as an energy supply. Of the total amount of energy available to the plant, about 16 per cent is used by the plant to supply the necessary energy for its own metabolism. This leaves about 84 per cent of the

FIGURE 7–7 Energy is transferred and lost from various trophic levels of a food series. E_T is the energy transferred; E_L is the energy lost from the food series. Lowest arrow in the diagram represents energy lost by reducer organisms.

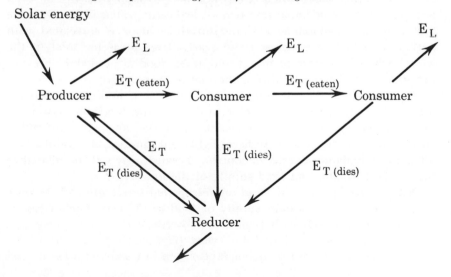

bound energy within a green plant available for higher trophic levels. It is estimated that throughout the world, about 5 per cent of this energy is lost because of forest and grass fires that ravage communities or parts of communities every year.

The distribution and abundance of food in a particular geographic locality often affects the behavior of the organism. Kluijver's (1951) study of the great tit, *Parus major,* demonstrates how territorial behavior (discussed in Chapter VI) may be related to the available food supply in the immediate area. Kluijver found that toward the end of summer the region was densely populated. Birds paired off during the autumn, and territories were established and defended by threat display and song. Establishment of territories reduced the density of the population because birds that failed to establish a territory left the area. With arrival of winter, territorial areas disappeared and the birds searched for food over wide areas, often in flocks. In spring, a brief mating period was accompanied by the establishment of territories. With hatching of the young after the mating season, territorial areas disappeared. The resumption of territorial behavior the following fall reduced the population density in that geographic locality and consequently prevented possible overcrowding which could have brought about a reduction of the food supply to a critically low level. The abandonment of territorial behavior during the winter allows a flock or individual birds the freedom of searching for food over a much wider geographic area than would be possible within the confines of a territory. Small fruits, seeds, and berries are eaten during the cooler portions of the year when insects, which are the main dietary staple during warm weather, became scarce in northern latitudes. The disappearance of territorial boundaries occurred again after the mating season when it was necessary to supply the five to seven nestlings with considerable numbers of leaf-eating caterpillars. Thus we find that the abandonment of territorial behavior is correlated with periods in which it is necessary to search large areas for food in the winter when it is least plentiful and when food is needed in greatest quantity by the young following the mating season.

Rodents such as the muskrat, *Ondatra zibethicus,* according to Errington (1944), are keenly aware of crowding as the breeding season approaches. Though there are no specific territories, an increased intolerance to overcrowding results in fierce fights and considerable cannibalism. Thus the population density is controlled, which may well be related to the available shelter and food supply of the locality.

Occasionally in nature we find organisms that starve to death in spite of an adequate or abundant supply of food in the area. Such a case is cited by Clark (1953) with regard to a beetle, *Chrysomela gemellata,* that feeds on the leaves of St. John's wort (*Hypericum perforatum*). The adult beetle may feed on plants of *Hypericum* in woodland areas if food becomes scarce in open grassland areas, but it seldom lays eggs on plants in woodland areas. Thus the plants in this habitat are unavailable as a food supply for the developing young owing to their feeble powers of dispersal as immature organisms. Where stands of St. John's wort are relatively dense in open grassland areas, populations may continue to increase until defoliation becomes so acute that starvation results among the immature organisms. Yet in areas only a short distance away, often a matter of fifty meters or less, are adequate numbers of healthy plants that would serve as a food supply for the starving population. But because of the weak powers of dispersal of these immature insects, this often plentiful food supply within the same environmental area is unavailable and consequently there is a localized extinction of the entire colony.

QUANTITATIVE RELATIONSHIPS OF FOOD MATERIAL

The total mass of organic food that can be manufactured in a particular area for a certain period of time is referred to as the **productivity** for that region. It is the net yield of the producer and consumer elements of a food series and as a consequence, it will govern the amount of living matter that may reside in a particular area. Productivity in terrestrial areas is limited to a stratum of about 100 meters above the earth's surface, with only a few exceptional aerial forms (birds and insects) actively feeding on organic material found in this area. Below the surface of the soil, chemosynthetic organisms and consumers with a relatively high productive rate are numerous in the first meter or so, but below this rather shallow stratum the density of organisms decreases rapidly with increased depth. In aquatic communities, the producer element of the food series is situated within the upper 100 meters in oceanic areas, and the upper 20 to 50 meters in ponds or lakes, depending upon the turbidity. Below this depth, light penetration is so radically reduced that the phytic limit is reached; no photosynthetic plants can survive and hence no food production by the photosynthetic producers occurs. Most of the more active consumers are limited to the upper, more productive, photic zone of water. The bottom dwellers or organisms living at lower depths (consumers and decomposers) must rely on the "rain" of organic debris from above. Individuals inhabiting deeper waters tend to be more sedentary in habit, with relatively low metabolic rates. Recent work indicates that populations in these deeper portions of lakes and oceans are not so sparse as was once supposed.

Biomass is usually expressed as air-dry weight per unit surface of a certain habitat. But in studying aquatic areas, soil strata, and certain microhabitats such as logs and so on, it is sometimes more convenient and meaningful to express biomass as volume or weight per unit volume of habitat. In biomass calculations it is important to remember that no allowance is made for nonnutritious parts of organisms such as shells, skeletons, and other parts that cannot be digested or taken as food. Biomass determinations have been made in oceanic and freshwater areas, but few have been conducted in terrestrial communities. Ecological use of the term **crop** differs from biomass in that it refers to the nutritional portion of one or so related species (not all of the living components situated in the immediate environment) in terms of total quantity (weight or volume) produced within a certain period of time. **Standing crop** is the total quantity of organic matter available at a given time and place.

Measurement (or at least an attempt to measure) of the productivity of a community encounters such difficulties that no single determination or accumulative determinations involving single factors will yield an adequate picture of community productivity. Workers have attempted to measure productivity based on the quantity of chlorophyll that can be extracted from the producer element per unit area or volume. This would appear to give a reasonable index to the potential productivity of an area. But difficulties arise: for one thing, chlorophyll is often located in the lower reaches of lakes and oceans where photosynthesis (productivity) cannot take place because of reduced light. Such organisms have just entered these lower zones from upper levels where they were formerly active. Then too, some plants may contain a large quantity of chlorophyll, but because of weak or intermittent light they may not be able to carry on photosynthesis at a maximum rate. The two basic types of chlorophyll, chlorophyll A and chlorophyll B, differ in their innate efficiency to carry on photosynthesis. Some investigators have attempted to measure productivity by calculating the biomass for a particular habitat. Such figures are valuable in that they indicate the total energy available to a particular segment or several segments of a food series. However, the relation of biomass to productivity varies with the proportion of consumers and producers in the community and this proportion fluctuates within a community from time to time, just as it fluctuates in communities of the very same type. It must be emphasized once again that biomass computations also include structures of little or no nutritional value such as integuments, skeletons, spore cases, and so on. This will give a distorted impression of productivity within any community.

One must also not lose sight of the fact that biotic productivity, even under ideal conditions, is inefficient. This fact is apparent when we realize that at least 35 per cent of the solar energy striking our planet is reflected back into the atmosphere, primarily by cloud cover, so that over a third of the available energy is irretrievably lost. Of the remaining 65 per cent only a fraction is utilized because plants are not present in many areas. Cities, snow, bare rock, and sterile soil account for their absence in many cases. Seasonal changes leading to periods of dormancy in plants and the physical factors such as temperature, water supply, minerals, carbon dioxide, and trace elements, if limited or absent, can seriously inhibit or completely disrupt photosynthesis. Finally, the loss of energy at each trophic level and a mean efficiency of about 0.09 per cent of land plants to utilize solar energy reaching stem or leaf surfaces offer, at best, a rather inefficient conversion of incoming solar energy into biotic productivity.

In any quantitative discussion of foods, the amount of food ingested by the consumer levels of a food series will have a direct bearing on the productivity of an area. A number of methods have been devised for calculating the food consumption of a trophic level in various environments. The most obvious method is that of direct observation of organisms in their natural habitat from a suitable observation point. If the observation area is some distance from the feeding location, binoculars may be used to make a tentative estimate of the amount of food consumed, the length of the feeding period, and the manner in which the organism ingests the food. With prior preparation and greater familiarity with the feeding area, it is possible to construct a blind located much closer to the organism that is under observation, which would allow, in certain cases, an estimate of the amount of material consumed by young and adult animals. Many difficulties will transpire; one such difficulty is the limited observation and assessment of the quantity of food consumed by nocturnal species.

Any method involving laboratory feeding must always take into account that animals in their natural environment will need greater quantities of food because their increased activity will involve a higher metabolic rate than is true when they are confined in a laboratory cage or enclosure. Exposure to the natural elements and escape from predators will greatly increase the energy expenditure and consequently increase food intake. Under laboratory conditions many species are under a considerable amount of stress—that is, many of them are not able to adapt themselves psychologically to an enclosure. As a consequence, the amount of food intake will be drastically altered. In many instances, it may be nearly impossible to duplicate the same type of food that would be available in the natural environment. The substitute offered under laboratory conditions may not be accepted or ingested in the same quantities as the preferred food in the wild.

One of the most valuable methods of estimating food consumption in the past and at present is the careful analysis of gut contents. Such work has yielded considerable information regarding food selection as well as quantitative data. These analyses are often more tedious and difficult than the uninitiated worker might at first suspect. Identification of food items (type) are often difficult and at times impossible owing to a combination of two digestive activities: mastication (physical breakdown of foods) that often occurs in the mouth cavity, and the subsequent action of digestive enzymes (chemical breakdown of foods) that occurs along the remainder of the digestive tract. The latter may reduce material to such an amorphous paste that only chemical tests would give any idea as to the possible source. One of the initial steps in such a procedure is the separation of various identifiable food matter, which is then weighed or measured on a volume basis. From these measurements quantitative data can be obtained. For example, the per cent of volume or weight of a particular food item may be determined by using the following formula:

$$\text{Per cent of total volume (or weight)} = \frac{\text{Volume (or weight) of food item}}{\text{Volume (or weight) of total amount of food in gut}} \times 100.$$

An alternate approach to the determination of the amount of food ingested by consumers is a combined analysis of the excreta and feces. Though this analysis involves time-consuming chemical analyses of materials discharged by the organism, it offers the added advantage of the determination of the volume of food material absorbed and ultimately converted into wastes and the quantity of the material that will pass through the digestive tract and never be absorbed by the organism, provided that figures for food intake are available. Such data must depend on laboratory observations and collections and a unit time period over which the excreta and feces are collected. Many unresolved problems are unavoidably encountered in such a method because much depends on the age, sex, health, and seasonal condition of the organism. Thus, during certain portions of the year, when the animal is storing considerable quantities of food prior to hibernation, these materials will not be excreted. It has been previously mentioned that animals under laboratory conditions will not feed as they would in nature. Since these measurements can be made only under laboratory conditions, there will be some unavoidable variance in results.

In calculating the food consumed by individual organisms, we can say, in general, that body surface area is a better indication of the nutritional requirements for a particular species. It is found that total surface area is a far more reliable index than body weight. Several factors will lead to a variation in food intake. One such factor is age: younger organisms often have a higher metabolic rate and so will require greater quantities of food than will older or aged members of the population. Although animals can live for long periods of time on minimal or even subminimal quantities of food, breeding, health, and the general vigor of the population will be adversely affected. With plentiful food sources, greater quantities of food will be consumed, generally more than will be required for maintaining normal body functions. The season or time of the year will cause variations in food consumption. Hibernating or dormant organisms will survive on a very low metabolic level with no active ingestion, but stored food will be utilized to maintain this basal rate of metabolism. Reproductive cycles will have an effect on animals, especially pregnant or nursing females, because they will require more food during this interval. Homoiothermous (warm-blooded) animals—birds and mammals—will require a greater amount of food during colder weather to maintain body temperature, but poikilothermous (cold-blooded) organisms will generally require less food because they are inactive during this period.

Food is stored in variable quantities by plants and animals in order that they may survive periods of hibernation, estivation, or dormancy. These stored foods will also allow organisms to survive unfavorable periods in the ecosystem. Plants generally store food in the form of starch, which can be hoarded in any organ of the plant (roots, stems, leaves, seeds, or fruits). Some species of plants have special storage structures, such as tubers, bulbs, rhizomes, and tap roots. Many animals store excess food internally, often in the form of fat or small quantities of glycogen. But other consumers depend on external storage of food in the form of honey, nuts, fruits, grasses, grains, and countless other foods that will be hoarded and stored in a burrow or den during periods of plenty. The lemmings (*Lemmus* and *Dicrostonyx*) store roots of plants in burrows under stones, and the arctic fox (*Alopex lagopus*) will place ptarmigan in ice crevices during periods when these foods are plentiful in the tundra areas of the far north.

A quantitative discussion of the nutritional problem in nature would be incomplete without consideration of **carrying capacity**—the total number of organisms of a particular species that can survive in a particular ecosystem. Of course, the entire concept of carrying capacity is broad in meaning, since it must take into consideration all of the vital activities that will transpire during an organism's life cycle, such as breeding sites, adequate shelter, adequate room for the establishment of territories or homesites in the territorial species, and adequate food supplies for the nourishment of the population. Our direct concern here is the carrying capacity for any particular area and species with respect to the nutritive factor. We find that the carrying capacity for any particular group of animals in any one location will tend to vary from week to week and from season to season, dependent upon the quantity and type of food available at that particular time. Measurements of carrying capacity are extremely difficult because food sources undergo temporal changes, and populations of the consumers, in addition to the physiological changes such as variability in sex ratios, age, and reproductive activity, are never static. Environmental changes impose additional headaches for any investigator concerned with such measurements; sudden temperature changes, prolonged drought, or extensive inundation of terrestrial habitats are a few of the common disasters that upset even the most detailed studies.

Under natural conditions, the carrying capacity of a particular area is seldom attained by a population. A number of environmental factors prevent a population from reaching the saturation level for that particular area. One of the most widespread and effective controls is predation. Man's intervention often upsets the delicately balanced nutritional factors of an environment, many of which are subtle and escape initial of casual investigation. The Kaibab Plateau of Arizona supported a population of approximately 4,000 deer in 1918, an aggregation that was far below the carrying capacity of the area, since it was estimated that 30,000 deer could have inhabited the region. However, many of the deer's natural predators, including wolves, coyotes, and pumas, were killed to the same extent as were the wolves by 1926. This reduction in predation pressure resulted in a maximum population of 100,000 deer during the winter of 1924–25. An excess number of ungulates, exceeding the carrying capacity of the areas, depleted the food supply and caused the starvation of 60,000 deer during the next two years. Surviving members of the population were undernourished and more susceptible to disease. The depletion of the initial food supply resulted in a continued attrition until only 10,000 deer were estimated to inhabit the area in 1940. Intensive trapping of carnivores such as civets, jackals, and mongooses in parts of Africa has resulted in increases of rodent populations. These resultant populations have increased to such an extent that they exceed the carrying capacity of their native bush environment, causing them to invade grain fields to supplement their nutritional requirements.

QUALITATIVE RELATIONSHIPS OF FOOD MATERIALS

Even though food items may be plentiful and present in more or less equal amounts in any ecosystem, a species generally displays a preference for a certain food type. Preferences are often linked with pleasant flavor, palatability, or odors emitted from various nutrients. Selection of foods has evolved as a result of nutritional requirements of amounts of protein, carbohydrates, fats, vitamins, and other components of a food that are necessary for the metabolic requirements of the species. The preferred foods are ingested as a result of basic chemical (smell, taste) or physical stimuli (shape, touch, color). When an organism must feed on an alternate food, the variance in the basic food components causes a reduction in the speed of development and reproductive potential (number of young produced and the health of the offspring). The buprestid beetle *Melanophila californica* lays its eggs under the bark scales of the ponderosa pine in the northwestern part of the United States. The larva hatches in approximately two weeks and enters the cambium of the pine. If the tree is unhealthy and nearly dead, the grub feeds and completes its larval development by the end of the summer. However, if the tree is healthy, the larva does not feed or grow normally and may remain as a grub for as long as four years, eventually dying. In this case, the larva has been forced to accept an alternate food, healthy cambium tissue, rather than the preferred diet of dead or dying cambial cells. This alternate type of food prolonged its developmental period and eventually caused its death. Many vertebrates deprived of their normal diet ingest alternate foods, often leading to a stunted growth and sterility or impaired reproductive ability.

Monophagous species—animals able to utilize only one type of food—do exist. They are at a very definite disadvantage as compared with **polyphagous** types of organisms. The geographic distribution of the former species is limited to the regions where the specific food type (plant or animal) is located. If the food type is removed or destroyed by some catastropic action, the species is destined, by sheer lack of nutriments, to disappear from the area if encysted or dormant stages of the life cycle are not present in the immediate environment. Recolonization would depend on a chance invasion of the area by the species at a later period, following the reestablishment of the food species or activation of the encysted or dormant stages. The milkweed butterfly, *Danaus plexippus,* lays eggs on milkweed plants of the genus *Asclepias.* The larvae are stimulated by the odor of the leaves. Prior to feeding on the plant the organism moves sensory (olfactory) receptors over the surface of the leaf; if the odor exuded is that of the milkweed plant, it then begins to feed actively. If eggs are removed from a milkweed plant and placed on another species, the organism, upon hatching, moves over the foreign plant without feeding. Unless it locates a plant of the genus *Asclepias,* it starves to death.

Invertebrates and the more primitive vertebrates, whether they are monophagous or polyphagous, usually locate and select food on the basis of olfaction (smell) or gustation (taste). Visual stimuli are utilized by some of the more advanced invertebrates (Mollusca and Arthropoda) and advanced vertebrates because it is only in these groups that visual discrimination has evolved to the point that shape and size are discernible. Raber (1949) found that the tawny owl recognized its prey on the basis of shape and/or movement. Bird models were recognized as prey on the basis of shape, but it was not necessary to incorporate moving parts into the model to arouse a capture response on the part of the owl. However, models of mice were captured only if they had moving legs; in this instance, shape alone was not sufficient to stimulate the predator. A knowledge of the environmental situation readily explains the difference in feeding behavior. The tawny owl is most actively searching for prey, with the approach of darkness. It is at this time that mice are likely to be moving, but many birds will be preparing to roost for the night and so present a relatively immobile form.

When favored foods have been exhausted or ruined by environmental conditions, the animal will seek other substances, some of which are of little nutritive value. This substitution will cause slow starvation. Or the animals may resort to some toxic materials, which may cause the sudden death of a major segment of a population. Laboratory feeding experiments have yielded considerable information about food preferences. However, the number of food items offered under laboratory conditions is necessarily limited to a far greater extent than it is under normal environmental circumstances. We find, therefore, that conclusions based on these methods are often subject to error. Some of the most valid work on food preferences relies on the capture of organisms of varying ages from their natural habitat and examination of the gut contents after sacrificing the individual. A sound method of comparing food preferences between the sexes and at varying ages can be determined by calculating the frequency index for different food items. A frequency index is obtained by using the following formula:

$$\text{Frequency index} = \frac{\text{Number of digestive tracts containing food item}}{\text{Total number of digestive tracts examined}}.$$

Thus, by way of example, if 300 organisms are examined during a certain portion of the year and 120 of these organisms contained a particular type of food item, then the frequency index would be 0.40 or 40 per cent. We would expect that each food item would have a different frequency index and that this index would also change considerably, depending upon the season of the year (and the availability of the particular food item). Needless to say, the greater the number of organisms examined, the more accurate the final conclusions will be.

There are countless examples of cases where the quality of a food must be altered before it is of any value to an organism. The host of microfloral and microfaunal organisms that thrive within the digestive tracts of vertebrates and some invertebrates are typical examples. Before ingestion and preliminary or partial digestive changes have occurred, this food material could not be utilized by these microorganisms. Dung- and carrion-feeding beetles and other associated organisms require some fundamental changes in the quality of the food. The larva of the wood wasp *Sirex noctilio* lives as a borer in the trunks and branches of pine, on cambium tissue that has been altered by a fungus (*Stereum*). The adult female introduces an inoculum of the fungus into the hole that she drills with her ovipositor at the time she lays her eggs. The fruiting bodies of the fungus are located in the accessory glands of the reproductive system of the female wasp. The fungus spreads from the initial site of inoculation over an area several inches wide and several feet long and kills the cambial cells in this area. The larva feeds in this area for a certain period of time. If the fungus is not inoculated or if it dies, the larval wasp does not survive. How the quality of the food (cambium) is altered is not as yet known. Perhaps some substance is added to the cambial tissue, which alters its chemical condition; or perhaps the death of the cambial cells eradicates or inactivates some substance that would normally be toxic to the larva during a critical stage of development.

Nutritive values of any one food type will vary from place to place and from season to season. The producer element will exhibit variation as the growth season progresses. The food value will usually increase because of a proportional increase in stored carbohydrates, fats, and proteins. The nutritional value of different plant organs will vary. Stems and leaves, for example, will tend to lose some of their food value as the reproductive season progresses, resulting in the setting and maturation of fruits. Another factor that must not be overlooked when considering the food value of plants is the soil type and innate fertility of this medium, because this element can and will make a big difference. Consumer levels will demonstrate as much variation as do the lower trophic levels (producers) because they will reflect changes in nutritional content of consumed foodstuffs, as well as seasonal changes in keeping with reproductive cycles, hibernation, estivation, age, sex, and other related factors. The rate at which food deteriorates depends upon the type of food and the kind of weather during any seasonal period. Cooler weather tends to retard the rate of spoilage, while higher temperatures and increased moisture in terrestrial areas will generally hasten the rate of nutritional loss.

We find, in nature, that often there is more food available in the immediate environment than can be utilized by a particular species of animal. This is fortunate, for it will allow for considerable flexibility in terms of population size or sudden invasion of areas by migrating groups

FIGURE 7–8 Measurement of food utilization entails enclosing an area (sample block *A*) with a fence to prevent feeding, while another region within the community boundary (sample block *B*) is left open. Paired random samples of the vegetation (quadrats with diagonal lines) are then removed and compared.

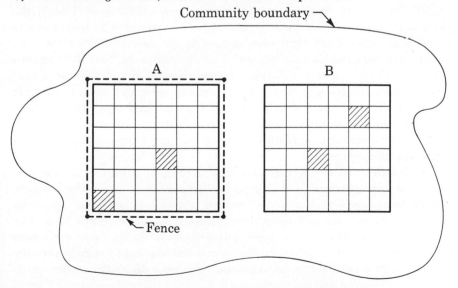

without disastrous results. However, uncontrolled reproduction and the subsequent population explosion that will at times occur in nature may exhaust food sources and bring about massive emigrations or widespread starvation. Environmental catastrophes such as fires, floods, prolonged droughts, the inaccessibility of a food source, trampling, or rapid deterioration may also eradicate extensive numbers of consumers periodically. Ecologists can measure the utilization of any food item in the environment by means of the following technique. A portion of the feeding range of a species is measured and divided into sampling quadrats of equal size (Figure 7–8). Using an unbiased approach, random quadrats are paired, with one member of the pair inclosed or effectively isolated from the consumer element. Effective isolation may often pose difficult problems for the ecologist because such methods may disturb or alter the productivity of the food source. The other member of the pair of quadrats is easily accessible to the animal population for a certain prescribed period of time, often referred to as the feeding period. At the end of the feeding period both areas are isolated and the food is removed. In the case of plant material, it is customarily removed down to within an inch of ground level. The nutrients from these quadrats are air dried and weighed to compare the degree or amount of utilization. An index of utilization is calculated by means of the following formula:

$$\frac{Y - X}{Y} = \text{index of utilization,}$$

where Y is the air-dry weight of food in the inclosed or isolated quadrat, and X equals the air-dry weight of food in the accessible area. If 5,000 grams of food were recovered from the control (isolated) plot and only 2,300 grams from the area open to feeding, the index of utilization would be 0.54, or 54 per cent of the total food available utilized by the feeding element over a unit period of time. A number of objections to such a technique can rightfully be raised: the period of time involved may be inadequate to give a valid idea of utilization, and the methods used to isolate areas may also be open to question. Everyone should realize that an ecologist would be the first to agree that such techniques often yield only an indication of the actual situation. In addition, environmental conditions impose such varied and complex conditions on any problem that it is difficult to devise any experimental situation that is above reproach.

Full utilization of food in any area is seldom, if ever, realized. One very important reason is the quantity of food often wasted by animals. Another reason is that many of the fruits and seed produced by plants drop to the ground and deteriorate. This, however, may not be a complete food loss because the seed will germinate if favorable conditions transpire and subsequently replenish any reduction or losses in the producer level of the food series. Also, an abundance of food in nature often results in considerable waste. Predators tend to kill more prey than they will eat before the organism deteriorates, if prey species abound in an area. Consumers dependent upon vegetation will waste food as the amount of usable nutrients increases, because they become more selective and eat only the tastier parts of the plant and leave structures that, though not as flavorable, may be as nutritious and be eaten during periods of a less plentiful food supply. Organisms that characteristically store food to provide nourishment during unfavorable or less favorable periods of the year will often gather more food than will be utilized. Such excessive hoarding leads to waste and may actually deprive other members of the population an adequate store of food. Additional means of waste can be cited. Trampling of vegetation by larger mammals, barking trees, and browsing on young shoots will often stunt or retard growth of the producer element, which will waste food in an indirect manner. There will be a reduction in the amount of food that would have been produced if not for the wasteful intrusion of certain species.

Range managers and agricultural specialists are often faced with problems involving overutilization of feeding areas. Overutilization is simply the failure of producer or consumer groups in a food series to provide enough food for the trophic level dependent upon them. If the annual use of any food exceeds the annual productivity of that particular food in some locale, a condition of overutilization is said to exist. Continued overutilization in the form of overgrazing and extensive browsing and overkilling of prey will most certainly reduce the ability of food populations to recover from such adverse conditions for some time. Such overutilization will inevitably affect the populations dependent on these food sources. Long-lived species may live in such regions for some time, causing greater damage to the habitat. The younger, older, and weaker members of these populations will generally die first, and the stronger individuals may survive in an emaciated condition for some time. However, if no radical change in the environmental situation occurs, they are destined to die, which will lead to a complete disappearance of the population until the proper food materials are reestablished and the species is reintroduced by emigration.

In arctic or subarctic areas there is often a scarcity of food, which is not a result of overutilization by the fauna, but rather of severe climatic conditions. These harsh conditions in northern areas will limit the productivity of vegetation because the growing season is shorter than it is anywhere on earth. Frozen subsoils make growth difficult even during the short growing season, and day length as well as type of wavelength of the sun's rays reaching the earth's surface varies in these northern areas. The fauna, particularly predators, must change their feeding habits in keeping with the seasonal availability of food. For this reason many of them become omnivorous during the more adverse periods. The snowy owl (*Nyctea nyctea*), which normally feeds on lemmings and other rodents, eats carrion and fish, and the purple sandpiper (*Erolia maritima*) of northern Norway becomes herbivorous. Birds during these periods will accept foods they never touch during times of plenty. This ability to vary a diet in relation to environmental availability is one basic reason that the avifauna have been so successful in these inhospitable northern areas. The arctic fox will feed on mollusks and various types of fish when rodents (especially lemmings) are scarce, just as the polar bear resorts to robbing birds' nests of eggs or to eating plant food when seals and walruses cannot be found.

FOOD AND THE COMMUNITY

The character or general type of community that exists in an area is dependent to some extent upon the foods that are available. Unless, for example, eucalyptus groves were to become a permanent flora in other continental areas, there would be little danger of the koala bear becoming a permanently established resident in these other areas because this animal is dependent on eucalyptus leaves for subsistence. The entire structure of the community (living biota) will depend on available food sources. Even casual observations and comparisons between newly established ponds and mature ponds will reinforce this contention. In an older pond a greater variety of plants and hence animals are present, but in a young pond or in a pond that is periodically drained and the excess vegetation removed, the number of endemic species are low in number. In terrestrial communities where succession is occurring (see Chapter X), such as a rock outcrop, the pioneer communities comprised of lichens and mosses will have a small number of endemic animal species. But as time passes and the flora becomes more diverse in terms of species numbers (greater food diversity), the total numbers of species will also increase in proportion.

Selected References

Aldous, S. E. 1938. Beaver food utilization studies. Jour. Wildlife Manag., 2:215–222.

Allen, W. E. 1934. The primary food supply of the sea. Quart. Rev. Biol., 9:161–180.

Arnold, J. F. 1942. Forage consumption and preferences of experimentally fed Arizona and antelope jack rabbits. Tech. Bull. Ariz. Exper. Sta., 98:51–86.

Arnon, D. I. 1960. The role of light in photosynthesis. Sci. Amer., 203:104–118.

Bohning, R. H., and C. A. Burnside. 1956. The effect of light intensity on rate of apparent photosynthesis in leaves of sun and shade plants. Am. Jour. Botany, 43:557–561.

Brues, C. T. *Insect Dietary* (Cambridge, Mass.: Harvard Univ. Press, 1946), pp. i–xxvi, 1–466.

Clark, L. R. 1953. The ecology of *Chrysomela gemellata* Rossi and *C. hyperici* and their effect on St. John's Wort in the Bright District, Victoria. Austral. Jour. Zool., 1:1–69.

Cook, J. G. *The Fight for Food* (New York: Dial Press, 1957), pp. 1–208.

Daiber, F. C. 1952. The food and feeding relationships of the freshwater drum *Aplodinotus grunniens* Rafinesque in western Lake Erie. Ohio Jour. Sci., 52:35–46.

Dalke, P. D. 1935. Dropping analyses as an indication of pheasant food habits. Trans. No. Amer. Game Conf., 21:387–391.

Errington, P. L. 1937. What is the meaning of predation? Smithson. Rept., 1936, pp. 243–252.

———. 1944. Ecology of the muskrat. Rep. Iowa Agric. Exp. Sta. (1944), pp. 187–189.

———. 1946. Predation and vertebrate populations. Quart. Rev. Biol., 21:144–177, 221–245.

Evans, F. C. 1950. Relative abundance of species and the pyramid of numbers. Ecology, 31:631–632.

Fitch, H. S., and H. Twining. 1946. Feeding habits of the Pacific rattlesnake. Copeia, 1946: 64–71.

Hill, R., and C. P. Whittingham. *Photosynthesis* (New York: John Wiley, 1955), pp. i–vii, 1–165.

Kluijver, H. N. 1951. The population ecology of the great tit, *Parus m. major*. Ardea., 39:1–135.

Lauckhart, J. B. 1957. Animal cycles and food. Jour. Wildlife Manag., 21:230–234.

McAtee, W. L. 1912. Methods of estimating the contents of birds' stomachs. Auk., 29:449–464.

Meyer, B. S., D. B. Anderson, and R. H. Bohning. *Introduction to Plant Physiology* (Princeton, N.J.: Van Nostrand, 1960), pp. i–v, 1–541.

Morse, M. 1939. A local study of predation upon hares and grouse during the cyclic decimation. Jour. Wildlife Manag., 3:203–211.

Murie, O. 1935. Food habits of the coyote in Jackson Hole, Wyoming. U.S. Dept. Agric., Circ., 362:1–24.

Palmer, L. J. 1944. Food requirements of some Alaskan game mammals. Jour. Mammal., 25:49–54.

Pechanec, J. F., and G. D. Pickford. 1937. A comparison of some methods used in determining percentage utilization of range grasses. Jour. Agric. Res., 54:753–765.

Pitelka, F. A., P. Q. Tomich, and G. W. Treichel. 1955. Ecological relations of jaegers and owls as lemming predators near Barrow, Alaska. Ecol. Monogr., 25:85–117.

Popham, E. J. 1942. Further experimental studies of the selective action of predators. Proc. Zool. Soc. London, 112:105–117.

Raber, H. 1949. Analyse des Balzerhaltung eines domestizierten Truthahns (*Meleagris*). Behaviour, 1:237–266.

Rudebeck, G. 1950. The choice of prey and modes of hunting of predatory birds with special reference to their selective effect. Oikos., 2:65–88.

Ryther, J. H. 1956. The measurement of primary production. Limn. and Oceanogr., 1:72–84.

———. 1959. Potential productivity of the sea. Sci., 130:602–608.

Schomer, H. A. 1934. Photosynthesis of water plants at various depths in the lakes of northeastern Wisconsin. Ecology, 15:217–218.

Scott, T. G., and W. D. Klimstra. 1955. Redfoxes and a declining prey population. So. Ill. Univ. Monog. Ser., 1:1–123.

Stegeman, L. C. 1937. A food study of the white-tailed deer. Trans. No. Amer. Wildlife Conf., 2:438–445.

Verduin, J. 1956. Primary production in lakes. Limn. and Oceanogr., 1:85–91.

Vogtman, D. B. 1945. Flushing tube for determining food of game birds. Jour. Wildlife Manag., 9:255–257.

Weese, A. O. 1939. The effect of overgrazing on insect populations. Proc. Okla. Acad. Sci., 19:95–99.

VIII. Population Ecology

A population may be defined as all of the individuals of a particular species or several related species occupying a certain area at some specific time. A population consisting of individuals that are members of one species is often referred to as a monospecific population; if several species are included, it is called a mixed, or polyspecific, population. There are some ecologists who will argue that any polyspecific population constitutes a community rather than a population. But population ecologists have probably dealt with mixed groups as often as they have with monospecific aggregations. Population ecology is an important and basic part of modern ecology, because the ecology of any single organism cannot be completely understood until the relationships between individuals of a species are known. Following the same line of reasoning, any investigation is further enhanced if the influence of related species is fully appreciated. One must realize that populations share certain characteristics such as dispersion, fluctuation in numbers, sex ratios, birth rate, and death rate that can never be displayed by a single organism.

POPULATION GROWTH

If favorable environmental conditions exist in a specific region and there is a means by which a species may be introduced into the area, a group of individuals exposed to such an environment will increase in numbers with the passage of time. We find, however, that environments seldom remain continuously favorable or unfavorable with regard to the myriad of components involved. Instead, there is usually a fluctuation from favorable to unfavorable conditions for the particular species involved, which acts as a natural check on population numbers. Even if conditions were to remain continuously favorable for the species, the population would be able to inhabit only that area or region of the earth's surface where those conditions prevailed. Population growth depends upon the presence of both sexes in sexually reproducing forms if self-fertilization is impossible or unlikely. A number of methods have been proposed over the years to estimate the size of populations, periodically, and to determine the rate of growth. One principle that any prospective ecologist must recognize is that population counts made under different climatic conditions and at different seasonal periods, or even at different times of the day (or night), are seldom comparable because differences in habits or patterns of activity over any unit period of time may account for grossly different results.

MEASUREMENT OF POPULATIONS

Census techniques have been one of the most common methods of estimating the population size of plant populations and macrofaunal components of the environment. In some cases, when one is dealing with relatively small areas or microenvironments, it is possible to isolate the entire population and take a complete census. Direct census methods are usually more appropriate when one is dealing with plant populations, because the mobility of most faunal aggregations (with the exception of sessile forms) precludes this procedure. Counts of animal populations often depend upon some type of trapping technique. The manner in which animals may be trapped and counted depends upon the type and size of the organism involved. Figure 8–1 shows several different types of trapping devices, one of which is quite different from our general idea or concept of a "trap." Spring traps are used to estimate the population size of small or large mammals; the most efficient type of spring trap holds the animal securely but causes a minimum of injury. When it is practical, most ecologists prefer cage traps. A pitfall trap is used for small invertebrates. The trap usually consists of a small wide-mouthed jar, with a lip diameter of two or three inches, filled one-third to one-half its capacity with 50 per cent alcohol; it is buried so that the opening is flush with ground level. This trap is left in some environmental situation for a specified period of time, then is removed and the preserved organisms are counted. In this instance, some of the animals are killed; the survivors would be too small to mark effectively, so they cannot be released. In aquatic areas, trapping of large individuals can

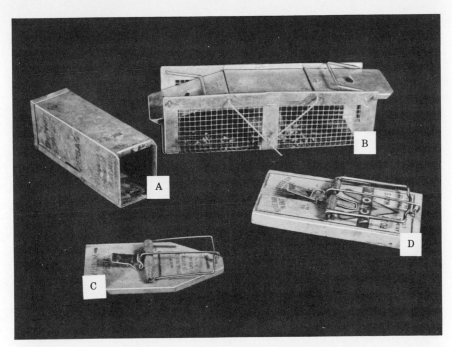

FIGURE 8–1 Several different traps used for capturing small mammals and birds under varying situations are shown. Trap *A* is a Sherman trap; trap *B*, a Havahart animal trap; trap *C*, a Museum Special snap trap; trap *D*, a Victor snap trap; and trap *E*, a Havahart sparrow trap used to capture small birds.

be accomplished by using seine nets or any variety of fish traps devised by ichthyologists.

Removal of trapped animals from their environment may cause serious errors in population estimates; consequently, trapped individuals should be marked (by banding, by clipping toes and ears, or by some other means that will help to differentiate individuals) and then released so that they may return to their natural environment. This preliminary trapping period during which animals are marked and then released will be followed by a final trapping period that will last for an equivalent period of time. During the final trapping period a careful record of marked and unmarked individuals is kept. An estimate of population size may then be made by taking the recorded figures and using the formula suggested by Lincoln (1930), known as the Lincoln Index.

During the final trapping period, say, we trap 48 marked and unmarked animals. Let us call this number T. The number of individuals trapped during the preliminary period and subsequently marked is 63. We shall use the symbol m to represent this factor. The number of marked individuals trapped during the final period is 28, which we may represent by the symbol g. By using the formula

$$\frac{T \times m}{g},$$

we can determine the estimated population size based on our trapping results. By using the figures previously given, we can calculate the size of this hypothetical population to be

$$\frac{48 \times 63}{28} = 108.$$

This would mean that there are about 108 wolves, mice, rabbits, or whatever mammals we were attempting to census in the immediate environment (in the vicinity of the trapping area).

Random sampling techniques have been used by ecologists with considerable success. Many ecologists prefer random sampling because the results may be analyzed statistically, which gives the investigator a number of useful items of information about the population. Although random sampling is discussed more fully in the section "Sampling Populations" in Chapter XIII devoted to statistical procedures, it might be well to point out here the general theory of random sampling. If we wish to estimate the population size of some group of organisms (such as invertebrates or a species of vegetation), the entire area is subdivided into sampling units as shown in Figure 8–2. Usually, these units, which are called quadrats, are square if the investigator is sampling a terrestrial population. The size of any quadrat depends on the size of the organism being sampled, so that if we are concerned with trees, a quadrat might be an acre or some fraction of this unit; for some of the smaller

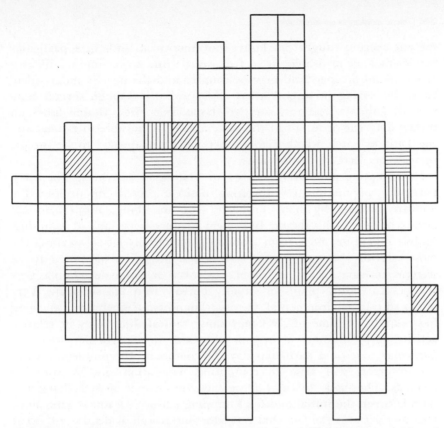

FIGURE 8-2 A typical community of irregular outline subdivided into a number of quadrats. The community has been randomly sampled on three different occasions as indicated by the three different shading patterns used on the quadrats. From *Sampling Methods in Forestry and Range Management* by F. X. Schumacher and R. A. Chapman (Duke University School of Forestry, Bulletin 7, 1948). Used by permission.

invertebrates it might be several square centimeters or a square meter. A random sample could conceivably be a sample of organisms trapped in a sweep net by making so many passes over vegetation, or a sample of organisms removed with a dredge from the substrate of an aquatic area. A certain number of sample units are gathered, the fractional amount of the total sample area is computed, and an estimate of population size is then calculated for any particular stratum or seasonal period.

Another method that is used basically to compare either populations between several portions of an environmental area (spacial comparison) or population density over a unit period (temporal comparison) is known as a **density index.** Students must realize that a density index does not yield information about the actual number of individuals present per unit area as is true of trapping and random sampling techniques, but merely gives an indication of the abundance of a particular species. A density index of fish may be calculated by counting the number of fish (of one species) caught per hour; the number of birds of a particular species that an ornithologist sees or hears while traversing a unit area of woodland or open field may be counted and the density index calculated. By fishing in several areas or by walking through several comparable habitats, one can compare population sizes. If one fishes on several different occasions in the same area, it is possible to estimate on the basis of catch whether the fish population appears to be on the increase or decrease in that area.

In estimating population size or attempting to determine whether a particular population is exhibiting positive growth or decline, the ecologist is beset by many problems. For one thing, animals do not always behave as he should like them to during periods of sampling. Mobile organisms move from place to place rapidly, often escaping the most carefully planned census techniques. Many animals tend to be secretive in behavior and are often overlooked or escape detection as they scamper to hiding places or rapidly burrow into the substrate. Very often, certain environmental factors (humidity, temperature, enemies, food supply, or time of day) may cause radical differences in relative activity of the number of organisms present in a particular area at a particular time on a particular day. To compound the problem, a number of errors will arise in computing population size by trapping methods. The main difficulty arises over the amount of time that transpires between the initial and final trapping period. An investigator must take into account the fact that reproduction as well as deaths will occur during the intervening period, which may appreciably alter population size. He must also assume that there is no differential mortality caused by the sudden invasion of the area by predators or disease and that there is no emigration (escape) or immigration (invasion) of the species that would alter the size of the population. Some organisms tend to develop an awareness of trapping devices and stay away from areas they associate with traps. In other words, they alter the extent or location of their home range after having been trapped in a specific area. Such trap-shy organisms may very well escape the second census period.

Individual members of populations will exhibit their own unique embryonic and postembryonic rates of development, fecundity or capacity to reproduce, and longevity (life span). All of these factors vary from organism to organism, being governed by a vast complex of factors, including anatomical and physiological variation, controlling the innate capacities of the organism. In addition to the internal metabolic efficiency of the animal, there are external (environmental) factors that must be reckoned with if we include all of the effective factors that are to be included. Since there is such a range of individual differences in developmental rate, fecundity, and longevity of the organism, it is necessary to deal with mean values for the population. Thus accumulation of population data entails mean or average values of critical factors. Too often, in the past, the population ecologist has ignored the internal or innate factors and considered only the surrounding environmental data. It must be emphasized that the most valuable studies must yield information about the innate abilities of a population as well as the surrounding environment.

FACTORS AFFECTING POPULATION GROWTH

Natality. A vast array of factors influences the rate of growth of any population in nature. The **reproductive potential** of a population is based on natality and mortality, intraspecific competition for food, shelter, mates, predation, and parasitism. All of these factors enter the total picture and often radically change population growth patterns. Natality, or the production of new generations of organisms by sexual or asexual reproduction, is obviously vital for population growth. The **maximum, or potential, natality** refers to the greatest number of organisms that can possibly be produced by a parent organism over a unit period of time. This implies that these terms are synonymous with the reproductive potential of a species, which in reality is a theoretical figure, assuming that all circumstances relative to reproduction are ideal. Such an ideal situation is never attained under normal environmental conditions because of limiting factors and **environmental resistance** (environmental conditions that would operate against the population from the standpoint of increase in numbers). To realize a reproductive potential would necessitate optimal ecological, genetic, morphological, and physiological conditions. Although some members of populations may approach this theoretical value, many others fall far short of the figure.

A **normal, or realized natality** rate is an observed population birth rate occurring under normal circumstances for the species. A number of factors play a part in governing the total number of young produced within a unit period of time. Some of the more obvious factors are the sex ratio and age ratio in regard to the reproductivity mature individuals and the mortality rate of actively reproducing organisms. Ecological conditions such as a lack of nesting or mating sites, unfavorable weather, a qualitative or quantitative deficiency of food, unfavorable temperatures or humidity, a disease epidemic, high predation, or parasitic incidence, all will have their effect on the birth rate either singly or in combination. Finally, variations in the degree of fertility brought about by psychological, physiological, or ecological causes will have an effect on population birth rates. The actual computation of a birth rate for any population is simple, as it is merely based on the number of individuals born over a specific period of time (day, week, month, or year). Thus, according to a formula, we might represent natality (birth) rate in the following manner:

$$\frac{B}{t} = \text{natality rate,}$$

where B is the number of births and t equals the time unit.

Mortality. The mortality of individuals at any age, from time of conception until senility, will affect population growth as drastically as will natality. Causes of mortality in any population are numerous. Although, often, one factor alone may not cause the death of an organism, if two or more such factors happen to appear at the same time, they may have such an adverse effect that the organism will die. Hereditary diseases that cause abnormal embryos or postembryonic deficiencies of a physiological or anatomical nature and an unfavorable physical environment in terms of temperature, humidity, and catastrophic events may cause an early death. Health and the age of the mother are important during the embryonic period; an unfavorable uterine environment is responsible for an unduly high mortality rate among certain segments of any population because this is often the most critical period of life. Diseases (nonhereditary), predation, competition, and parasitism—all must be considered as possible contributing causes when one is attempting to trace the reason for deaths within certain aggregations of plants or animals. Competition among plants frequently develops when root systems vie for soil minerals and water and when aerial portions of the plant contend for available light. Animal competition usually involves a struggle for available shelter, food, territorial rights, and mates; at times this competition may become so intense that death is the end result. Parasitism among plants and animals may or may not cause the immediate death of the host, but it may seriously weaken an organism so that some other adverse factor, in combination with parasitism, will cause the plant or animal to succumb.

The mortality, or death, rate in a population is computed in much the same way that we determine birth rate,

$$\frac{D}{t} = \text{mortality rate,}$$

where D represents the number of deaths, and t represents a suitable time unit. However, though the mortality rate is easily computed mathematically, it is often very difficult to determine the total number of deaths within a population. Dead organisms are reduced to unrecognizable remains by scavengers, bacteria, and a host of other organisms that subsist on decaying materials. If predation is the cause of death, there is often no trace of the organism, so that an investigator would be forced to examine the gut contents of a number of predators. This is a tedious task and yields limited results. For population size to remain stable, there must be a definite relationship between natality and mortality toward the end of the growth phase in most established populations. An intrinsic adjustment in ratio of natality rate to mortality rate takes place. Extensive mortality in a population during a certain period is often followed by a period of increased reproductive activity, which helps to maintain a stable aggregation in that area. Usually a population will produce more reproductive units than is necessary to maintain normal density because some members of the group will succumb to disease, predation, and other adverse conditions previously cited. An increase in birth rate in stable populations yields a proportionately higher mortality rate as competition becomes keener, and only the stronger, healthier individuals survive.

From the foregoing discussion, it is obvious that when birth rate exceeds the death rate, a population exhibits positive growth. An increase in death rate over birth rate yields negative growth or a population decline. However, the rate of population increase or decrease on a quantitative basis, which involves the number of births and the probability of death, varies with the age of the organism. Lotka (1925) formulated the changes in birth rate and death rate in accordance with the age of the organism. He referred to the basic value as the intrinsic rate of natural increase. The statistic r_m (intrinsic rate of natural increase), first used by Lotka in reference to human populations, was later found to be applicable to populations in nature, and the following formula was created:

$$b - d = \frac{N}{t},$$

where b is the birth rate for a specific population of a specific mean age and d is the population death rate for a specific mean age. N and t refer to the number of animals and time, respectively. In actuality the difference in birth rate and death rate is equivalent to the innate capacity for increase, r_m, so that

$$r_m = \frac{N}{t}.$$

The innate capacity for increase, or r_m, is in reality an abstract statistic because it would not apply in a natural population. The actual or natural capacity for increase, r, is subject to environmental fluctuations such as weather, parasitism, predation, food availability, and many other variables. The basic value of the abstract statistic r_m is that it does provide an indication or rough approximation of what could occur under ideal conditions.

POPULATION GROWTH CURVES

Population ecologists employ growth curves to present graphically an increase (and possibly the subsequent decrease) in population numbers over a unit period of time under certain environmental conditions. In sparsely colonized areas, a population may grow at nearly the theoretical rate of increase because often predators, disease, and competition are minimal in such localities (Figure 8–3). But with the passage of time, this growing population will be faced with various phases of environmental

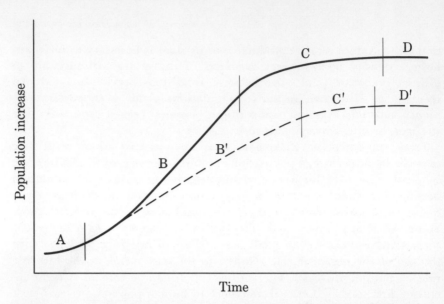

FIGURE 8–3 A theoretical growth curve showing the critical phases of growth in a population. *A* represents the positive acceleration phase, *B* the logarithmic growth phase, *C* the negative acceleration phase, and *D* the upper asymptote. The dotted line represents the actual growth curve of a hypothetical population, where *B'* is the logarithmic growth phase, *C'* the negative acceleration phase, and *D'* the upper asymptote of the hypothetical population.

resistance that will gradually shift the actual population size further and further away from theoretical or potential growth rates. In a typical population curve, the abscissa (horizontal axis) represents a time interval that may be measured in minutes, days, weeks, years, or any unit of time that conforms with the population growth rate. Fruit fly (*Drosophila*) populations would be observed and measured for a number of days, whereas mammalian populations might be calculated over a much longer period (months or years). The ordinate, or vertical axis refers to the total number of individuals (or a reasonable population estimate) in a certain area for a particular interval of time. This number is commonly referred to as the **population density.** A population growth curve exhibits a rather slow increase in numbers because the numbers of interbreeding organisms are small and there is often little initial mating as the organisms become adjusted to the area and establish shelters, homesites, and nests. This period during which an aggregation is beginning to show only a gradual increase in total numbers is the **positive acceleration phase** of the curve. Following this initial period there is a **logarithmic phase** during which population growth or increase in total numbers is maximal. Such a change is caused by a sharp increase in natality rate (in contrast to minimal mortality) brought about by increased numbers of organisms of reproductive age, establishment of homesites, and adequate protection of the young. This rapid rate of

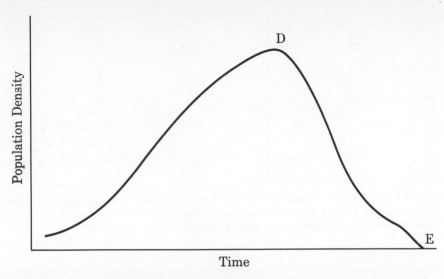

FIGURE 8–4 A J-shaped population curve produced by an environmental factor becomes intolerable at point **D** on the curve, leading to a rapid population decline and to extinction of the entire aggregation at point **E**.

growth, which will ensue for a variable period of time, is inevitably followed by a decrease in population growth rate, the **negative acceleration phase.** Actually this latter period is a reversal of the positive acceleration interval caused by an increase in environmental resistance in some form. It follows that as populations increase, predators, competition, and the probability of parasitism and disease invading a population also increase. If such factors increase disproportionately, it will lead to a population decline (as indicated in Figure 8–4), and possibly extinction, as even the strongest members of a population are not able to contend with conditions as they exist. The J-shaped curve is indicative of catastrophic conditions that decimate and at times completely destroy a population that has been flourishing and increasing at almost a theoretical rate.

POPULATION DENSITY

The **density** of a population is the total number of individuals inhabiting a specific area of the habitat for a particular time period. It becomes apparent that density is a numerical concept, a measure of the population size for a sample area; or, in a broader sense, it may refer to the total numbers of a species within some natural habitat. It is easily computed by using the density formula as follows:

$$D = \frac{n/a}{t},$$

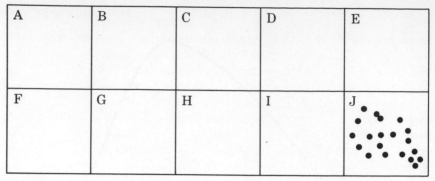

FIGURE 8-5 Twenty organisms within a sample area give a density of 2.0 or two individuals per quadrat. In this instance all of the organisms are situated in a single quadrat (quadrat *J*), yielding a frequency value of 0.1, or 10 per cent.

where D = density, n = the number of individuals, a = the area, and t = the time unit. Although density figures are valuable because they give us information about the magnitude of the population, these values yield no picture of the distributional pattern within the environment. For example, as shown in Figure 8-5, suppose that we have an environmental area that has been subdivided into 10 quadrats (sample units)

FIGURE 8-6 A frequency-density graph of several species of *Tomocerus*. In this case height of each bar is a measure of percentage frequency, and the width of the bars indicates density. From Clifford B. Knight, "The Tomocerinae (Collembola) in Old Field Stands of North Carolina," *Ecology, 42*:140–149, 1961. Used by permission of Duke University Press.

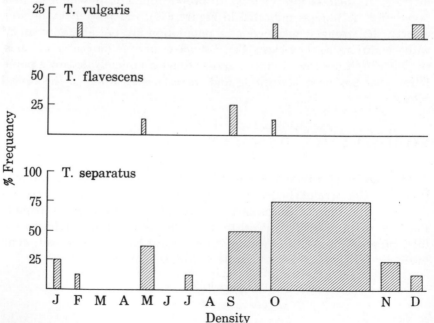

and there are 20 individuals of the species in these quadrats. The result is a density of 2, or an average number of 2 individuals per sample unit, but all of these individuals could have conceivably come from a single quadrat! However, if we combine density data with **frequency**, we have a fundamental idea of the total number of organisms as well as their distribution relative to sample plots. Frequency, in an ecological sense, is the per cent of sample plots occupied by a particular species regardless of number. Thus, according to our previous example, if all 20 organisms were located in a single quadrat (and there was a total of 10 quadrats), the frequency would be 0.1, or 10 per cent, indicating that the population was located in only one plot out of ten—a very poor distribution of the species in this case. Figure 8–6 illustrates a frequency-density graph of the collembolan *Tomocerus*. The width of the bar represents the organism's density, and the height of each bar represents the frequency of the springtail for each interval. By combining these population characteristics (frequency and density), any interested reader may quickly grasp the distributional and numerical aspects of any population.

Any population may reach a maximum density known as the **saturation point**. The saturation point for a particular species within a certain environment is unalterable because even if the amount of food or number of shelters is increased, the saturation point remains fixed; no change in the total number of organisms inhabiting an area is possible. The saturation point is often reached in breeding areas where territories of fixed size limit the number of breeding pairs able to inhabit the area (see Chapter VI, "Home Ranges and Territoriality"). Overcrowding of confined populations, particularly in microhabitats, readily results in the establishment of a saturation point and may under extreme circumstances lead to cannibalism. Such activity has been noted among flour beetles (*Tribolium*) and the mealworm (*Tenebrio*); populations of these organisms reach a level (saturation) beyond which weaker adults, larvae, and eggs are killed and eaten by the stronger adults. The **carrying capacity** of any region can be changed with the improvement of shelters and breeding areas, and increases in food available to the population. The carrying capacity may be defined as the total number of individuals of a species that will live in an ecosystem (or habitat) under certain conditions. If these conditions are altered either by improvement or regression, the carrying capacity will subsequently change, increasing or decreasing, respectively. If the area changes for the better, the carrying capacity increases until a point is reached where the carrying capacity cannot be altered. This is the point of maximal density, or the saturation level. The carrying capacity will change over a period of time because seasonal changes alter the environment with respect to food availability, shelters, territories, and so on. These continual changes will cause changes in the carrying capacity of any area, just as different stages of the life cycle of any organism will alter the carrying capacity. For example, if we consider the life cycle of a lepidopteran (moths, butterflies), we find that the larval stage is comprised of leaf feeders; hence the carrying capacity is determined by the amount of leaf material available. If the caterpillar is a specific feeder (feeding on only one species of plant), the carrying capacity is determined by the amount of leaf surface of that particular species of plant. Many adult lepidopterans feed on nectar so that at this stage of the life cycle, carrying capacity would be determined by the number of flowers found in the locality.

Overpopulation or underpopulation drastically affect the density attained by any organism. Overpopulation tends to decrease the density for several obvious reasons. Competition becomes keen for food, shelter, and mates; this often brings about premature deaths among the weaker members of the population. Predation will also become more severe in overpopulated regions because prey are more easily located in these overcrowded situations. This results in an increase of the carrying capacity for the predator until the prey population is reduced in size or, in some instances, decimated by predation. Disease and parasitism very often gain critical footholds in overpopulated areas, not only as a result of increased accessibility of host organisms, but also of overcrowding that weakens many individuals and renders them more vulnerable to attack.

Underpopulation may often result in density increases as food, shelter, and mates are more abundant. Among social animals, underpopulation may be as disastrous as overpopulation is for solitary organisms for the reason that collective behavior among social groups maintains or establishes environmental conditions that are vital necessities for the survival of the population. The common honeybee (*Apis mellifera*) maintains a constant temperature within a hive by collective behavior of hive members. The hive is cooled by wing movement in summer and warmed by metabolic heat in the winter. But constant temperature is maintained only if a certain population level is maintained within the hive. The bobwhite (*Colinus virginianus*) suffers under conditions of underpopulation during cold periods because tightly huddled coveys of birds, according to Gerstell (1939), are able to survive low environmental temperatures that would be fatal to isolated birds. When populations decrease beyond a certain point, they may become extinct over a certain area for a period of time. Repopulation is then dependent on immigration from other regions or on reintroduction of the species by wild animals or by man transporting a few members from distant points. If the population should be limited in distribution or reach critical levels of underpopulation everywhere, there would be no population reserve and the species would then become extinct throughout the world. The passenger pigeon (*Ectopistes migratorius*) was at one time so numerous that flocks darkened the skies for hours at a time. By 1890 the passenger pigeon was far less numerous than it had been even fifteen years before, and by 1900 it was a rare bird. The last known passenger pigeon died in a Cincinnati zoo in 1914. Some ecologists maintain that extinction was due to overhunting and subsequent underpopulation—that is, flocks became smaller and the reproductive capacity was critically affected. Other naturalists believe that the wholesale destruction of forests, which served as cover and nesting sites for the species, may have been the predominant cause of extinction. It is likely that both factors contributed to dissolution of the population, although either factor over a longer time period could have achieved the same unfortunate result.

The heath hen, or black grouse (*Tympanuchus cupido*), a close relative of the prairie chicken, which was found until recently on an island (Martha's Vineyard) off the coast of Massachusetts, is another example of an organism approaching extinction because of underpopulation. In 1880 heath hens were abundant throughout the middle and southern New England states, but as was true in the case of the passenger pigeon, overhunting reduced the population to 200 birds by 1890. Extinction would probably have occurred within a short time as a result of over-hunting, but the bird was protected after 1890. Twenty-six years later there was a population of about 2,000 birds. A severe fire, coupled with adverse weather conditions, reduced the population of black grouse to 50 breeding pairs in the latter part of this same year (1916). This severe population reduction caused by diminishing areas offering suitable shelter and nesting sites as well as available food, and most probably reduced reproductive activity because only one male represented the species by 1928. Allee (1938) reported that a herd of 25 elephants is about the smallest number that can persist and maintain a surviving population in South Africa. Reindeer inhabiting the tundra areas of northern Eurasia must maintain herds of 300 to 400 individuals if the population is to preserve stability, because smaller herds gradually die out. Herds of antelope that have been decimated by severe hunting by man are less likely to survive if the aggregation has been reduced to less than 12 or 15 organisms. As is true of the reindeer, small herds of these ungulates can be forced to stampede and scatter by packs of coyotes and wolves. The immature and older, weaker members are killed first, and the few survivors are then easily eradicated by concerted attacks of roaming predators.

Knowledge of the decimating effect of underpopulation among animals can be of importance to applied science in some instances. For example, entomologists have discovered that it is not necessary to eradicate the tsetse fly completely from certain areas of South Africa, because small populations will eventually disappear. This information may eventually be utilized in eradication of pest species and eliminate the necessity and danger of saturating natural environments with massive doses of insecticides. From these forementioned studies on underpopulation, it becomes apparent that immigration of a species into an unpopulated area (unpopulated by the species) to be successful must necessarily include a critical number of individuals. One fascinating aspect of this problem is that every species will undoubtedly require a different number of organisms to maintain itself under the existing environmental circumstances. These critical population values are seldom known, but it promises to be an interesting problem for present and future groups of population ecologists.

In laboratory populations it has been known for some years that reduction in the density of certain ciliate protozoans (Robertson, 1921) reduces the rate of division (reproductive capacity of the population). He theorized that the reproducing individuals released into the medium a stimulating substance that became more concentrated and subsequently more effective as a reproductive stimulus with greater population densities. This substance has never been isolated and it is doubtful that there is any scientific evidence for such a hypothesis. Under natural conditions, if the population density is below a particular level, the chances of a reproductively active female encountering a mature male are less probable.

Underpopulation may also lead to an increased death rate as a result of increased predation. This has been described many times in the literature and numerous examples have been reported, particularly in the case of food series involving invertebrate prey and vertebrate predators. One of the most dramatic examples of increased death rate as a result of underpopulation was reported by Birch and Andrewartha (1941) in Australia, involving the grasshopper *Austroicetes cruciata* that served as a prey for several groups of predaceous birds. From 1935 to 1940 the environmental conditions were so favorable for the prey species that it attained very large population levels. While such large populations were sustained, the chances of any particular grasshopper serving as a prey for birds were rather small. But during the winter and spring of 1940–41 a severe drought withered grass, so that only in a few isolated humid areas was there enough food to support the grasshopper population. This drastic underpopulation of the prey resulted in a drastic reduction of the fauna because the predaceous birds sought out every grasshopper in many of these small moist areas and increased the chances of every prey organism of being ingested by the predators. The population of these predators had not increased during the previous favorable period, from 1935 to 1940, because food during the period of the year when grasshoppers were unavailable was not present in great enough quantity to support large populations of predators. Thus the great losses inflicted on the prey species were not a result of predator populations being larger than they had been in previous years, but, instead, of a severe underpopulation of the prey decreasing individual chances of longevity.

Social species that normally travel in flocks or herds or maintain colonies are generally most severely affected in respect to reproduction by underpopulation. Darling (1938) has found that some groups of gulls (particularly the herring gull, *Larus argentatus*) are reproductively more successful in large groups. In small populations, it has been found that some mammals become sterile as a result of excessive inbreeding. Several species of the field mouse (*Peromyscus*) become sterile, in some cases within four generations, if they are continually inbred in the laboratory. This most certainly would limit population size and finally lead to its extinction if a population were in a state of numerical decline.

POPULATION FLUCTUATION

Population size is in a constant state of change. Whether the aggregation is increasing, decreasing, or is in a stage of relative stability, there will always be variations in numbers over a period of time. When the birth rate exceeds the death rate

$$\frac{nB > nD}{t},$$

there is a growing population where nB represents the number of births, nD the number of deaths, and t the period of time. However, if the birth rate is less than the death rate

$$\frac{nB < nD}{t},$$

there is a declining population. While the population is demonstrating the typical sigmoid growth curve so common for aggregations introduced

FIGURE 8–7 Following the negative acceleration phase in population growth indicated by *N*, there is always some fluctuation in a natural population caused by environmental factors such as predation, competition, disease, weather, and so on.

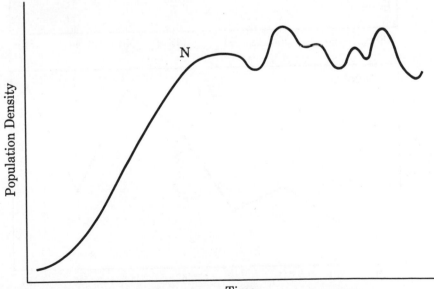

into new areas, the fluctuation is most definitely oriented toward a greater number of births and very few deaths. Shortly after this logarithmic period of growth, during the interval of negative acceleration, the number of births begins to decrease and the number of deaths increases as environmental resistance in the form of one or more adverse factors tends to limit population size. If the population is to maintain itself in the area, there will be periodic fluctuations in population size, as is indicated in Figure 8–7, following the period of negative acceleration.

Factors bringing about fluctuations are numerous and, generally, as is true of many ecological events, many conditions are in operation that

FIGURE 8–8 Population numbers of *Choristoneura fumiferana* (spruce budworm) in terms of defoliation of balsam fir and the effect of precipitation on population size. Note the one-year shift in the cause and effect relationship. From W. G. Wellington, J. J. Fettes, K. B. Turner, and R. M. Belyea, "Physical and Biological Indicators of the Development of Outbreaks of the Spruce Budworm, *Choristoneura fumiferana* (Clem.) (Lepidoptera: Tortricidae)," Canad. Jour. Res. D. *28:*308–331, 1950. By permission of the National Research Council, Ottawa, Canada.

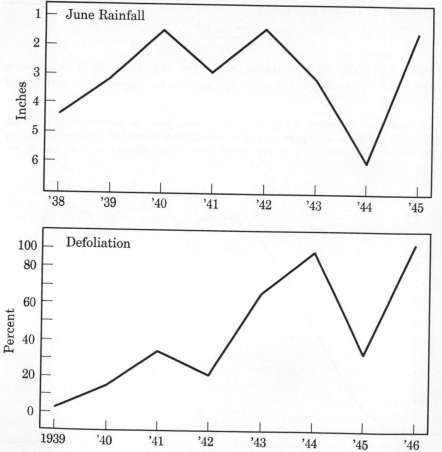

cause the observed changes in population numbers. The spruce budworm (*Choristoneura fumiferana*) is indigenous to North America; it causes extensive damage to vast tracts of spruce, balsam fir, and other coniferous species by ingesting buds, flowers, and the tender leaves of these trees. Outbreaks of the insect will sometimes last for five or more years, and if the insects are numerous they may defoliate spruce trees in some areas. Wellington (1952) and Wellington, *et al.* have indicated the relationship between outbreaks of the spruce budworm and associated weather conditions. This is apparent if we compare the per cent of defoliation, which is an indication of population size, with the precipitation as shown in Figure 8–8, taken from Wellington's paper (1950). Records kept by the Hudson's Bay Company showing the number of pelts of the lynx (*Lynx*

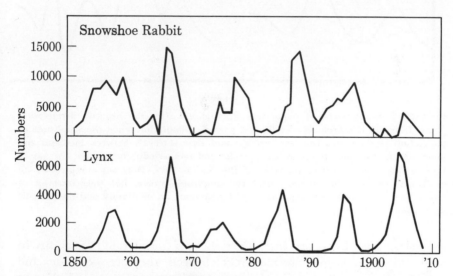

FIGURE 8–9 Population oscillations as indicated by the number of pelts recorded by the Hudson Bay Company in Canada over a period of sixty years. The amplitude of the populations is not cyclic, but oscillates considerably; both predator and prey populations demonstrate the interrelationship of such changes in total numbers. Reproduced from C. Elton and M. Nicholson, "The Ten-Year Cycle in Numbers of Lynx in Canada," Jour. An. Ecology, *11*:215–243, 1942. Used by permission of Blackwell Scientific Publications, Ltd., Oxford, and the authors.

canadensis), taken from 1736, demonstrate the population fluctuation experienced by this organism. This animal and its chief prey, the snowshoe hare (*Lepus americanus*), undergo periodic fluctuations, with maximal populations occurring every ten years (Figure 8–9). The fluctuations exhibited by the lynx and snowshoe hare are not cyclic because the amplitude of the fluctuations is too variable. Dymond (1947) has pointed out that the maximal numbers exceeded minimal numbers of the lynx in a ratio of 100 to 1 in northern British Columbia and 20 to 1 in the

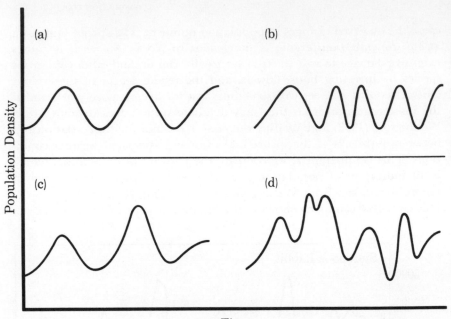

FIGURE 8–10 Patterns of population fluctuations after the negative acceleration phase. Diagram *a* represents a cyclic and periodic fluctuation when the amplitude of population size remains constant (cyclic), and time intervals between increases and decreases are constant. Diagram *b* is a cyclic and nonperiodic fluctuation; the amplitude is constant, but time intervals of fluctuation vary. Diagram *c* represents an oscillatory, periodic fluctuation where the amplitude varies, but time intervals of population change do not vary. Diagram *d* represents an oscillatory and nonperiodic fluctuation.

southern parts of this province. Since there is considerable variability in amplitude, populations are not cyclic; instead, they are oscillatory and periodic, because the turning points indicating an increase or decline in population numbers do occur at regular intervals (Figure 8–10). Other oscillatory and periodic fluctuations are known; Table 8–1 indicates some common North American vertebrates and the interval between population peaks.

Many factors contribute to the extreme variability (oscillation) of population numbers and to the aperiodic occurrence of population peaks and minima. Disease in epidemic proportions, uncontrolled parasitism, and catastrophic events in the form of hurricanes, tornadoes, and violent tropical storms are usually more common and the results (destruction of habitats, shelters, food supply) may be more severe. A chance immigration of predators or an accidental introduction of predator species into an area may cause drastic decreases in population density. If predation continues with equal intensity, it may lead to the possible extinction or certainly a reduction in numbers to such an extent that the population never fully recovers.

TABLE 8-1. *List of Common Vertebrates Known to Exhibit Population Peaks and Average Interval (in years) Between Peaks**

ANIMAL	INTERVAL (IN YEARS)
Pink salmon (*Oncorhynchus gorbuscha*)	2
Horned owl (*Bubo virginianus*)	9–11
Ruffed grouse (*Bonasa umbellus*)	9–10
Rough-legged hawk (*Buteo lagopus*)	4
Mink (*Mustela vison*)	9–10
Lemming (*Lemmus trimucronatus*)	4
Field mouse (*Microtus pennsylvanicus*)	4
Red fox (*Vulpes fulva*)	9–10

* Adapted from H. G. Andrewartha and L. C. Birch, *The Distribution and Abundance of Animals* (Chicago: Univ. of Chicago Press, 1954), pp. i–xv, 1–782. Used by permission.

Cyclic, periodic fluctuations are rarely apparent in nature. Usually reproductive cycles in these cases are periodic, occurring as the female mammal enters the estrus period after a unit interval of time. The subsequent birth of animals increases the population size. Disease, predation, and other adverse factors will then reduce the size of the species aggregation. This is followed by another period of estrus, and so on, in periodical and at times in cyclic fashion. The usual situation, particularly among invertebrates and plants, is an oscillatory and usually aperiodic fluctuation because of the differences in natality, mortality, individual resistance to disease, and parasitism within any natural aggregation of plants and animals.

POPULATION TURNOVER

All populations, whether plant or animal, will experience a turnover from time to time. New individuals will enter the aggregation periodically as a result of reproduction (natality) or immigration from surrounding geographic areas. At the same time other individuals are permanently lost from the population by emigration or mortality. New additions to the population may exceed population losses when the entity is experiencing growth, but if a population is on the decline, these new members will fall short of the losses. The amplitude of any population turnover depends on a number of factors: mortality rate, natality rate, habits of the species relative to dispersal, and migration are a few of the contributing causes.

The migrations of members of a population have been discussed earlier (Chapter VI, "Migration"). These mass movements are confined to the breeding portion of a population and do not result in a widespread dissemination of the species or the establishment of a portion of a population in a new territory. Movements of members of a population away from a populated area where population pressure is becoming increasingly more acute because of competition is called **dispersal.** Increased power of dispersal favors species survival, since it prevents an annihilation of a population by predation in a localized area. The ability to disperse also enables members of a population to locate themselves in more suitable areas with respect to shelter and food. This ability is quite important in areas where there is a dramatic seasonal change. Food and shelter in any specific area will change, and in many instances a population must disperse to new areas as food and, at times, suitable shelter disappear from the former region of habitation. Ernst Mayr (1947) emphasized the almost universal aspect of dispersal among animals in his statement that "there is a dispersal phase in the life cycle of every species."

In recent years it has been established that dispersal of a population is not always stimulated by population pressure (increased density of the population) or other unfavorable factors, but that instead an inherited behavioral pattern is responsible for the movement into other areas. Several thousand adults of *Drosophila pseudoobscura* were released by Dobzhansky and Wright (1943, 1947) to determine the rate of dispersal. The flies were orange-eyed mutants that were easily discernible among members of the wild population in the area. Two traplines were set up in the shape of a cross so that the lines intersected each other at their centers. Flies were released from the center trap initially and then counted and released from traps along each arm of the cross at the same time on successive days. The investigators stated that if the dispersal were random in direction, then one would be able to plot a normal curve of distribution (Figure 13–4) from the data obtained along a line of traps. By random, in this case, we mean that there is no definite directional orientation, and the presence of members of the population has no effect on dispersal. If, however, dispersal is randomized with respect to direction and other organisms (of the population), but the rate of dispersal is more rapid (or slower) than would be anticipated, the distributional curve will be distorted. In other words, the curve will be steeper or flatter than normal. If the rate of dispersal is slower than would be expected, the curve is steep; a flat curve would represent a rapid dispersal of the species. The degree of kurtosis, or variation from the normal curve of distribution, may be calculated by the following formula:

$$Ku = \frac{n\Sigma r^4 f}{\Sigma r^2 f},$$

where Σ is the summation of values, n is the total number of flies caught in all traps, r is the distance between the point of release and the trap, and f is the number of flies caught in the trap. The Ku value is 3.0 for a normal curve of distribution; a steeper than normal curve yields a value of less than 3.0; a flat curve yields a value greater than 3.0.

Because of high values of kurtosis, a more accurate estimate of dispersal was obtained by the calculation of variance according to the following equation:

$$s^2 = \frac{\pi \Sigma r^3 \bar{f}}{\Sigma r \bar{f} + c}.$$

In this equation, s^2 is variance, r is the distance of the trap from the center of the cross, $\bar{f}$ is the mean number of flies found in traps at this distance from the center of the cross, and c is the number of flies caught in the central trap. If flies continue to disperse in the area, the variance continues to increase in amount; conversely, a decrease in rate of dispersal yields a corresponding decrease in the variance increments over a period of time. Dobzhansky and Wright (1943) found that there was a continuous increase in variance, indicating that despite a decrease in density over a period of time, the instinct to disperse was still exhibited by the population.

This innate behavioral drive to disperse has been noted for a number of different groups of organisms. In some cases, dispersal has not been attributable to adverse environmental conditions, because members of a population tend to move away from inhabited areas despite adequate food, optimal climatic conditions, and suitable density values for the species. For some segments of the population, dispersal or migration flights previously reported in the literature are in actuality neither dispersion nor migration. A case in point is the frequent flights of the swift, *Micropus apus,* an insectivorous bird common in Europe. Flights of this bird have been reported as late spring migration, early autumn migration, or as after-nesting dispersal because they occurred sometime after the breeding season in summer. Koskimies (1947) has asserted that these movements are none of these activities from the standpoint of the breeding population. He has found that flights occur when the organism is exposed to a warm front associated with a low pressure cell in the immediate vicinity. This type of weather front, characterized by rain and descending air currents, practically excludes insects from the atmosphere. Since the swift feeds on insects caught in flight, it is probably the lack of available food rather than the weather conditions *per se* that cause the prolonged flights away from the area. Although the immature, nonbreeding members of a population may permanently leave the area (hence it may be considered a dispersal flight), the adult birds with nestlings always return to the original nest site. The nestlings of the swift can survive for as long as seven days without food; most insectivorous species would starve after two foodless days. Distances covered by these birds are often great; they have been known to fly over 1,000 kilometers in a twenty-four-hour period.

Selected References

Allee, W. C. *The Social Life of Animals* (New York: Norton, 1938), pp. 1–298.

Andersen, J. 1957. Studies in Danish hare population. 1. Population fluctuations. Dan. Rev. Game Biol. 3:85–131.

Andrewartha, H. G., and L. C. Birch. *The Distribution and Abundance of Animals* (Chicago: Univ. of Chicago Press, 1954), pp. i–xv, 1–782.

Baumgartner, L. L. 1938. Population studies of the fox squirrel in Ohio. Trans. Third No. Amer. Wildlife Conf., 685–689.

Birch, L. C., and H. G. Andrewartha. 1941. The influence of weather on grasshopper plagues in South Australia. Jour. Dept. Agric. So. Australia, 45:95–100.

Bodenheimer, F. S. 1937. Population problems of social insects. Biol. Rev. 12:393–430.

Cahalane, V. H. 1941. A trap-removal census study of small mammals. Jour. Wildlife Manag., 5:42–67.

Cole, L. C. 1951. Population cycles and random oscillations. Jour. Wildlife Manag., 15:233–252.

———. 1954. Some features of random population cycles. Jour. Wildlife Manag., 18:2–24.

Darling, F. F. *Bird Flocks and the Breeding Cycle: A Contribution to the Study of Avian Sociality* (New York: Cambridge Univ. Press, 1938), pp. i–x, 1–124.

Dice, L. R. 1938. Some census methods for mammals. Jour. Wildlife Manag., 2:119–130.

Dobzhansky, T., and S. Wright. 1943. Genetics of natural populations. X. Dispersion rates in *Drosophila pseudoobscura*. Genetics, 28:304–340.

———. 1947. Genetics of natural populations. XV. Rate of diffusion of a mutant gene through a population of *Drosophila pseudoobscura*. Genetics, 32:303–324.

Dymond, J. R. 1947. Fluctuations in animal populations with special reference to those of Canada. Trans. Roy. Soc. Canada, 41:1–34.

Edwards, R. Y., and C. D. Fowle. 1955. The concept of carrying capacity. Trans. 20th No. Amer. Wildlife Conf., 589–602.

Errington, P. L. 1957. Of population cycles and unknowns. Cold Spring Harbor Sympos. Quant. Biol., 22:287–300.

Gerstell, R. 1939. Certain mechanics of winter quail losses revealed by laboratory experiments. Trans. Fourth No. Amer. Wildlife Conf., 462–467.

Hayne, D. W. 1949. Two methods for estimating populations from trapping records. Jour. Mamm., 30:399–411.

———. 1949a. An examination of the strip census method for estimating animal populations. Jour. Wildlife Manag., 13:145–157.

Koskimies, J. 1947. On movements of the swift *Micropus a. apus* L., during the breeding season. Ornis Fenn., 24:106–111.

Lack, D. 1951. Population ecology in birds. Proc. Tenth Intern. Ornith. Congr., Uppsala, 1950, 409–448.

————. 1952. Reproductive rate and population density in the great tit: Kluijver's study. Ibis., **94**:167–173.

Lincoln, F. C. 1930. Calculating waterfowl abundance on the basis of banding returns. U.S. Department of Agriculture Circ. **118**:1–40.

Lotka, A. J. *Elements of Physical Biology*. (Baltimore: Williams & Wilkins, 1925).

MacLagan, D. S. 1932. The effect of population density upon rate of reproduction with special reference to insects. Proc. Roy. Soc. B., **111**:437–454.

Mayr, E. 1947. Ecological factors in speciation. Evolution, **1**:263–288.

Morris, R. F. 1960. Sampling insect populations. Ann. Rev. Entomol. **5**:243–264.

Nicholson, A. J. 1954. An outline of the dynamics of animal populations. Austr. Jour. Zool., **2**:9–65.

————. 1954a. Compensatory reactions of populations to stresses, and their evolutionary significance. Austr. Jour. Zool., **2**:1–8.

Park, T. 1948. Experimental studies of interspecies competition. 1. Competition between populations of the flour beetles, *Tribolium confusum* Duval and *Tribolium castaneum* Herbst. Ecol. Monog., **18**:265–308.

————. 1954. Experimental studies of interspecies competition. 2. Temperature, humidity, and competition in two species of *Tribolium*. Physiol. Zool., **27**:177–238.

Pearl, R. *The Biology of Population Growth* (New York: Knopf, 1925), pp. i–xiv, 1–260.

————. 1927. The growth of populations. Quart. Rev. Biol., **2**:532–548.

Robertson, T. B. 1921. Experimental studies on cellular reproduction. II. The influence of mutual contiguity upon reproduction rate and the part played therein by the "X substance" in bacterized infusions which stimulates the multiplication of Infusoria. Biochem. Jour., **15**:612–619.

Rowan, W., and L. B. Keith. 1956. Reproductive potential and sex ratios of snowshoe hares in northern Alberta. Canad. Jour. Zool., **34**:273–281.

Stickel, Lucille F. 1946. Experimental analysis of methods for measuring small mammal populations. Jour. Wildlife Manag., **10**:150–159.

Taber, R. D. 1956. Uses of marking animals in ecological studies: marking of mammals; standard methods and new developments. Ecology, **37**:681–685.

Wellington, W. G., 1952. Air mass climatology of Ontario north of Lake Huron and Lake Superior before outbreaks of the spruce budworm, *Choristoneura fumiferana* (Clem.), and the forest tent caterpillar, *Malacosoma disstria* Hbn. (Lepidoptera: Tortiricidae; Lasiocampidae). Canad. Jour. Zool., **30**:114–127.

Wellington, W. G., J. J. Fettes, K. B. Turner, and R. M. Belyea. 1950. Physical and biological indicators of the development of outbreaks of the spruce budworm, *Choristoneura fumiferana* (Clem.) (Lepidoptera: Tortiricidae). Canad. Jour. Res. D., **28**:308–331.

IX. Community Ecology

A monospecific assemblage of living organisms is a population. A group of several or many species living together in the same locality is a community. Examples of a community would be a mixed stand of pine and dogwood trees or a squirrel in an oak tree. These are extreme, hypothetical examples because in nature there are countless species associated with the latter illustration. In addition to this particular oak tree, there would probably be a number of different species of oaks (black oaks, red oaks, white oaks, possibly post oaks, and so on) as well as other hardwoods (dogwood, ash, hickory, sourwood), vines, and possibly shrubs and herbs as well. The squirrel would represent only one vertebrate inhabiting this forest community. Birds of different species, amphibians (toads, tree frogs), and mammals (deer, fox, mice, shrews) are other common examples. Invertebrates are far more numerous than vertebrates in most forests in terms of species numbers as well as population counts. Snails, slugs, beetles, flies, butterflies, and annelids would begin to give us a more complete picture. But even this assemblage, much of which is visible to the eye, is only part of the story. Within the leaf mold, in the soil, and inside the floral and faunal components we have mentioned there would be vast numbers of parasites, commensals, and so on, in the form of bacteria, fungi, protozoa, nematodes, and algae that would begin to yield a very complex picture. We have used a forest community as an example. But we might use a prairie, a desert, a pond, or an estuary as examples. We would find that even though the total number of species and the population levels might be lower in these communities, each would harbor a truly complex array of animals and plants. Only in pioneer communities, where we are dealing with the first assemblage of organisms colonizing a particular locality, would we expect to find a relatively simple community situation. E. C. Williams (1941), while studying the fauna of the forest floor in Panama, estimated that there were at least 40,000,000 organisms per acre, representing over 400 species, and this did not include the protozoa, bacteria, fungi, or higher plants. By definition, a community includes only the living entities of the environment. If nonliving factors, together with the living entities, are considered, then we are dealing with an **ecosystem.**

COMMUNITY CLASSIFICATION

In the ecological literature, reference is often made to abstract and concrete communities. An **abstract community** is a mental image of a particular type of community, an assemblage that does not exist except in one's mind. This mental image can be realized only if a person has had experience with a community of this type in nature and has some idea of its structure. A common example of an abstraction is not difficult to conjure. Suppose we mention the word "chair." Immediately one person may mentally picture a rocker, another an easy chair, and still another might form a mental image of a straight-backed wooden chair. As long as this "mind picture" remains as such, we are dealing with an abstraction. Thus, a desert community, a pond community, or a grassland community are all abstractions that will result in mental pictures of such areas, provided we have seen examples of such aggregations in nature or in pictures. A **concrete community** is a specific area, one that can be observed directly. It is an assemblage of plants and animals that actually exists and from which ecological data can be gathered by the ecologist.

Communities are classified on a basis of hierarchical arrangement. The community hierarchy descends, in a graduated series, from the largest possible assemblage of organisms to the most restricted assemblage. The **global community** is an immense mass of life, embodying all of the plants and animals in the world. Because of its enormity, study of this all-inclusive community is obviously impractical. The global community is divided into **continental communities** and **oceanic communities.** As the terms imply, all of the plants and animals living on a particular continent and all of the biota found within a particular ocean comprise such communities. The distribution of any species and the great variability of climatic factors in such vast areas make any comprehensive study futile. A somewhat more restrictive community is the **regional community**, or **biotic province**. Within any continental or oceanic community there are climatic variables. Using thermal values as one criterion for climatic variation, we find that oceanic and many continental areas can be subdivided into arctic, subarctic, temperate, subtropical, and tropical areas. In addition, other climatic factors must be considered such as moisture, wind, air pressure, and so on. Dice (1952) aptly summarizes the concept of a regional community as follows: "A biotic province may best be thought of as a considerable geographic area over which the climate is relatively uniform, though often locally modified by physiographic features.... Each biotic province, therefore, is a unit of climate, or physiography, and of soil types." Figure 9–1 illustrates a division of the North American continent into a number of biotic provinces. We find that regions differing radically in climate are known as regional communities, or biotic provinces; the entire assemblage of plants and animals in these geographic areas comprises

FIGURE 9–1 The biotic provinces of North America according to Lee R. Dice. Reprinted from *The Biotic Provinces of North America* by Lee R. Dice by permission of The University of Michigan Press, 1943.

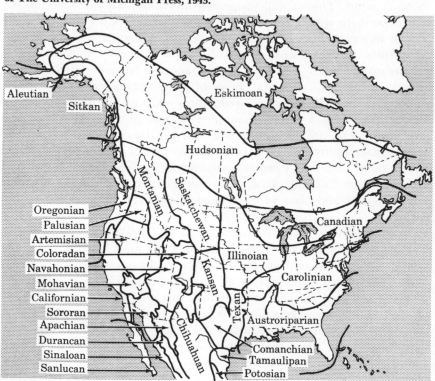

FIGURE 9–2 An open field association, with a forest type association in the background. The open field dominated by broom sedge (*Andropogon*) is gradually being invaded by seedlings of loblolly pine (*Pinus taeda*) that will convert the field into a pine woodland if left undisturbed.

such a community. There are regional communities within any oceanic province, for arctic temperate and tropical waters harbor groups of plants and animals restricted to these climatic zones. These have been less intensively studied.

Community categories that have been listed so far are abstract communities. Such a vast area that a continental or a regional community comprises is most certainly too extensive to study. Although we may examine a small portion of a biotic province, and despite the fact that a particular province does exist, it is an abstract community. An **associational community,** or **association,** might be considered a transitional type of entity, partially abstract and partly concrete, based on ecological criteria. An association is a particular type of vegetational community such as a forest, grassland, or a pond located within the regional area (Figure 9–2). There may be literally hundreds of ponds or many different types of forests (pine, beech-maple, oak-hickory and so on), but they are considered as part of an association—that is, a pond association or a forest association. In some instances, a portion of an association may be very extensive, covering hundreds of square miles (the coniferous forests of Canada and the tropical rain forests of South America); in others, portions of associational communities may be very small. Since portions of an association are small enough to be surveyed and studied by the ecologist, a small part of the association may be considered a concrete community. But it still remains an abstraction when it is considered in its entirety.

A **stand** is a localized example or portion of an associational community; thus it is one forest of many forests, one river of many rivers,

FIGURE 9–3 The irregular boundaries of several wooded communities with intervening ecotones (diagonal lines) of variable width between the pure stands.

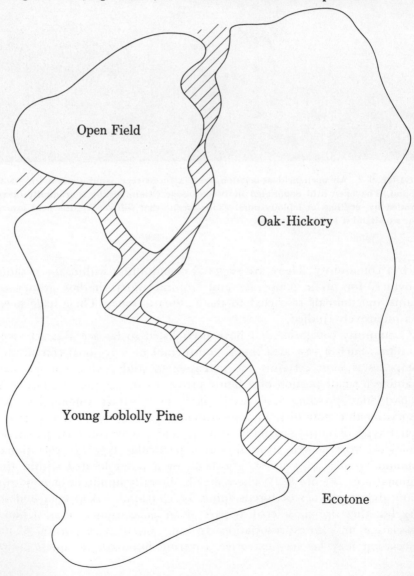

FIGURE 9–4 An example of a microstand in a wooded community. This log will exhibit variability with regard to microenvironmental factors throughout its structure. Within this log is a thriving community (microcommunity) of diverse organisms including plants and animals.

and so on. A stand is the largest concrete community included in our scheme of community classification, for this is a particular forest, river, swamp, meadow, or lake that can be seen, observed, measured, and worked over by the ecologist. A stand will exist for a specific interval of time and it will occupy a specific area. Characteristically, the boundaries of stands are irregular (Figure 9–3), unless such boundaries are artificially maintained by man. **Microstands** (Figure 9–4), the smallest community within our classification, is a small localized area within a stand. These small communities should not in actuality be considered as a subdivision of a stand, because a stand is an entity in itself. Once this entity is subdivided literally or figuratively, we have destroyed the structure and the environmental factors that are an integral part of such an aggregation. Furthermore, microstands are too diverse, too scattered, and too numerous to be considered as subdivisions of a stand, though they are located within the stand and are directly dependent on the environmental conditions prevalent therein in order to maintain their own microenvironment. Each individual plant or animal, with its associated parasites, epiphytes, and commensals may be considered a microstand, just as a rotting log, cattle droppings, an exposed rock outcrop, or a bird's nest fall into the same category.

Although this scheme of classification might conceivably satisfy some ecologists, it is not acceptable to others, partly because ecology is still young and dynamic in comparison to some of the other related biological disciplines. Ecology is still experiencing "growing pains." As a consequence there are synonymous terms used for basic community levels previously described. Also, the system of classification used often depends upon the part of the world in which a particular ecologist received his training. The system or systems used by European ecologists do not agree with those used by North American workers. There is even disagreement among ecologists in the United States. Dice's concept of a biotic province

FIGURE 9–5 An aerial photograph showing the location of cultivated communities maintained by man to produce agricultural crops and intervening woodland environments. Courtesy of the Soil Conservation Service, U.S. Department of Agriculture.

is not acceptable to some of them. An exhaustive list of synonymous names of the various types of communities used by different ecologists would be futile and confusing. It is necessary, it would seem, to organize an international system of community classification in order to establish a uniform terminology. However, this would not only present formidable problems, but it is most certainly unlikely that such a system would enjoy unanimous approval by ecologists.

Besides the established and semipermanent communities mentioned previously, there are special, temporary communities that exist throughout the world. One such type is the **mobile community** in the form of insect colonies or herds of vertebrates moving from one geographic area to another. These aggregations, together with the inevitable parasites, predators, and associated vegetation of the area, comprise a dynamic community. Cultivated areas that require continual attention from man to combat wild (weed) species, to supply the necessary mineral requirements in the form of fertilizers or compost material, and even to supply water are examples of temporary communities that would yield to tree and weed species were it not for man's continual attention (Figure 9–5). Areas of this type exist in many regions throughout the world, particularly in the heavily populated regions, in the form of gardens, lawns, and man-made clearings in forests or jungles. **Aerial communities** are even more temporary than those previously mentioned. Birds, insects, spiders, bacteria, spores, and seed of some plants make up a community that is often in a dynamic state of change. Most of the inhabitants of such a community spend but a brief period as airborne individuals. Many birds and insects feed and mate while in flight. Some insects and spiders are transported from one region to another by air currents, (thermal updrafts) and many remain in this aerial community for a considerable period of time. Planktonic communities of freshwater and marine areas with zooplanktonic and phytoplanktonic components, thrive for variable periods, but often during the spring and fall overturn, these populations may reach a considerable size in terms of total number of individuals.

BRIEF HISTORY OF THE COMMUNITY CONCEPT

The community concept dates back to the time of Theophrastus (mentioned in Chapter I). He recognized the existence of plant communities or associations of species in different environmental areas. Many centuries later, Grisebach in 1838, recognized the "plant formation" (community) as an important vegetational unit. Several years later Edward Forbes, in studying the molluscan fauna of the Aegean Sea, noted the provinces of depth and the fact that each area was distinctive because each was characterized by associations of species (communities) found at each depth. Verrill and Smith (1874) recognized three primary assemblages of animals in the region of Vineyard Sound off the Massachusetts coast, which, they stated, were dependent upon and limited by physical conditions of the water: (1) animals of bays and sounds, (2) animals of estuaries and other brackish water areas, and (3) animals of cold waters of ocean shores and outer channels. The study emphasized the fact that animals were confined to certain areas by the physical conditions that existed in the area. Both men were more impressed by the relationship between animals and physical factors than by the association of different species.

The first solid beginnings of community studies began to materialize in the latter part of the nineteenth century with the previously cited work of Mobius, first published in 1879, and the work of S. A. Forbes, who expanded Mobius's ideas of a community concept. Forbes recognized the fact that a community could not be maintained unless the birth rate and death rate of a species balanced. Furthermore, Forbes realized that if a predator-prey relationship existed, population numbers had to be maintained by both; otherwise, the community would be destroyed within a short period of time. Shortly after the turn of the century (1902), two botanists, Schroter and Kirchner, introduced the term **synecology** (the prefix syn- is a Greek derivative meaning "together") to refer to plant species living together on the ocean bottom as an association or community. In 1907, McAtee introduced the quadrat method of sampling of the flora and fauna of a community. This heralded the beginning of quantitative studies based on sampling techniques, which have gradually increased in amount and improved in accuracy over the years. Studies of succession—the change and gradual replacement of communities—first received serious attention during this early period of ecological work. (These studies are discussed briefly in the following chapter.) More recently, community studies have become involved with migration studies, community rhythms, microcommunity investigations, and population densities within communities, and there is a growing interest in marine communities.

COMMUNITY PERIODICITY

SEASONAL PERIODICITY

Any distinct community is a dynamic entity, constantly changing in various respects in keeping with the seasonal aspect as well as with the diel (twenty-four-hour) cycle. We find that both the biotic and abiotic factors that prevail for any one period will generally be quite different at a later time. The degree of difference will often limit the type of organism that can exist in an area. Such fluctuations may be recurrent after a certain time interval and, in fact, may appear over and over again in rhythmic fashion. Rhythmic fluctuation implies a cyclic pattern of events within the natural environment and will often control the activity (motor and physiological) in living organisms. These recurrent patterns of activity are so often under such complex systems of control (hormonal and metabolic cycles) that some animals, when removed from such natural conditions, will still follow various behavior patterns, even though they may be exposed to entirely different conditions for a period of time. Some of these changes are obvious to even a casual observer, but others are far more subtle. The latter changes tend to challenge some of the most modern ecological equipment and advanced methods of research. We may consider two basic types of changes: (1) abiotic fluctuations involving temperature, moisture, wind speed, and a number of other factors, and (2) biotic variability of the flora and fauna, which are influenced by (and can also alter) the existing abiotic elements of the immediate environment.

Community aspect, or the seasonal succession of events that transpire within a community, are cyclic and follow a definite pattern or sequence of events. The nonecologist recognizes four seasons—winter, spring, summer, and fall or autumn—based on weather conditions that prevail during these intervals. Ecologists have subdivided this annual cycle into six basic phases to correlate with such events as blooming of vegetation, fruiting of shrubs and trees, the emergence from hibernation, and migration of certain vertebrates. Figure 9–6 shows the differences in the appearance of a community during the several seasonal aspects throughout an annual cycle. In temperate regions of North America the ecologist recognizes the following aspects in sequence: A **prevernal period** (early spring), beginning in early March and terminating in mid-April, is an interval during which some of the hardier vegetation begins its growth and blooms, many of the hibernating mammals begin to emerge, and some of the birds are migrating northward on their way to summer nesting sites and territories. Late spring is called the **vernal period** and lasts usually about a month and a half (from late April through May) during which period, soil temperatures rise in harmony with atmospheric temperatures, trees leaf, a large number of insects hatch, birds are completing their migratory flights, some of the early blooming plants begin to set fruit. The next two periods comprise the summer interval: early summer (June through early July) is called the **estival** (or **aestival**) period; late summer (late July through early September) is called the **serotinal period**. During these periods there is maximum activity. Conditions for growth of plants and animals are optimal, though a period of drought may occur during either the estival or serotinal

(A)

FIGURE 9–6 Variation in the seasonal appearance of a forest community is indicated when photograph *A* is compared with photograph *B*. *A* was taken during the winter, and *B* in midsummer from the same location.

periods, causing an **estivation** of some of the biota. Such activity is associated with either higher temperatures or extremely dry conditions (or both) that cause a lowered organismal metabolism similar to the physiological depression exhibited by hibernating individuals during the hiemal period.

The **autumnal period,** which begins in mid- or late September and terminates in early November, is often an interval during which lower

(B)

temperatures and frosts will occur. There is a gradual defoliation of the deciduous vegetation, a general movement of many animals from the exposed strata to protected habitats or portions of a habitat, and the annual migration of the avifauna southward. There are less extensive migrations of invertebrates from the exposed open fields and grassland areas into the forest area and vertical migrations from the upper strata of the forest down to protected areas in the soil and leaf litter of the forest floor. These "micromigrations" are reversals of the activity that has occurred during the vernal and early estival intervals. During the autumnal period, many of the vertebrates collect food and prepare their **hibernicula** (areas in which the winter will be spent) for the adverse weather that soon materializes. The **hiemal period,** or winter interval, begins sometime in mid- or late November in most temperate areas and lasts until the end of February. In many areas this is a period during which precipitation in the form of snow, frozen rain, or rain is plentiful. The average temperatures are usually freezing or somewhat above. Most of the organisms that are intolerant of these lower thermal values have hibernated, encysted, or have been killed. The hardier species are usually less active than they would be during warmer periods of the year, for food is scarce and accelerated activity would merely raise the metabolic rate and the subsequent food requirements.

In nature, there is no sharp commencement or termination of any of the seasonal aspects just described. Every community is undergoing a gradual succession of changes, every day and every week. No single day is exactly like a preceding or succeeding one in terms of the multitude of abiotic factors and their continual fluctuations. These slow, ever-changing conditions occurring in extratropical regions are most graphically evident on the basis of thermal values and type of precipitation. Thermal fluctuations will cause subsequent changes in the availability of food in many instances. Some animals (birds and some insects) will frequently migrate to other areas where food is more plentiful. Others (bears and many reptiles) hibernate in a suitable cave, burrow, or similar homesite. These animals maintain a metabolic rate just adequate for survival and depend upon fat stored during the preceding period (prehibernal interval). Some organisms (insects, squirrels) will exhibit semihibernal reactions during such periods. They have prepared for the cooler season by storing food within their homesite and will exhibit reduced activity, though they will feed and be somewhat more active than the truly hibernal organism. Cooler temperatures will cover lentic localities with ice, provided that atmospheric temperatures are freezing or below; this in turn modifies the aquatic area, altering the amount of light penetrating the ice and affecting the rate of photosynthesis. These conditions, combined with the lower water temperatures and the basically poikilothermic fauna that dominates most aquatic areas, reduces activity, for the activity of a poikilothermous organisms is definitely affected by surrounding thermal values. Since they are not capable of maintaining body temperatures markedly different from the surrounding environment, they become lethargic and finally inactive if temperatures continue to drop.

The term **phenology** has been used to designate events associated with seasonal succession in natural communities. Shelford (1929) first used the term to correlate the appearance of certain seasonal events. Six years later the committee on nomenclature of the Ecological Society of America defined phenology as the science dealing with the appearance of certain characteristic events during the life cycle of any organism found in nature. In deserts, although there are no sharply defined seasonal changes, changes in weather conditions can bring about astounding changes in the flora and fauna. In most deserts there are only brief and occasional periods of rainfall. It is while this harsh environment is exposed to precipitation that many plants must complete the active portion of their life cycles. There are two rainy periods in the Sonoran Desert of North America: one occurs during the hiemal aspect, the other during the estival period. There are certain species of plants with a life cycle so adjusted to these hiemal rains that seeds germinate, grow, flower, and produce seed—all within a short interval of time. Another group of flora are activated by estival rains to complete the same series of events and then remain dormant until the following year (Figure 9–7).

Latitude and altitude are important factors that must be considered if one is studying the length of seasonal aspects. If we compare the length of seasons in different portions of the temperate zone, it is apparent that the cooler parts of the year will be more prolonged than is so in the southern part of the zone. The vernal, estival, and serotinal periods will be abbreviated in northern areas; the autumnal, hiemal, and prevernal intervals, collectively, last for a longer time interval. If we

FIGURE 9–7 Yucca plants in blossom in a desert environment in Arizona. Courtesy of the U.S. Forest Service.

become concerned with latitude on a worldwide scale—that is, particularly the seasonal changes occurring in the Southern Hemisphere—a reversal of seasons is apparent. This reversal is brought about by the position of the sun in relation to the equator at different times of the year (discussed in Chapter V, "Climatology"). In the vicinity of Rio de Janeiro, Brazil, the prevernal period begins in late August and terminates in September. The sequence and months for the rest of the year are as follows: vernal (October and November), estival (December and January), serotinal (February and March), autumnal (April and May), and the hiemal period (June, July, and early August). Two periods of flowering occur in this part of the world: a prevernal peak appears in late August; a second, longer estival-serotinal peak, begins in December and ends in March.

The altitude at which any community exists will modify the length of seasonal aspects throughout the year. In general, as the altitude increases above sea level, cooler portions of the year are prolonged, with a consequent decrease in total length of the warmer intervals. This is apparent, of course, only where considerable changes of altitude are involved (mountain ranges). Here we find that not only is the vernal-estival-serotinal interval abbreviated, but the average thermal maxima are generally lower than those recorded at lower altitudes in the same geographic locality. The longer cooler periods at high altitudes (autumnal-hiemal-prevernal interval) will also have lower thermal minima. An approximate 1,000-foot increase in altitude is equivalent to moving 300 miles closer to the nearest pole at the lower altitude, in terms of thermal conditions. The mule deer (*Odocoileus hemionus*) migrates from one altitude to another in the western part of the United States in keeping with the seasonal periods. This species occupies high slopes during the summer, but migrates to lower altitudes with the first snowfall in early fall. The spring migration to higher altitudes is apparently stimulated, according to Russell (1932), by increase in plant growth and necessary fodder that becomes available. Appearance of fodder at higher altitudes is dependent on the disappearance of snow and increased temperatures. Mule deer will migrate only in response to plant growth, not the latter two conditions; if suitable food is present at lower altitudes they do not migrate to summer feeding grounds.

The geographic position of any locale in relation to the seacoast will definitely influence the climate and seasonal intervals. We find that maritime communities will have seasonal intervals that are modified by marine currents in their vicinity. Cool currents such as the Humboldt Current that passes along the west coast of South America will lengthen the cooler seasons of the year. Warm currents (Gulf Stream) along the southeastern part of the United States will prolong the warmer seasons. In fact, a number of biologists in the past have stated that palm trees would be a common sight in southern New England if the Gulf Stream should ever shift its course and move closer to the northern shores of the continent, rather than move seaward as it does at the present time. Any shift in oceanic currents would of necessity bring about considerable changes in the duration of seasonal intervals.

DIEL PERIODICITY

Superimposed on the seasonal fluctuations in any natural community are **diel rhythms.** The term *diel* refers to the entire twenty-four-hour interval. This twenty-four-hour period can be subdivided into several units based on the total amount of illumination received by the environment. Of course, as shown in Figure 9–8, other environmental factors will also vary. Carpenter (1935) divided the diel period into the **auroral period** (dawn) and the **diurnal period** (interval of full daylight). During the auroral period, nocturnal species become increasingly more quiescent and begin returning to their shelters. At the same time, diurnal species become more active, for the diurnal period will shortly ensue. Following this prolonged period of full daylight is the **vesperal period,** which some biologists use synonymously with the term **crepuscular,** though the latter term, as Carpenter recommended in his *Ecological Glossary* (1938), embraces the dawn and dusk interlude or associated activities. During the vesperal interim, there is a complete reversal of the activities associated with the auroral period; the diurnal organisms gradually become quiescent and seek shelter, and the nocturnal fauna begins to stir and appear in increasing numbers. The fourth span of time is the

FIGURE 9–8 Graphic representation of light, thermal, and humidity changes ensuing over hourly intervals in a natural community near the southern end of Lake Michigan during late spring. From *Principles of Animal Ecology* by W. C. Allee, A. E. Emerson, T. Park, O. Park, and K. Schmidt. Used by permission of W. B. Saunders Company, 1949, and the authors.

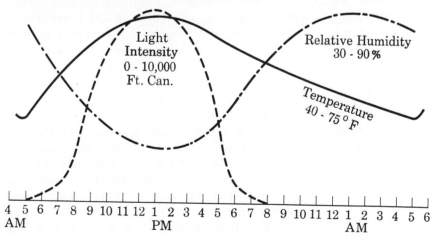

nocturnal period, when the illumination received in any natural environment is low in comparison to the diurnal interim, for the moon or bioluminescent organisms are the only source of visible light. This is a period of maximum activity for nocturnal species—a period which we unfortunately know less about owing to our limitations of visibility.

The daily activity of plants and animals is controlled by temperature, humidity, and variations in light intensity as well as the continual, long-term (seasonal) changes that transpire. Light intensity, measured in terms of foot-candles of light reaching the environment, obviously controls the rate of photosynthetic activity in plants. Flora located in areas of less than 1 per cent of full sunlight have surpassed a point, known as the **phytic limit,** where light intensity is not great enough to support vegetation on the basis of photosynthetic activity. Such plants (bacteria) must manufacture food by means of chemosynthesis. Vital processes that must transpire in order for the higher plant to complete its life cycle—growth, flower production, and seed development—are governed not only by light intensity but also by length of the period of illumination (or in some cases the length of the period of darkness), better known as **photoperiod** by plant physiologists. Some animals utilize different portions of the diel cycle to seek out prey or feed on vegetation. Crepuscular animals are most active during the auroral or vesperal portions of the cycle, or both. Nocturnal organisms appear in the absence of sunlight (direct or indirect). Some are extremely sensitive to light intensity. The deermouse (*Peromyscus maniculatus*) is so sensitive to light it avoids full moonlight, which is only 1/500,000 of the intensity of full sunlight.

Just as sunlight will affect large segments of the biota directly or indirectly, moonlight exerts a strong effect on some organisms. **Lunar rhythms** are most effective in areas where phases of the moon and time of moon rise and moon set affect the tides. The marine biota living in shallow water, especially the intertidal or sublittoral zones, will experience more dramatic effects from the standpoint of tidal amplitude. Many of the intertidal organisms remaining in this zone will become inactive as the tide recedes and exposes them to the atmosphere. Such cyclic changes definitely control the amount of time available for feeding or producing food. Lunar cycles are closely correlated with reproductive cycles in some marine forms, such as the grunion (*Laurestes tenuis*), a small fish of the Pacific coast that breeds and appears along the lower California area in large numbers during a long tidal rhythm. The Atlantic palolo worm (*Leodice fucata*) in the Bermuda and Carribean areas will spawn in June and July during the third quarter of the moon, and to a lesser extent during the first quarter. It is believed that the gradual changes in total time of exposure to moonlight as well as the length of exposure time are important.

Nearly every organism, and perhaps all life, is controlled by the sequence of activity that occurs during the course of seasonal and diel cycles. We find that man is adjusted to a twenty-four hour cycle on the basis of metabolic activity and that if he is transferred from one time zone to another, it requires several days for him to adjust to the new time zone. But it has been found that various body functions such as daily (diel) change in body temperature, blood pressure, hormone secretion, kidney function, and a number of other occurrences (many of them as yet unknown) require a much longer period, often several weeks, before they become reestablished at their own individual rate to the new time schedule. Dr. P. R. Lewis and Dr. Mary Labban (Cambridge University) studied three groups of men during the arctic summer of continuous daylight. One group, the control unit, lived on a twenty-four hour schedule, a second group on a shorter time span, and the third group on a longer time span. The abnormal schedule of the latter two groups suggested, on the basis of their study, that these men were less efficient and under greater physiological stress than was the control group.

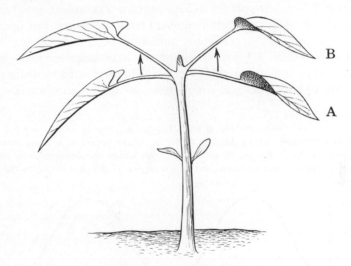

FIGURE 9–9 Leaves of a bean plant rise from position *A* to *B* as a result of light stimulation for a brief period after being kept in dim light for some time.

Wilhelm Pfeffer, the German plant physiologist, was one of the first biologists to demonstrate the presence of a diel rhythm in young bean seedlings. The first pair of leaves above the cotyledons were elevated during the day and dropped some distance at night. However, this was not a response brought about by variations in temperature or illumination, because these same responses occurred when both of these factors remained unchanged. More recently it has been discovered that this response may be reset by subjecting the plants to illumination at night and darkness during the day. After a few days of repetitive cycles during which the diel cycle is reversed in this way, the leaves of the seedling will be elevated at sunset and will fall at dawn, under conditions of unvarying light intensity. Erwin Bunning, a German plant physiologist (University of Tubingen), has discovered that bean seedlings under continuous dim light, if exposed to a brief period of bright illumination at the time the leaves are depressed, will exhibit a partial elevation of these leaves shortly afterward (Figure 9–9). More amazing than this, however, is the fact that these seedlings will continue to follow this rhythm during the diel period, despite the absence of further stimuli.

A large array of vertebrates and invertebrates are controlled by varying environmental conditions that in general will be of survival value in most cases. Fiddler crabs (*Uca*) are known to increase the distribution of pigment and become darker at dawn and decrease the quantity and distribution of superficial pigments during the vesperal interval. This diel rhythm may be reversed, however, by exposing them to illumination at night and darkness during the day. Further experimentation has shown that if *Uca* is immersed in ice water for a certain interval that the rhythm resumes its activity after removal from the water, but is resumed at the point where the crabs are immersed in the ice water (Figure 9–10). Diel rhythms are superimposed on long-range seasonal changes. In many plants and animals this diel periodicity is automatically slightly altered throughout the year in correlation with variations in photo-

FIGURE 9–10 The pigmentation of *Uca* changes in keeping with a diurnal rhythm from a dark individual during daylight hours to a light organism at night. Submersion in ice water in the lower graph stops the cycle, which continues after a return to normal temperatures, but six hours out of phase (curve *B*) in contrast to the normal cycle (curve *A*).

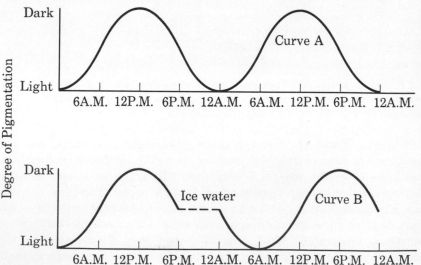

periods. Such changes will affect the reproductive process of many diverse groups of living organisms, generally causing them to become reproductively active at the most suitable time of the year with regard to conditions of survival.

Two hypotheses have been advanced to explain the diel and seasonal periodicity that exists almost universally among plants and animals. One hypothesis assumes that the organism responds to rhythmic changes in the external environment. The implication is that changes in light, temperature, humidity, and a number of other environmental changes will in turn affect body functions and bring about a set of behavioral patterns that conform with current conditions. The other hypothesis postulates that over the long evolutionary sequence that has transpired, a complex set of internal biochemical and metabolic systems developed that controls the behavioral sequence and that these mechanisms, on the basis of survival, necessarily parallel the external environmental conditions. It is quite likely that both hypotheses are operative to a variable degree.

ARHYTHMIC FLUCTUATIONS

Not all natural events can be predicted nor anticipated to the same degree of regularity as the rhythms just discussed. In fact, even climatic fluctuations such as temperature, humidity, and precipitation can become quite arhythmic because of localized disturbances or abnormal changes that may erupt and affect diel or seasonal rhythms. Climatic factors vary in certain geographical areas to such a degree that they are seldom similar for any two successive years. There are "wet years," "dry years," cool summers, warm winters, and so on. In fact, the Midwest and parts of New England experienced an exceedingly dry late summer and fall interval in 1963, much drier than many of the more aged residents could recall in their lifetime. Fluctuations in climatic factors can severely modify the community (see Chapter V, "Climatology"). Floods, droughts, and fires are arhythmic occurrences that transpire with considerable frequency in some regions.

Fires are caused by lightning or volcanic activity under natural circumstances. **Crown fires** are the most destructive for several reasons. This type of fire incinerates the forest canopy as well as surface debris, and brings about a wholesale destruction of vegetation. Temperatures that prevail while the fire is in progress may reach 1300° F. in the litter environment, but three quarters of an inch below this level, in the mineral soil, temperatures may be between 77° and 217° F. Thus, though temperatures may be severe on the surface, at a short distance below, the thermal conditions may not be incompatible with life. This type of fire may practically incinerate much of the surface biota that cannot

(A)

FIGURE 9–11 Photograph *A* represents an area exposed to a crown fire in Flathead National Forest, Montana, as compared with photograph *B*, an area that has been subjected to a surface fire in Osceola National Forest, Florida. Courtesy of the U.S. Forest Service.

(B)

escape or move rapidly enough to avoid the rapid passage of fire. Destruction of the vegetation results in massive erosion, because vegetation is necessary to prevent the rapid passage of rain to the soil and the subsequent runoff that will rapidly carry away the smaller surface soil particles, along with the rich humus that had formerly been an integral part of the soil. The fauna that have managed to escape the ravages of fire are a displaced group, having lost their former home ranges and refuges. Many are lost by predation by being forced into unfamiliar areas or into other territorial areas of the species. For those that survive, harsh conditions will sometimes ensue as a result of exceeding the carrying capacity for an area, the difficulty of establishing a homesite, a home range, and a territory amid unfamiliar surroundings.

Surface fires (Figure 9–11) are not as severe in terms of results as are crown fires because the thermal extremes are far below those cited for crown fires. Surface fires, as the name implies, are limited to surface debris and vegetation of modest height, such as shrubs and seedlings that are relatively close to ground level. Periodic but arhythmic surface fires often will reduce the possibility of a crown fire because much of the debris that could promote the latter is reduced to a minimum. Fire climaxes are maintained in some areas where surface fires are frequent and the vegetation is not replaced by the normal successional series of communities for the climatic area. An excellent example of such a community are the extensive stands of longleaf pine located through certain areas of the southeastern United States. The young seedlings have protective circlets of fire-resistant needles surrounding the apical meristems. Frequent surface fires bring about a more rapid breakdown of organic material, which in turn aids the bacterial disintegration of material. The result is a fertile soil that supports a lush ground cover and a remarkable array of biota.

THE ECOTONE

The existence of varying climatic conditions, man's intervention, or the presence of aquatic areas limits the extent of terrestrial communities. Under natural conditions, the vast array of climatic and physical factors become more adverse as we approach the outer limits of a terrestrial community until finally, for the particular inhabitants of a community, a limit of tolerance is encountered. At this point a different aggregation of plants and animals representing another community becomes apparent. In nature, there is never discernible a sharp line or point indicating the beginning of one community and the end of another; instead, there is a zone of transition, or tension, in which the conditions for each of the adjacent communities becomes more adverse and there is often an intermingling of species from both communities (Figure 9–12). Such a

FIGURE 9–12 A narrow ecotone of small trees and shrubs located between an open field (pasture) and a mature oak-hickory forest community.

region is known as an **ecotone,** or a **tension zone.** The extent of such an intervening area is variable, for in instances where the physical factors change abruptly, the ecotone is narrow. This is often so where marshes, bogs, ponds, and other bodies of freshwater interrupt communities; the transition from land to water can be quite abrupt, yielding only an extremely narrow zone of transition. On the other hand, when one community merges gradually with another, a relatively wide, spacious ecotone may exist. At times, the extent of a functional ecotone has been exaggerated by some biologists; zones between major continental communities, sometimes nearly 100 miles or so wide, have been considered as ecotones. A "transitional zone" of this vast extent, in all likelihood, should be treated as a distinct community or series of communities. As Allee, *et al.* have succinctly stated (p. 477): "... ecotone as a term covering a more or less sharply defined competitive zone between two self-supporting communities, the concept becomes reasonably concise. As a synonym of biome intergradation it loses its usefulness, since it could be argued that we have a single area of intergradation from pole to equator."

A general characteristic of the ecotone is that very often there are a greater number of species. In addition the density of many of these "edge species" is higher than it is for the neighboring communities. Such a unique feature has been designated, in the past, as the **principle of edges.** The reason for the greater number of species found in an ecotone is that there is an intermingling of the most tolerant species of the bordering communities and of other species that are characteristic of this tension zone and not indigenous to either of the bordering communities. A terrestrial ecotone that has probably received more intensive investigation than has any other single type is the forest-edge ecotone of the Midwest. This ecotone, situated between the mature poplar forest and prairie communities (Figure 9–13), is of limited width, usually only a few meters to 50 or 100 meters. There are scattered trees, scattered prairie grass, and shrubs and bushes that are found only in this transitional area. During the period in which such an ecotone has existed, there have been animals from both forest and prairie that have established themselves. Other organisms have entered this region briefly, but they have returned to their own particular communities because they have been unable to tolerate the peculiar biotic and abiotic conditions in the ecotone for any extensive period of time. A third group of animals has entered the zone and remained here exclusively (edge species).

The forest community is comprised of poplar (*Populus*), aspen (*P. tremuloides*), dogwood (*Cornus*), hazelnut (*Corylus*), and wintergreen (*Chimaphila*) vegetation. The characteristic fauna in this community includes the chestnut-backed chickadee (*Parus rufescens*), rose-breasted grosbeak (*Pheucticus ludovicianus*), rabbits (*Lepus*), wapiti (*Cervus canadensis*), shrews (*Sorex*), and many insects and spiders. Within the forest-edge ecotone are aspen, snowberry (*Symphoricarpos*), hazelnut and chokeberry (*Pyrus*), but red-backed voles (*Clethrionomys gapperi*), Franklin ground squirrels (*Citellus franklinii*), insects, spiders, red-eyed vireo (*Vireo olivaceous*), yellow warbler (*Dendroica petechia*), catbird (*Dumetella carolinensis*), brown thrasher (*Toxostoma rufum*), and snowshoe rabbits (*Lepus bairdi*) make up the predominate fauna.

The prairie community contains prairie grasses (*Poa, Andropogon,* etc.) and sunflower (*Helianthus*). Coyotes (*Canis latrans*), least weasels (*Mustela rixosa*), pocket gophers (*Geomys bursarius*), thirteen-lined ground squirrels (*Citellus tridecemlineatus*), prairie voles (*Microtus*

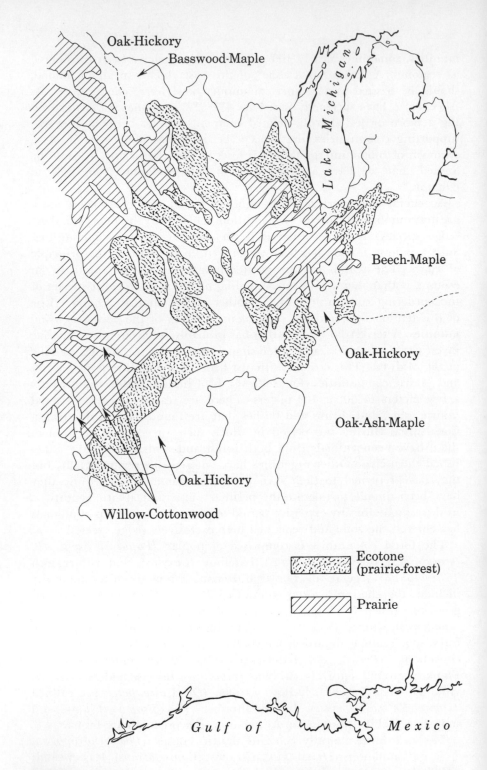

FIGURE 9–13 Forest-prairie ecotone area of the Midwest showing the extent and location of the ecotone, prairie, and forest associations.

ochrogaster), ants (Formididae), cutworms (Noctuidae), grasshoppers (Tettigoniidae), and click beetles (Elateridae) make up the associated faunal complex.

A tremendous variety of ecotones exist even in one geographic area— between different types of forest communities, between forest and grassland communities (Figure 9–14), bogs, or swamps, between coastal sand dune communities and maritime forests, and so on. Within aquatic communities, ecotones of limited extent may exist between two distinctly

FIGURE 9–14 An ecotone of shrub growth (left foreground) between a swamp and the surrounding forest community of red spruce, larch, balsam fir, alder, and white pine in New York. Courtesy of the U.S. Forest Service.

different communities. In these intermediate ecotones, physical factors such as substrate or dissolved gases may differ from those in both bordering communities. The intermediate ecotone is entirely dependent upon the continued existence of both adjacent communities for maintenance of its biotic and abiotic factors. If one or both communities are changed or altered by man or some catastrophic event, the ecotone will either disappear completely or undergo extreme changes. Gradual changes will take place in this intermediate tension zone if the adjacent communities are subject to ecological succession. Often the changes that occur may be very gradual, especially in the advanced stages of succession.

Despite the importance and tremendous variety of ecotonal areas throughout the world, relatively little ecological attention has been focused on this interesting area. This neglect is more apparent as regards ecological research dealing with the various invertebrate groups. A more thorough knowledge of the microenvironmental conditions and the invertebrate organisms present in some of these areas would be an important addition to the ecological literature at the present time. In the ecotone and bordering communities there exists a natural laboratory where variability of such factors as temperature, wind, humidity, precipitation, light intensity, rate of evaporation, and many other physical conditions could give us greater insight into the reasons for seasonal migrations, diel rhythms, and oscillations in density and frequency. Hall has stated (pp. 48 and 49): "When in the marginal part of its geographical range, a species is sharply restricted to a particular fraction of its environment, ... the chances are that several features of the environment are intolerable for the species. By noting, in the marginal part of the range, which feature of the environment is common to the places in which the species does live, the most important positive distributional factor for the species throughout its range can often be ascertained more quickly than through study of areas near the center of the geographic range.... For these reasons study in the marginal rather than in the central part of the range of a species often is profitable."

THE COMMUNITY VERSUS THE CONTINUUM

Within the past dozen years or so, some ecologists investigating communities of the Midwest have introduced the **continuum** concept into the ecological literature. "Continuum" implies that there are no distinct communities with well-defined boundaries, but rather there is a gradual change in space and time along a gradient of some sort. The gradient may be in the form of moisture, temperature, soil type, amount of insulation, altitude, or any number of abiotic factors. To conform with the gradients established within the area, the species of plants and animals will exhibit parallel changes. Thus we find that there are no sharp borders or changes in species composition in areas where a continuum can be demonstrated. For convenience of study, an investigator can recognize subcommunities or associations within the continuum in keeping with the density and frequency of organisms in localized areas.

Recent work by Curtis and McIntosh (1951), Whittaker (1951, 1953), and Curtis (1955) has strengthened the continuum school of thought in ecological work. Much work has centered around the prairie and prairie-forest regions of Wisconsin, where, according to Curtis and McIntosh, no distinct groups of stands were apparent. Instead, there was a definite gradient from initial stages composed of pioneer species to terminal stages of climax species. Such a gradient, according to the authors, may be regarded as a vegetational continuum. Whittaker has attacked the existence of an ecotone by implying that a transitional area between two types of vegetation may be very broad and gradual so that it is impossible to recognize any basic discontinuity but only a gradient from one vegetational area to another. According to Whittaker, the observed discontinuities produced locally by environmental differences tend to telescope the transitions. Or the incompatibility of the species with regard to environmental differences tends to steepen the rate of change along a

FIGURE 9–15 A land slide caused by an earthquake in Yellowstone National Park (August, 1959) brought about the destruction of the existing vegetational community. This photograph was taken in the Gibbon Falls area of the Park. Courtesy of the National Park Service, U.S. Department of the Interior.

(A)

FIGURE 9-16 The destructive effect of a hurricane on a terrestrial community altering the entire environmental complex of the area. Both photographs were taken in Massachusetts, recording the effects of the 1938 hurricane. Courtesy of the U.S. Forest Service.

gradient. The same author states that the traditional community concept of communities extending along an unchanged gradient to some community-wide limit of tolerance where it is finally replaced by another community is untenable. Curtis, in studying the prairie vegetation in Wisconsin, found that the flora was affected more by soil and moisture factors than by any other single environmental element. He found there were no discrete groups of plant species but rather gradients of species governed by edaphic and moisture factors in the immediate area. Furthermore, with regard to succession, Curtis explains that there is succession on a microsite; but no large areas are involved, since no region of any extent is in the same stage of successional development. Consequently, there is no opportunity to differentiate developmental communities.

It is difficult for one to render an unbiased appraisal of the continuum versus the community approach. It seems doubtful, at this time, that the community concept that has been so valuable and utilized by generations of ecologists will ever be completely forsaken. One important fact must be taken into account: the continuum concept has been applied to few

(B)

geographic areas to date, and though it may be a very logical and useful approach in some regions, it may fall far short of expectations in other localities. All ecologists are aware of gradients that exist within communities. It is the degree of variability of one or more of these environmental gradients that determines whether or not a community is replaced by another vegetation type. In short, whether one considers an area a continuum or a community, at the present time, depends upon one's personal outlook and past training.

COMMUNITIES OF THE PAST

One of the fundamental principles of ecology, community succession, implies that there will be a sequence of communities in any one area over a period of time. These changes in communities may be caused by catastrophic events, climatic changes, or intrinsic factors. It certainly is not difficult to visualize how catastrophes of climatic nature could destroy a thriving community. Severe fires caused by lightning, earthquakes ripping large fissures through communities or causing vast landslides (Figure 9–15), the erosion of soil and the transport of fauna and their subsequent drowning by floods, the devastation caused by hurricanes, tornadoes, typhoons, and volcanic eruption (Figure 9–16)—all are examples of the destructive natural catastrophes that occur periodically on our planet. Climatic changes are not as easily perceived except through careful study because the disappearance of species and their replacement by more tolerant types is usually a gradual affair. This does not mean that changes in amount of rainfall or thermal variation are any less destruc-

FIGURE 9–17 The distribution of Cretaceous seas over the North American continent indicates oceanic areas in black; inland seas in dark-gray; and areas submerged for only part of the period in light-gray. This represents but one period of inundation in the geological past and like time lapse photography, it gives an idea of the land areas submerged during only one particular interval of time. From *Introduction to Historical Geology* by Raymond C. Moore. Copyright 1949. McGraw-Hill Book Company. Used by permission.

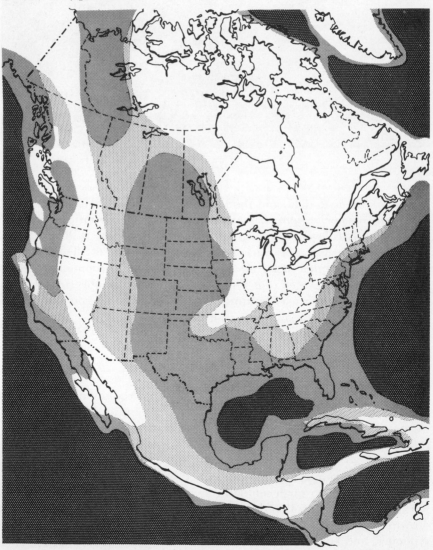

tive than the forementioned catastrophic events. Climatic changes generally affect large geographic areas and they are more insidious than is any earthquake.

In the past, communities throughout the world were quite different from what they are today. If we were to gradually turn back the clock ten thousand years, a hundred thousand years, a million years and observe the flora and fauna living in some particular locality, we would find that in each time interval these communities would exhibit considerable differences. Man's recent intervention, geological changes, climatic variability, and glaciation—all have had their effect on the living aggregation. Geological events such as the rise of mountain ranges, which changed the altitude (and climate) of specific areas, erosion in one region and sedimentation in others, as well as invasion and recession of oceanic waters in continental areas (Figure 9–17) caused gradual but permanent changes in the landscape. The glacial periods that

FIGURE 9–18 The maximum extent of glaciation during the Quarternary period. Glaciers did not cover the entire area represented at any one time. This is a composite representation of all of the glacial advances covering the North American continent. From *Introduction to Historical Geology* by Raymond C. Moore. Copyright 1949. McGraw-Hill Book Company. Used by permission.

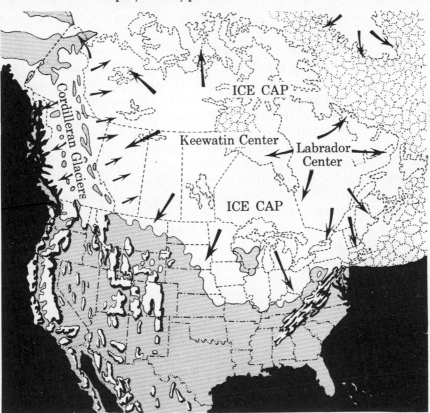

brought about major thermal changes and transported tremendous masses of soil and rock long distances southward and the intervening warm, moist periods certainly altered the communities in the north (Figure 9–18). During each ice age, vegetation and sessile or sluggish animals were destroyed, while more active animals were forced to retreat southward in order to survive. If we add to this man's management (and more often his mismanagement) of natural areas, it is little wonder that the same geographic area in any of the past eras is not recognizable when it is compared with its present-day appearance.

A recent publication, *The Ecology of North America*, by Shelford (1963), describes North America, from an ecological standpoint, as it appeared in the sixteenth century. This publication gives a clear idea of the biotic communities that existed throughout the North American continent before disturbance by the early European settlers and allows one to compare the changes that have occurred over the past several centuries.

PALEOECOLOGY

One specialized field of ecological research, **paleoecology,** deals with the environments and living aggregations of past eras of time. Careful study and a knowledge of the tolerance of certain species to existing conditions of the past have enabled the paleoecologist to reconstruct entire communities, including the species, topography, and the climate, as they existed at some particular interval in prehistoric time. The types of communities that prevailed within any particular area may be inferred from **relic species,** pollen analysis, or fossil deposits. A relic species is an organism, either plant or animal, that has managed to survive within a geographic area, despite the gradual disappearance of other species in the community. Such a species is usually able to survive because of its extreme tolerance to changing ecological conditions; but in some cases, protective structures or inactive and resistant spores or cysts have enabled the organism to maintain itself in the area.

In the past few decades, examination of pollen cores removed from bog areas has enabled the paleoecologist to determine the vegetation that inhabited areas surrounding the bog. A core of bog sediment is removed and pollen samples that are extracted at different points along the core are identified as to species. The pollen from the lowest portion of the core, having been laid first, represents the earlier communities. By identifying the species of pollen at different intervals along the core, it is possible to trace the succession of communities that occurred in the vicinity of any bog as indicated in the diagrammatic transect in Figure 9–19. A careful survey of fossil deposits in any area can reveal a surprising amount of information. A list of species and any unusual structures consistently found on fossil species will often yield valuable clues about the environmental conditions in the area. The general nature of fossil beds will provide information about the general terrain. If fossils are deposited in a small area, it often indicates a small community, such as a mountain top, a small depression, a valley, or a small stream or pond. However, a large area covered by fossil specimens of a particular species would certainly indicate that a large plateau, a lake, an ocean, or an extensive forest once existed in the vicinity. The paleoecologist is faced with a number of difficulties when attempting to piece together the ecological conditions and the populations that once existed in certain areas. Past floods or windstorms could have carried pollen and other fossil material extensive distances from their native habitat. Many soft-bodied or delicate fossils are never preserved because their delicate structure cannot withstand the pressures and stresses to which it is exposed during fossilization. One final point: as time passes, different varieties and subspecies of plants and animals will appear. These variants will have a different degree of tolerance to certain environmental conditions than had preexisting populations. Consequently, inferences made about environmental conditions, based solely on a knowledge of species present, should be discouraged or considered with an extreme degree of caution.

Within recent years the geologist, paleontologist, and paleoecologist have been able to determine the age of various rock strata by measuring very carefully the amount of radioactive material in mineral or fossil deposits. The basic theory of radioactive dating is based on the fact that over a unit period of time certain radioactive parent materials will decay or change into measurable quantities of daughter substances. If the rate of decay is known, then a measurement of radioactive parent and derived material formed by the disintegration will yield the age of the deposit. For example, if we have a pure crystal of a mineral, such as uraninite, which contained no lead at the time of its formation, the mineral will gradually build up a deposit of lead according to the radioactive decay constant for the mineral. If we know the decay constant (the rate at which the uranium will disintegrate over a unit period of time) and can measure the amount of uranium and lead within the ore, we can determine the age of that particular mass of mineral. In some cases, when crystals are formed, a tight system is organized which will last for billions of years without disturbance. In others, a loose system or crystal is produced that allows for a diffusion and an exchange with other elements in the environment. If we are to determine the age of a particular deposit, it is necessary to have a tight crystal system from which there will be no loss or gain of material. There must be measurable quantities of radioactive parent material and measurable amounts of daughter product present. It is also necessary to determine the amount of daughter product originally present in the crystal at the time of formation.

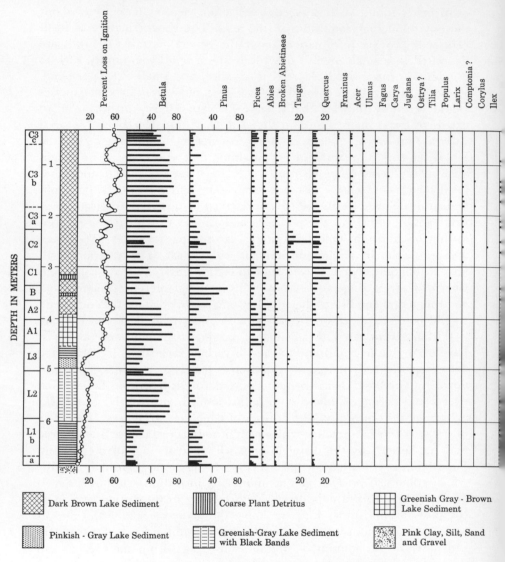

GILLIS LAKE, RICHMOND COUNTY, NOVA SCOTIA

FIGURE 9–19 A diagrammatic bisect of a pollen bed, indicating the layered appearance of the pollen deposits, with the various vegetational components listed along the upper margin of the diagram and the depth of the core in meters indicated by the enlarged numerals near the left margin. The L_1 layer demonstrates a high sedge density; L_2 denotes an increase in birch and a decline in sedge, ferns, and conifers. A high frequency of spruce and birch indicates a boreal forest in the A_1 layer. The pollen analysis of the A_2 stratum indicates an increase in fir followed by an increase in pine in the *B* stratum. Hardwood forests appear in the C_1 layer (oak),

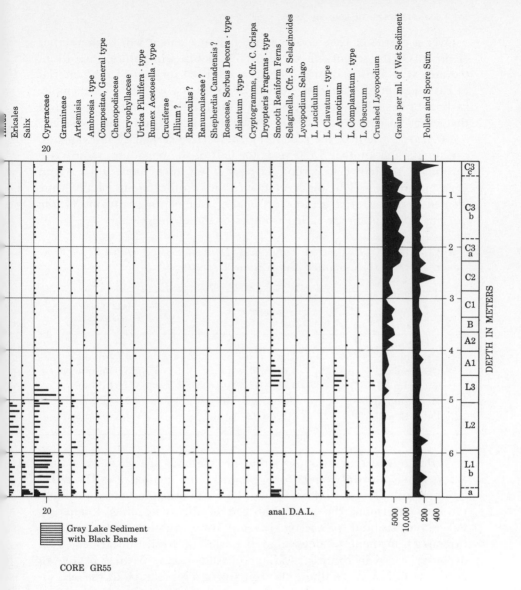

followed by an increase in hemlock (C_2) indicating moister conditions. This is followed by a decline in hemlock and rise in frequency of birch (C_3) as a result of lower temperatures. The black bar near the left-hand margin of the graph indicates the level of material with a radioactive date of $Y = 524$ (10,340 ± 220 years). From D. A. Livingstone and B. G. R. Livingstone, "Late Glacial and Post Glacial Vegetation from Gillis Lake in Richmond County, Cape Breton Island, Nova Scotia," Amer. Jour. Sci., *256*:341–359, 1958.

Over a period of time a radioactive parent element will form another element. Of the seventy-three radioactive isotopes in nature, each disintegrates at a particular rate. The time required for half of the material to disintegrate into another element is called its **half-life**. For example, carbon 14 has a half-life of 5,730 years, the time required for one half of the atoms to change to carbon 12. It will then require an additional 5,730 years for half of the remaining radioactive carbon 14 to change to carbon 12, and another 5,730 years for half of the remaining radioactive carbon 14 to change to carbon 12, and so on. (See Table 9–1.) Atoms with an atomic weight different from that of other atoms of the same element because of a greater or smaller number of neutrons in the nucleus of the atom are called isotopes of the element.

T A B L E   9 – 1 .   *Radioactive Substances, Derivatives, and Half-Life of Some Common Materials Encountered in Natural Deposits*

SOURCE	DERIVATIVE	HALF-LIFE (IN YEARS)
Uranium (U^{238})	Lead (Pb^{206})	4.5 billion
Uranium (U^{235})	Lead (Pb^{207})	713.0 million
Thorium (Th^{232})	Lead (Pb^{208})	13.9 billion
Rubidium (Rb^{87})	Strontium (Sr^{87})	50.0 billion
Potassium (K^{40})	Argon (A^{40})	1.3 billion

At the present time, it appears that two methods of radioactive dating are yielding practical results for geologists. One method uses the calculation of rubidium-strontium ratios; the other uses the potassium-argon ratio to determine the geological age of different mineral deposits. Paleontologists and paleoecologists are using another technique, the carbon 14 method, to determine the ages of fossils unearthed from deposits formed in the past. Carbon 14 emits a beta particle having an energy of 0.15 Mev (million electron volts). This isotope of carbon can be produced within a neutron pile by exposing nitrogen 14 to neutron bombardment. Under natural conditions, neutrons liberated by cosmic radiation transform atmospheric nitrogen (nitrogen 14) into carbon 14 (Figure 9–20). The carbon is soon oxidized into carbon dioxide. The bombardment of nitrogen by neutrons will take place in the atmosphere at an altitude of about 30,000 feet or higher. This isotope of carbon will remain in the atmosphere for an average period of five years.

It has been estimated that C^{14} may remain in the surface layers of the ocean or land for a period of five more years and in the deeper parts of the ocean for 1,200 years. Since living organisms consist of large amounts of carbon and water, any C^{14} that is available becomes concentrated in

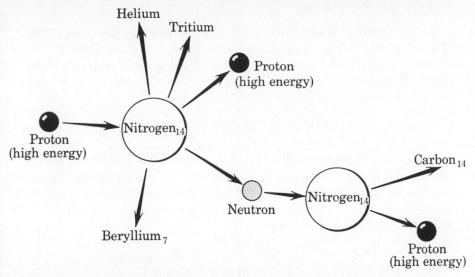

FIGURE 9–20 Diagrammatic representation of the formation of carbon-14 from atmospheric nitrogen by means of high energy protons and neutrons.

living tissue. Living biological organisms, as a result of metabolic activity, have the same proportional amount of C^{14} in their carbon compounds as the surrounding biosphere. After death, there is no further carbon exchange with the environment; the C^{14} decays without replacement and its depletion is in keeping with the isotopic half-life (5,730 years). Thus, the concentration of C^{14} in any fossil gives us an accurate idea of how long it has ceased to live.

Radioactive dating developed by Libby (1955, 1961) and his coworkers has enabled research workers to calculate the age of large numbers of fossils recovered from different areas. The actual measurement can be made on either solid or gaseous forms of carbon by placing the carbon in a counting chamber and reducing the background radiation to a level that will allow accurate detection of the weak beta emission from carbon 14. Background radiation arises from three sources: alpha radiation, which is emitted by the construction materials of the detector; cosmic radiation; and gamma rays from surrounding substances in the laboratory. Effects of background radiation are reduced by surrounding the counting chamber with a protective shield of iron or mercury and installing a group of anticoincidence counters that correct for stray cosmic radiation. Unshielded samples may be exposed to background radiation on the order of five hundred counts per minute; however, eight inches of iron shielding may reduce this value by 80 per cent.

It should be realized that it is not practicable to determine the age of fossil deposits that exceed twenty thousand years in age without using special techniques, as the radioactivity in older deposits is so slight that accurate measurements are difficult to assess because of background radioactive disturbance. Based on a value of 5,730 years for the half-life of carbon 14, which was the half-life value adopted by the Fifth Radiocarbon Dating Conference at Cambridge University in July 1962, the length of time since the death of the organism can be computed by using the following equation:

$$SA\ C^{14} = 15.3 \exp\left(-0.693\ \frac{t}{5,730}\right).$$

In this equation SA C^{14} is the specific activity of the sample in disintegrations per minute per gram of carbon, and t is the age of the organic material in years. After recording the value in disintegrations per minute per gram of carbon (dpm/g) it is a simple calculation to solve for t, the unknown value in the equation.

EVOLUTION OF COMMUNITIES

Extrinsic and intrinsic changes with respect to the community, whether terrestrial, freshwater, or marine, have resulted in the evolution of each. External forces that tend to change the character of a community are often at first purely physiographic factors involving geological and climatic events. The elevation of landmasses (altering the altitude and climate), the erosion or base leveling of mountains, or the gradual disappearance of physical barriers—all will lead the way to changes in community structure. For with these initial physical and climatological changes, the type of life that will achieve success must be tolerant of the existing conditions. Species interaction in community situations are of three basic types according to Ross (1962), involving coexistence, exploitation, or mutualism. As Ross states (p. 218): ". . . as soon as geomorphic changes resulted in a mixing of species, these mixtures evolved into the first biological communities which had the same fundamental characteristics as those occurring today. Competition, chance inherent differences in the species, and innate ecological differences within the range of mixtures would interact and constitute the mechanisms of evolution." In a general sense, all of the species making up a community are coexisting, but in a more restricted sense we find that conditions of coexistence become more acute when two or more species are competing for the same food or shelter within a limited geographic area. It is believed that direct competition for food between several species denoted the primitive conditions in community organization from which more specialized means of coexistence gradually evolved over the course of time.

In spite of Gause's Law that no two animal species could occupy the same ecological niche at the same time in the same community, indirect evidence from the past tends to refute this generalization. It is believed that in primitive communities, animal species did compete for the same type of food and shelter at the same time of year. However, after an interval of time, natural selection favors one of the species. There must be a structural modification (mutation) to allow for some change in diet with regard to the second species; otherwise, it may be doomed to extinction. Thus, over the course of time, the process of evolution tends to support Gause's Law, though initially the situation may have been quite different. In highly competitive associations, it has been found that certain weather conditions will favor one species during one portion of the year, while a normal seasonal change will favor the other species during the remainder of the year; hence, the two populations are able to coexist in the same area, though they may display a considerable oscillation in population size. Other ecological conditions may also allow coexistence in a limited area. Utida (1957) discovered that two parasites of the azuki bean weevil *Callosobruchus chinensis* were able to coexist as a result of differences in host density. *Neocatolaccus mamezophagus* is the predominant organism when the weevil population is high, but a reduction in the host population favors the other parasite *Heterospilus prososipidis* because adults are capable of locating the host larvae more readily. Needless to say, a direct and continuous competition takes place among the plant species of a community for soil water, minerals, and in some cases, sunlight. An increasing shortage of some factor intensifies the competitive interplay so that a prolonged shortage may result in the death of one or more of the plant species that formerly held an integral place in the community complex.

As communities have evolved in the past with a gradually increasing number of species, a stratification of the vegetation has resulted in a reduction of direct competition. The animal populations have become stratified as selection pressures have tended to favor groups that have moved into certain stratal regions of the community. Thus competition has become more indirect, over the course of time, as this spacial separation due to stratification has become established in natural communities. In a number of community studies, it has been observed that as the number of competing species increase, there is a tendency toward dietary restriction. In other words, a single species may have formerly subsisted on a fairly general diet of insects, seeds, and fruits, but as the number of competing species increase, the diet of any one species is restricted to a particular type of food. The exploitation of populations within a community has undoubtedly existed as a very real form of interaction nearly as long as coexistence. The complex avenues of predator-prey and parasitic relationships have increased species interaction and the organization of food chains in natural areas. As the number of predator species increase in a community, the more likely it is that prey species will exist in moderate numbers. This, in turn, reduces the dangers of highly competitive relationships in a food chain and allows a greater number of prey species to coexist. Intrinsic factors regulating community change are usually confined to the species. The degree of competition, predation, cooperation, and rate of reproduction gives some picture of the direction in which the community evolution is progressing.

Accidental introduction of a new species into a community by wind, animals, or water can change the nature of the entire community. Predation and competition may be only potential dangers in some cases, but in other areas they may govern the outcome of an intracommunity struggle. The rate at which a newly introduced species spreads throughout a community will depend on the mobility of its young and adults as well as the speed of dissemination of the reproductive units (seeds, spores, and cysts).

In general, the larger the community in terms of members of a species and total number of species, the more slowly it will evolve. In larger populations, there is a large gene pool with a large number of gene variants that continue to diffuse through the community. Some of these mutations will be beneficial to the population and through natural selection will insure the success of that particular species and a tendency toward greater community stability. Very often small isolated communities exhibit a more accelerated evolutionary rate. New species, as a result of accumulative mutations and a limited gene pool, are not uncommon in such situations. A more thorough discussion of ecological evolution—better known as **succession**—follows in the next chapter.

Selected References

Allee, W. C., A. E. Emerson, O. Park, T. Park, and K. Schmidt. *Principles of Animal Ecology* (Philadelphia: W. B. Saunders, 1949), pp. i–xii, 1–837.

Anderson, E. C., and W. F. Libby. 1947. Radiocarbon from cosmic radiation. Science, 105:576–578.

Barick, F. B. 1950. The edge effect of the lesser vegetation of certain Adirondack forest types with particular reference to deer and grouse. Roosevelt Wildlife Bull., 9:1–146.

Brown, F. A., Jr. 1959a. Living clocks. Science, 130:1535–1544.

———. 1959b. The rhythmic nature of animals and plants. Am. Sci., 47:147–168.

Carpenter, J. R. 1934. Diurnal fluctuations in communities adjoining the forest edge near Urbana, Illinois. Proc. Okla. Acad. Sci., 14:29–31.

———. 1935. Fluctuations in biotic communities. I. Prairie-forest ecotone of central Illinois. Ecology, 16:203–212.

———. 1936. Daily fluctuations in insect populations in the prairie-forest ecotone of North America. Proc. 12th Int. Congr. Zool. Lisbon.

———. *An Ecological Glossary* (Norman, Okla.: Univ. of Oklahoma Press, 1938), pp. i–viii, 1–306.

Cloudsley-Thompson, J. L. *Rythmic Activity in Animal Physiology and Behavior.* (New York: Academy Press, 1961), pp. 1–263.

Curtis, J. T. 1955. A prairie continuum in Wisconsin. Ecology, 36:558–566.

Curtis, J. T., and R. P. McIntosh. 1951. An upland forest continuum in the prairie-forest border region of Wisconsin. Ecology, 32:476–496.

Dice, L. R. *The Biotic Provinces of North America* (Ann Arbor, Mich.: Univ. of Michigan Press, 1943), pp. 1–78.

————. *Natural Communities* (Ann Arbor, Mich.: Univ. of Michigan Press, 1952), pp. i–x, 1–547.

Dorf, E. 1960. Climatic changes of the past and present. Amer. Sci., 48:341–364.

Elton, C. 1946. Competition and the structure of ecological communities. Jour. An. Ecol., 15:54–68.

Forbes, E. 1843. Report on the molluscs and Radiata of the Aegean Sea, and on their distribution considered as bearing on geology. Rept. Brit. Assoc. Adv. Sci., 13:130–193.

Griesbach, A. 1838. Ueber den Einfluss des Climas auf die Begranzung der naturlichen Floren. Linnea., 12:159–200.

Hall, E. R. *Mammals of Nevada* (Berkeley, Calif.: Univ. of California Press, 1946), pp. i–xi, 1–710.

Harker, J. E. 1958. Diurnal rhythms in the animal kingdom. Biol. Rev., 33:1–52.

Hedgpeth, J. W. 1957. Treatise on Marine Ecology and Paleoecology. Geol. Soc. Amer., Mem., 67:i–viii, 1–1296.

Johnson, V. R. 1947. Breeding birds of the forest edge in Illinois. Condor, 49:45–53.

Ladd, H. S. 1959. Ecology, paleontology and stratigraphy. Science, 129:69–78.

Leopold, A., and S. Jones. 1947. A phenological record for Sauk and Dave Counties, Wisconsin, 1935–45. Ecol. Monogr., 17:81–122.

Libby, W. F. *Radioactive Dating* (Chicago: Univ. of Chicago Press, 1955), pp. 1–175.

————. 1961. Radioactive dating. Science, 133:621–629.

————. 1963. Accuracy of radiocarbon dates. Science, 140:278–280.

Livingstone, D. A. 1955. Some pollen profiles from Arctic Alaska. Ecology, 36:587–600.

McAtee, W. L. 1907. Census of four square feet. Science, 26:447–449.

Pearse, A. S. 1946. Observations on the microfauna of the Duke Forest. Ecol. Monogr., 16:127–150.

Potzger, J. E. 1956. Pollen profiles as indicators in the history of lake filling and bog formation. Ecology, 37:476–483.

Ross, H. H. *A Synthesis of Evolutionary Theory* (Englewood Cliffs, N. J.: Prentice-Hall, 1962), pp. i–xiii, 1–387.

Russell, C. P. 1932. Seasonal migration of mule deer. Ecol. Monogr., 2:1–46.

Schroter, C., and O. Kirchner. 1902. Die Vegetation des Bodensees. Schrift. Ver. gesch. Bodensees Umgeb., 31:1–86.

Shelford, V. E. *Laboratory and Field Ecology* (Baltimore: Williams and Wilkins, 1929), pp. i–xii, 1–608.

————. 1932. Basic principles of the classification of communities and habitats and the use of terms. Ecology, 13:105–120.

————. 1951. Fluctuation of non-forest animal populations in the upper Mississippi basin. Ecol. Monogr., 21:149–181.

————. 1951a. Fluctuation of forest animal populations in east central Illinois. Ecol. Monogr., 21:183–214.

————. *The Ecology of North America* (Urbana, Ill.: Univ. of Illinois Press, 1963), pp. 1–610.

Utida, S. 1957. Population fluctuation, an experimental and theoretical approach. Cold Spring Harbor Symposia Quant. Biology, 22:139–151.

Verrill, A. E., and S. I. Smith. 1874. Report on the invertebrate animals of Vineyard Sound and adjacent waters. Rept. U.S. Comm. Fish and Fisheries, 1871–1872; 295–852.

Weese, A. O. 1924. Animal ecology of an Illinois elm-maple forest. Ill. Biol. Monogr., 9:1–93.

Whittaker, R. H. 1951. A criticism of the plant association and climatic climax concept. Northwest Sci., 25:17–31.

————. 1953. A consideration of climax theory: the climax as a population and pattern. Ecol. Monogr., 23:41–78.

Williams, E. C. 1941. An ecological study of the floor fauna of the Panama rain forest. Bull. Chic. Acad. Sci., 6:63–124.

X. Ecological Succession

According to Webster's dictionary, succession is the "act or fact of succeeding or a following in order of time or place; a repeated following up of one (of that specified) by another . . ." Succession, from the ecological standpoint, refers to an orderly sequence of different communities over a period of time in some particular area. Two points must be kept in mind as we discuss succession in this chapter: There is a faunistic succession (a sequence of animal communities) as well as a floristic succession, whether we are concerned with the details of microsuccession or macrosuccession. There is a tendency to emphasize the sequence of plant communities in any discussion of this type—not because animal succession does not occur, for it most certainly does, but because vegetational succession is more readily apparent in the field. Also, it is the plant community that most radically effects and alters the environment. The faunal composite of any area will have much less effect on important environmental conditions. An extreme example is the environmental conditions found in a forest community prior to a lumbering operation and after excessive thinning or clear cutting has occurred. Environmental factors such as temperature, humidity, soil moisture, insolation, evaporation, and wind—all will be drastically altered. This wholesale destruction or alteration of the vegetational component of the area will necessarily change the entire animal community for many years. In some cases, particularly in the earlier stages of succession, we shall notice marked differences from one year to the next, but as we examine the terminal stages of any successional sequence, it becomes apparent that many years, and sometimes centuries, may pass without much change taking place in biotic composition.

BASIC TYPES OF SUCCESSION

Two general types of succession may occur in any of the three basic environments (terrestrial, freshwater, and marine areas). One type is **primary succession** in which the biota becomes established on a particular substrate for the first time; no living matter has previously colonized this particular substratum. The first group of plants and animals to become established is called the **pioneer community.** As the community becomes firmly entrenched in the area, the biota will gradually alter the abiotic factors; the pioneer species prepare and change the environ-

FIGURE 10–1 A pioneer community becoming established on bare rock surfaces. The lichens appear first, followed by mosses. A bare rock and lichen zone surround an "island" of more advanced vegetation including mosses (dark patches) and broom sedge (*Andropogon*).

ment for an entirely different assemblage of organisms. The aggregations that follow are **secondary communities.** All of the communities that will exist for an interval of time are collectively termed a **sere;** any one group of organisms, or community, is a **seral stage.** Suitable areas for the establishment of pioneer communities in a primary successional series can be cited for any of the basic environments. In terrestrial regions—bare mineral soil, exposed rock surfaces, volcanic ash, sand dunes (Figure 10–1), and new islands that often appear in streams or along coastal areas —all will serve as an ideal substrate. In freshwater environments—new dams, pier supports, rock exposed for the first time by waves or stream currents, and freshly eroded soils—all will support pioneer species for a brief interval of time. In marine areas—eroded soils carried into coastal waters by rivers, sand formed from the disintegration of coral, pier supports (Figure 10–2), breakwaters, Texas tower supports, and sunken

FIGURE 10–2 One of the marine communities of barnacles and bivalves that become established on a pier support along an estuary.

vessels—all will furnish suitable areas for pioneer communities. In fact, anyone who has scraped barnacles and other invertebrates from the submerged hulls of vessels will acknowledge the suitability of moving objects as a place for settling. In certain cases, we may cite living organisms such as aquatic vegetation, molluscan shells, and crab tests that serve as a place of attachment for pioneer communities. These organisms may in turn be replaced by other secondary aggregations of organisms.

The other general type of succession is **secondary succession.** In this type of sequence, the substrate has been occupied by aggregations of organisms in the past. But a catastrophic event, a change in climatic factors, or man's intervention has caused the community occupying that area to disappear. A fire caused by lightning or man (Figure 10–3), a flood or permanent inundation of a terrestrial community by construction of a new dam or excessive moisture, storms such as hurricanes, typhoons, tornadoes, lumbering, the mere abandonment of cleared land

FIGURE 10–3 The appearance of a terrestrial community (white pine forest) following a severe hurricane and fire in the Coeur d'Alene National Forest, Idaho. Courtesy of the U.S. Forest Service.

by man, or the introduction of commercial wastes or sewage into streams or coastal waters can destroy or alter the communities that formerly existed and pave the way for entirely different aggregations. Very often the seral stages that become established during the latter stages of succession may be similar or identical to the seral communities that would have occupied the area if primary succession had been allowed to run its course. It must be kept in mind that the earlier stages of secondary succession are radically different from communities that would have existed in this same locality if primary succession had transpired.

One abiotic factor that has a most drastic effect on the types of communities inhabiting an area is the amount of moisture present. Thus we find that whether we are concerned with primary or secondary succession, water or its relative absence will govern the entire character of the successional pattern. In regions where water is plentiful, a **hydrarch succession** will ensue. This sequence of communities will occur in ponds,

FIGURE 10–4 The emergent hydrophyte (*Typha,* cattails) that have become established along a segment of a young aquatic community.

lakes, streams, swamps, or bogs. In these areas, the conditions vary from one extreme, where animals and plants are completely submerged in water, to the other, where the water table is high and soil moisture values are consequently great enough to produce a soggy, water-bound environment. Plant species growing in such areas require greater amounts of water and are called **hydrophytes.** Such communities will vary—from the submerged hydrophytes such as pond weed, or water weed (*Elodea*), tape grass (*Valisneria*), bladderwort (*Utricularia*), milfoil (*Myriophyllum*), and hornwort (*Ceratophyllum*), found in ponds, lakes, and streams—to the emergent hydrophytes such as cattail (*Typha*), bulrushes (*Scirpus*), sawgrasses (*Zizaniopsis*), rushes (*Juncus*), sedges (*Carex*), and wild rice (*Zizinia*), and the swamp shrubs such as buttonbush (*Cephalanthus*) and alder (*Alnus*) that thrive in swampy localities (Figures 10–4, 10–5). Animal communities will vary—from the fish including the bluegill (*Lepomis*), carp (*Cyprinus*), crappie (*Pomoxus*), aquatic snails (*Helisoma, Physa*), bivalves (*Pisidium, Sphaerium*), insects such as water striders (Gerridae), whirligig beetles (Gyrinidae), water measurers (Hydrometridae), diving beetles (Dytiscidae), *Hydra*, cladocerans (*Daphnia, Bosmina*), and countless protozoans inhabiting a truly aquatic environment—to the amphibians including frogs (*Rana*)

FIGURE 10–5 A typical swamp community of the eastern United States, taken in Florida. Courtesy of the Soil Conservation Service, U.S. Department of Agriculture.

and salamanders *(Siren, Necturus, Plethodon)* and reptiles like the painted turtle *(Chrysemys)* and snapping turtle *(Macrochelys)* that live in the bogs. As we follow the sequence of plant and animal communities that thrive under such conditions, it becomes apparent that there is a trend toward a drier environment, with average quantities of soil water. Over the centuries, if areas are left undisturbed, natural conditions gradually convert ponds and lakes into bogs or swamps as soil erosion from surrounding areas silts in the bottom and the continual, gradual accumulation of organic detritus eventually decreases the water depth. After a swamp has evolved, succession continues uninterrupted, gradually producing a terrestrial community with average moisture conditions. Man's or nature's intervention can result in a prolongation or reversion of successional communities.

At the other extreme, we have a xerarch type of succession, when moisture is present in minimal amounts or is not available to plants and animals because of some intrinsic factor. Most persons tend to think in terms of desert communities when xerarch succession is discussed; certainly, desert regions, in terms of climate, are prime examples of xerarch communities. Dry deserts have little moisture over extensive periods of time, generally less than ten inches per year, though in many of the dry deserts several years may pass without any appreciable precipitation. The wet deserts have greater amounts of rainfall, often enough to support grassland or forest communities, but the distribution of rainfall is erratic. Torrential rains and flash floods occur only once or twice a year, on the average, and the substrate, which is often sandy, does not retain the moisture for any length of time. Aside from desert communities, there are other localities favoring a xeric type of succession as a result of physiological drought. In these instances, soil salts or freezing temperatures prevent consumption of adequate amounts of water, though precipitation in the form of rain or snow may be adequate. Bare rock and sandy soils, even though surrounded by marsh communities, will often represent little islands of xerarch type communities that are definite stages in xererarch succession. Plants (xerophytes) and animals such as reptiles and small burrowing mammals are tolerant of the dry conditions and will possess amazing structural, physiological, or behavioral adaptations that allow them to survive and often thrive under adverse conditions of moisture. A type of xerarch succession is discussed in detail in the section titled "The General Successional Pattern" in this chapter. Xerarch succession is slowest, but tends to progress toward communities with an average amount of soil moisture. A bare rock area where surface runoff or drainage is rapid will exhibit a xererarch type of succession in any climatic area.

A **mesarch succession** is an intermediate type, with moisture present in adequate amounts. The successional series is much shorter because moisture conditions are more ideal, and the initial water problems that must be resolved in a xerarch or hydrarch type of succession are nonexistent. In actuality, the conditions toward which hydrarch and xerarch communities are gradually progressing are those that prevail in the mesarch series, thus giving the latter type of sequential pattern a head start.

THE GENERAL SUCCESSIONAL PATTERN

Any succession under similar conditions of climate and abiotic factors will be comprised of the same series of communities in the same sequence, whether the areas are separated by a fraction of a mile or by many thousands of miles. The varying moisture conditions present in an area will result in **hydroseres, mesoseres,** or **xeroseres,** the types of successional stages that will ensue. In either primary or secondary succession, a pioneer community is the first seral stage to become established; the aggregate organisms in this community are called **pioneer species.** These pioneer species must be able to tolerate the adverse climatic and edaphic conditions that often exist in areas that have been depopulated or where previously existing communities have been destroyed, removed, or severely altered. Generally, there are relatively few species in a pioneer community. Anyone who has casually observed the initial stages of succession in an old field cannot fail to notice the homogeneous composition of such a community. The pioneer community generally exists for a short interval of time, in comparison with some of the later successional stages. During its brief existence, the environment is modified. Such changes in environment lead to increased tension and the gradual inability of species to cope with the altered conditions. As this situation continues, other species infiltrate into the area as the environment becomes more suitable for their establishment.

Secondary communities become established as the pioneer species gradually disappear. Each seral stage will appear, flourish, and finally disappear as the many environmental changes occur. The rate of change in seral stages will conform to the degree of alteration of surrounding factors some secondary communities exist for only brief intervals; others do not yield to other community types for extremely long time periods. If we were to watch the gradual succession on a bare rock surface, an example of primary succession, and carefully follow the secondary aggregations of organisms, we would find that lichens constitute the vegetational component of the pioneer community, beginning with the crustose types of lichens (Figure 10–6) such as *Grimmia laevigata* followed by fruiticose lichens (*Cladonia*). These lichens are of limited value in succession, for they are not mat-forming types. But they will begin the long, slow process of mineral decomposition. Associated with the flora are a few mites. The fauna is as sparse in terms of species composition as the flora and is limited to ants (Formicidae) and a few spiders that may spin webs in

FIGURE 10–6 Crustose lichens, the earliest pioneer to become established on a bare rock surface. Note that seedlings are beginning to appear in crevices of rock where pockets of soil can support these advanced vegetational stages.

cracks and crevices of the rock. These pioneer species are exposed to harsh environmental conditions—thermal extremes in summer and winter —with little protection normally found in the more advanced successional stages. Acids produced by the lichens initiate the disintegration of the rock substrate, and with the subsequent accumulation of dust in small quantities, the environment is altered enough to allow the establishment of secondary communities in a rather definite sequence. Scattered patches of moss (*Polytrichum* or species of *Selaginella*) begin to invade the environment that had hitherto been monopolized by lichens. The mites (Acarina) become more varied in terms of species represented; some small spiders (*Araneida*) and springtails (Collembola) as well as tardigrades (*Echiniscus*) become associated with this secondary community. As the mats of mosses become more extensive, more soil accumulates; much of the soil is blown in from surrounding areas during windy periods. More mineral material is added to the soil as acids leach out from the overlying vegetation and increase the depth of the mineral soil layer. Isolated sprigs of hardy garden weeds are followed by biennial and finally perennial grasses. *Andropogon,* commonly known as broom sedge, becomes a dominant grass in many areas. With the influx of grasses the fauna undergoes a quantitative and qualitative increase. Nematodes and larval insects, Collembola, ants, spiders, and mites appear in the gradually altered environment. Following the establishment of grasses, shrubs—including some species of sumac (*Rhus*) and other ericaceous shrubby growth—small tree seedlings appear, provided the climatic conditions are adequate for the existence of a wooded community. On a large rock outcrop, one can see all of the successive stages within a relatively small area, particularly if the colonization begins in the center of the bare rock face. The various seral stages become established in concentric rings, with the pioneer community located around the outer fringe of the vegetative zone, as illustrated in Figure 10-7. The more advanced stages are located successively back toward the center of the colony, so that there is an outer ring of lichens. Within this outer border is a ring of mosses, within this mass of bryophytes are the grasses, and inside this relatively broad zone are scattered trees (seedlings) that have become established as the underlying soil layer has become thicker from the outer boundary toward the center of this "raft" of vegetation.

Finally, if we were to follow our bare rock succession to its last stage of development, assuming that a forest community could be maintained in the area, a climax forest community would appear. The **climax community** is the last aggregation in the successional series. Provided the

(terminal Succession)

FIGURE 10-7 Vegetational zonation on a rock outcrop from the primitive pioneer community of lichens around the outer edge to more advanced stages (trees) located in the center of the outcrop where the soil is thickest (*R* represents bare rock).

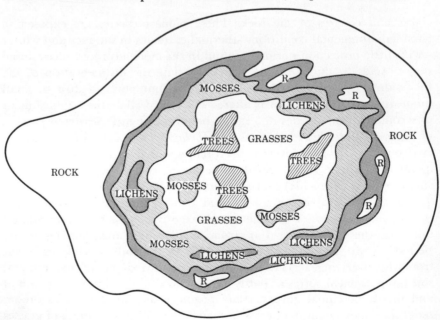

FIGURE 10–8 A climax oak–hickory community of the southeastern United States.

climatic conditions do not change and no catastrophic event alters the area, the community will sustain itself indefinitely. Climax communities are found in virgin forests or in areas that man or natural disasters have not denuded. The climax can maintain itself, since the conditions that exist within the area are ideal for the continual reproduction, nourishment, and normal biological activities of the aggregate species. The climatic climax community (Figure 10–8) can always be predicted for any region of comparable climatic conditions. The species will be similar in

TABLE 10–1. *Some of the Common Vertebrate Representatives of an Oak-Hickory Climax·Forest*

CLASS	COMMON NAME	SCIENTIFIC NAME
Mammalia	Gray fox	*Urocyon cinereoargenteus*
	Raccoon	*Procyon lotor*
	Eastern chipmunk	*Tamias striatus*
	White-footed mouse	*Peromyscus leucopus*
	Eastern mole	*Scalopus aquaticus*
Aves	Whippoorwill	*Caprimulgus vociferus*
	White-breasted nuthatch	*Sitta carolinensis*
	Ruffed grouse	*Bonasa umbellus*
	Acadian flycatcher	*Empidonax virescens*
Reptilia	Timber rattlesnake	*Crotalus horridus*
	Copperhead	*Agkistrodon contortrix*
	Black rat snake	*Elaphe obsoleta*
	Skinks	*Eumeces* spp.
	Box turtle	*Terrapene carolina*
Amphibia	Marbled salamander	*Ambystoma opacum*
	Red-backed salamander	*Plethodon cinereus*
	Wood frog	*Rana sylvatica*
	Common tree frog	*Hyla versicolor*

these climatic communities. Oak-hickory (*Quercus-Carya* association) forests are located in North Carolina and surrounding regions, along with the fauna, including slugs (*Philomycus*), snails (*Polygyra, Helix*), wire worms, millipedes (Diplopoda), centipedes (Chilopoda), ants, sow bugs (Isopoda), springtails, mites, squirrels (*Sciurus*), opossum (*Didelphis*), wood thrush (*Hylocichla mustelina*), southern flying squirrel (*Glaucomys*), short-tailed shrew (*Blarina brevicauda*), and a number of others, as shown in Table 10–1. In Ohio, Michigan, and southern Canada, a beech-maple forest (*Fagus-Acer* association) replaces the oak-hickory forest, which in this area is a **subclimax** stage in succession.

Other types of climax communities are situated within or border climatic climax communities because of variations in the abiotic or climatic conditions. The two most common variants in such areas are **edaphic** (soil) and **topographic** or **physiographic climax** communities. Edaphic climax communities have been investigated by Hills (1952), in southern Ontario. Hills found that although a beech-maple forest is the climatic climax for the area, on a wet soil in a warmer microclimate, a sycamore tulip tree community (*Platanus-Liriodendron* association) flourishes; on a dry soil in warmer microclimates an oak-chestnut forest (*Quercus-*

Castanea association) is the climax representative. Aside from the moisture factor, the soil type—clay, sand, silt, and various mixtures of these texture classes—will influence the type of climax vegetation by their effect on moisture, aeration, drainage, and many other related factors. A special topographical (the general contour of the land area) situation

FIGURE 10–9 A preclimax community of post oak and blackjack oak. Openings in the stand, as exist in the foreground, are characteristic of preclimax stands. Note the small diameter of the trees compared to those of climax and postclimax vegetation.

will also affect the vegetation type that becomes permanently established because a south-facing and north-facing slope or a deep gully will possess climatic conditions that are considerably different from conditions on a hilltop or an east-facing slope.

Two types of climax communities that are influenced by topography and moisture conditions have become so well recognized that ecologists have devised the terms **preclimax** and **postclimax** to differentiate these variants. The choice of terms may be unfortunate since the prefixes often have a far different connotation for the student, but the terms are so firmly entrenched in the literature that it would probably be unwise to propose a change in terminology. A preclimax community appears in a more xeric region (Figure 10–9) of the climatic zone. Such communities are often located on south-facing slopes, where the conditions are drier and warmer than surrounding regions. In North Carolina where a white oak-hickory forest predominates as the climatic climax, a preclimax community is comprised of post oak-blackjack oak vegetation. Preclimax stands are also situated along the southern extreme of a climatic climax region, where the temperatures will be higher. In a community of this type, the stand is open and irregular. Trees are smaller, gnarled, and scrubby in appearance in contrast to the thick growth found in a virgin white oak-hickory stand. A change in type of vegetation and its distribution affects the fauna inhabiting the area because the litter in a preclimax stand is sparse and is often entirely absent in scattered parts. Lichens and some mosses are more abundant in these areas, and the number of soil animals is reduced. Many of the vertebrates are merely transients.

Postclimax stands (Figure 10–10) are located in more hygric and cooler areas than are the climatic climax. Good examples of postclimax communities are found in lowland areas such as deltas or flood plains, north-facing slopes, and along the northern limits of a climatic climax zone. In contrast to the paucity of fauna indicative of a preclimax area, the soil animals and vertebrates are often recovered in large numbers. Amphibians including salamanders (*Ambystoma, Plethodon*) and tree frogs (*Hyla* spp.), reptiles like the blanding turtle (*Emys blandingi*), eastern box turtle (*Terrapene carolina*), wood turtle (*Clemmys insculpta*), brown skink (*Scincella laterale*), rainbow snake (*Abastor erythrogrammus*), and the ringneck snake (*Diadophis punctatus*), are among some of the more predominant forms. Some mammals such as the muskrat (*Ondatra zibethicus*), beavers (*Castor canadensis*), marsh rabbit (*Sylvilagus palustris*), swamp rabbit (*S. aquaticus*), masked shrew (*Sorex cinereus*), raccoons (*Procyon lotor*), round-tailed muskrat (*Neofiber alleni*), river otters (*Lutra canadensis*), marsh rice rats (*Oryzomys palustris*) and Virginia deer, or white-tailed deer (*Odocoileus virginianus*) are common inhabitants. Among some of the more obvious invertebrates are large populations of land snails such as *Mesodon pennsylvanicus, Allo-*

FIGURE 10–10   A postclimax community typical of moist environments.

gona profunda, Anguispira alternata, A. kochi, and *Haplotrema concava.*
Some of the birds common in postclimax communities are the swallow-
tailed kite *(Elanoides forficatus)*, the turkey *(Meleagris gallopavo)*, white-
eyed vireos *(Vireo griseus)*, prothonotary warblers *(Protonotaria citrea)*,
parula warblers *(Parula americana)*, pileated woodpeckers *(Dryocopus
pileatus)*, hermit thrushes *(Hylocichla guttata)*, and solitary sandpipers
(Tringa solitaria). Beech *(Fagus grandifolia)*, willow oak *(Quercus*

phellos), and sweet gum (*Liquidambar styraciftua*) are some of the more dominant overstory species found in these stands in the southeastern part of the United States.

Our discussion of climax stands would not be complete without a brief discussion of a **disclimax**. A disclimax implies that a particular type of vegetation and fauna maintain themselves in the area as a result of recurrent disturbance. The agent responsible for such a disturbance prevents the successful establishment of a climatic climax community. The disturbance may be caused by the biota, such as the recurrent browsing or grazing of animals. Or the continual thinning and cutting of timber or cultivation of fields by man prevents succession from continuing beyond a certain stage. For that matter, a front lawn, provided that it is mowed regularly, is an example of a disclimax, as it will be maintained for an indefinite period. Abiotic elements such as windstorms, floods, erosion, and periodic fires caused by lightning may result in the establishment of a disclimax. An example of a natural disclimax is the longleaf pine (*Pinus palustris*) forests that are so extensive throughout the southeastern portion of the United States. Such vegetation is maintained by recurrent natural fires caused by lightning during the hot, dry portions of the year. The dry grasses that exist in these vast savanna areas burn rapidly. The intense heat kills any deciduous seedlings that may have gained a foothold in the interim between successive fires. This prevents any continuance of the successional pattern, for if the fire factor were to be eradicated, hardwood species would gradually invade the area and replace the longleaf pine. The longleaf pine has managed to survive and thrive in these areas because its growing tips are surrounded by a circlet of fire-resistant needles that prevent any heat damage to the apical meristem tissue. With the effective and periodical removal of competing hardwood species, the pine is capable of maintaining its position in the community indefinitely.

In some cases it is possible to see what happens when the disturbing factor is removed from the immediate area. A pasture situated in areas of the eastern temperate zone of the United States is an example of a disclimax promoted by man for the nourishment of domestic livestock. If this livestock is removed or the area is abandoned and left undisturbed, it is only a short while before deciduous shrubs, hardwood seedlings, vines, and possibly scattered briar patches become established. Fast-growing deciduous trees such as black locust (*Robinia pseudoacacia*), honey locust (*Gleditsia triacanthos*), black cherry (*Padus serotina*), chokecherry (*P. virginiana*), pin cherry (*Prunus pennsylvanica*), laurel sumac (*Rhus laurina*), or in damp areas, poison sumac (*Toxicodendron vernix*), may become dominant in the area for a time; but this is merely a successional stage and will eventually be replaced by the climax species for the area.

THE MONOCLIMAX VERSUS
THE POLYCLIMAX THEORY

Two predominant theories concerning climax communities have been advanced by ecologists. Both theories have gained adherents either through appeal to one's personal philosophy or interpretation or to the influence imposed by past training, experience, and personal contact with different ecologists. One theory is referred to as the **monoclimax theory,** an interpretation championed by Frederick Clements, an American plant ecologist. Ecologists who subscribe to such an interpretation contend that there is only one climatic climax community for any geographic area. They believe that in time the edaphic or topographic climax will develop into a climatic climax community. This, of course, implies that given enough time, the topography and soil in any area will change, allowing a climatic climax community to appear. Such stands will be similar, though not identical, in terms of dominance and relative abundance of various flora and fauna. Since these stands exist as a result of localized climatic conditions that will be similar (though not identical) over considerable areas, the term **climatic climax** is in actuality a redundant phrase. Although some critics of the monoclimax theory hastily conclude that the monoclimax interpretation implies that an area with the same general climatic conditions would also have a more or less uniform flora and fauna, such is not the case. There are areas within the climatic zone that contain topographic irregularities and soil types (edaphic factors) of such permanence that the vegetation is not indicative of the climax type, and perhaps never will be, at least in the foreseeable future. In such areas, the monoclimax theory provides for such variations that are atypical in comparison to those in a regional or climatic climax community. For this very reason the terms, **subclimax, disclimax, postclimax,** and **preclimax** have been introduced into the literature to clarify the reasons for the recognized variant within a climatic zone.

The **polyclimax theory** recognizes a number of different climax communities in any geographic region—climatic climax, preclimax, postclimax, disclimax, edaphic climax, pyric climax, and topographic climax —contending that they are all climax communities. They are all self-reproducing and will be maintained for an indefinite period of time; in fact, they will remain unchanged for such long periods of time that it is unrealistic to consider them as subclimax communities as the monoclimax adherents do. In this sense, the term **climax** merely refers to the final or terminal community that will appear in that localized situation. Although the polyclimax philosophy does not rule out climatic climax communities, other variants within the area are given equal recognition and are not assigned to a minor category or passed off as a variant, with the climatic climax as the more important community in any geographic area.

Historically, the monoclimax theory was basically of American origin, proposed and staunchly defended by Clements, and in a somewhat milder manner, by Cowles. Gleason was one of the outstanding opponents of the monoclimax theory; in this respect, his ideas were more in keeping with the European school of thought. Although Europeans, in general, have been less concerned with succession (and climax communities), their interpretations and philosophy usually support the polyclimax view. More recently, there has been an inclination among plant and animal ecologists to follow the polyclimax theory and consider terminal communities, individually, in any successional pattern. Perhaps the entire problem of the monoclimax versus the polyclimax theory is purely academic and depends upon one's own outlook. Some ecologists refuse to take sides, but the problem still remains and still appears in the ecological literature.

SUCCESSION IN THE BASIC ENVIRONMENTS

Succession in a terrestrial environment will follow different patterns, depending on many variable factors such as the prevailing climate, soil type, type of fauna in the area, type and amount of precipitation. In general, as has been stated, there will be a tendency for succession to transform a xeric or hygric region into a more mesic one as time passes. The type of community—whether forest, prairie, or desert—that prevails in a particular region will be determined to a great extent by the distribution of precipitation throughout the year, the amount of precipitation, and the evaporation tension in that region. The fauna will display a successional pattern paralleling the botanical changes. The succession of botanical and zoological elements is mutually dependent. We find that even as certain animals cannot exist in an area devoid of certain botanical elements, succeeding groups of plants or animals (the more advanced seral stages) will depend on the preparation of the area by the preceding aggregations of flora and fauna that have inhabited the region in question.

OLD FIELD SUCCESSION

In a secondary succession, crabgrass (*Digitaria sanguinalis*) and horseweed (*Leptilon canadense*) are dominant species (Figure 10–11) and always precedes wild aster (*Aster ericoides*) and ragweed (*Ambrosia*

FIGURE 10–11 A first-year-old field stand with a dominant horseweed–crabgrass association typical of old field succession in the southeastern United States. The tall flowering stalks are wild aster that will become a truly dominant plant the following year, as shown in Figure 10–12.

artemisiifolia), shown in Figure 10–12, in upland old fields of the Piedmont area of North Carolina. Horseweed and wild aster are tall plants (two to four feet) that shade out or eliminate most of the first- and second-year vegetation that might ordinarily appear in such localities. This is evident when horseweed that is normally five feet or more in height in one-year-old fields is compared with stunted plants that may be only a few inches tall in second-year fields under ragweed and wild aster. Ragweed is usually more common on poorer soils, eroded fields, or in areas where soil nutrients are depleted. In three-year-old abandoned fields, *Andropogon*, or broom sedge, assumes dominance, with *Andropogon virginicus* as the most common species and *A. ternarius* and *A. elliottii* present in lesser numbers. Andropogon will maintain its dominance for some years; but, generally, two or three years after its initial establishment, pine seedlings appear between the tufts of broom sedge. Loblolly pine (*Pinus taeda*) is common in the Coastal Plain and the southern Piedmont, shortleaf pine (*P. echinata*) in the western Piedmont, and Virginia pine (*P. virginiana*) in the northern Piedmont of North Carolina and Virginia, according to Oosting (1942). Each pine

FIGURE 10–12 A second-year-old field stand showing the establishment of wild aster, the tall dominant weed that is in flower in the foreground. Ragweed is also present, but it is much shorter and hidden by the taller wild aster.

tends to develop pure stands, probably because of availability of seed source, but loblolly and shortleaf pine may occupy the same field.

As the vegetation changes following successional trends, the animal populations also vary in relation to the changing environmental conditions imposed, in part by, floral variation. In early stages of old field succession, the most likely mammals would be the least shrew (*Cryptotis parva*), meadow voles (*Microtus pennsylvanicus*), hispid cotton rats

(*Sigmodon hispidus*), house mice (*Mus musculus*), eastern moles (*Scalopus aquaticus*), woodchucks (*Marmota monax*), and the eastern cottontail rabbit (*Sylvilagus floridanus*). Birds found in earlier successional stages of old field areas, utilizing such areas as feeding sites, nesting sites, or breeding areas, would be the killdeer (*Charadrius vociferus*), bobwhite (*Colinus virginianus*), horned lark (*Eremophila alpestris*), common meadowlark (*Sturnella magna*), common nighthawk (*Chordeiles minor*), and the vesper sparrow (*Pooecetes gramineus*). The puffing adder (*Heterodon contortrix*), rough green snake (*Opheodrys aestivus*), the black snake (*Coluber constrictor*), the deKay snake (*Storeria dekayi*), hog-nosed snakes (*Heterodon platyrhinos*), corn snakes (*Elaphe guttata*), and the five-lined skink (*Eumeces laticeps*) are among the most common reptiles inhabiting open old field stands. A number of invertebrates including annelids, nematodes, springtails, mites, grasshoppers, field crickets, katydids, leafhoppers, beetles, spittlebugs and ants are located on the surface or at varying distances below the surface of the soil. In general, we find that with the exception of the grasshoppers and katydids, the number of invertebrates will increase as grass litter increases in thickness with the age of the stand. The litter will tend to increase the uniformity of environmental conditions in the soil throughout the year as well as serve as an ideal habitat for fungi and bacteria, which in turn are an important food source for many of the invertebrates.

With the appearance of pine, usually five to eight years after abandonment, the number of pine seedlings gradually increase, with the greatest number located nearest the available seed source. By the sixteenth year after abandonment, pines are generally ten to fifteen feet tall, and are the only vegetation making up the overstory and understory strata. In a typical loblolly stand, seedlings of loblolly pine, Virginia pine, and red cedar are present, though many of these conifers are destined to die as the stand becomes more mature. Hardwood species will soon reach a size where they will compete with the pines and create shade that these conifers cannot tolerate. Dogwood (*Cornus florida*), red gum (*Liquidambar styraciflua*), red maple (*Acer rubrum*), and black oak (*Quercus velutina*) begin to invade the stand. These hardwood species will remain, contributing to the formation of the transgressive, understory, or overstory strata (Figure 10–13). Shrubs and vines in many cases are species that have appeared early in the successional picture and will continue to remain within the community, but their numbers gradually decrease as the stand ages. Trumpet creeper (*Tecoma radicans*), several species of blackberry (*Rubus* spp.), sawbrier (*Smilax glauca*), and poison ivy (*Rhus toxicodendron*) are the most common species found in young pine stands. Herbs present in young pine stands include bermuda grass (*Cynodon dactylon*), broomsedge, several species of goldenrod (*Solidago nemoralis*) (*S. juncea*), thoroughwort (*Eupatorium hyssopifolium*), bedstraw (*Galium pilosum*), pipsissewa (*Chimaphila maculata*), and bush clover (*Lespedeza*

FIGURE 10–13 The hardwood species becoming established within a well-established seventy-year-old coniferous community. The straight, large trunks of loblolly pine are evident in the foreground of the stand.

repens). Bermuda grass, unable to tolerate the increasing shade of a maturing stand, soon dies out; but broomsedge, goldenrod, and thoroughwort will be eliminated gradually, and bedstraw, pipsissewa, and bush clover remain as characteristic herbaceous growth within the pine stand.

If the young pine stand just described were to remain undisturbed for 150 or more years after abandonment, a climax deciduous forest would eventually become established in the area. The pines would be unable to reproduce successfully because of their intolerance to shade. Hardwood species replace the older pines as they age and gradually die one by one. White oak (*Quercus alba*) is one of the predominant species in the over-story and understory of a climax stand, with several species of hickory (*Carya* spp.), black oak (*Quercus velutina*), southern red oak (*Q. rubra*), post oak (*Q. stellata*), and scarlet oak (*Q. coccinea*) present in overstory and understory strata. Other understory species that seldom attain over-story height include sourwood (*Oxydendrum arboreum*), dogwood, black gum (*Nyssa sylvatica*), red maple (*Acer rubrum*), and red cedar. Trans-gressive and seedling strata would include the species enumerated be-cause a climax stand is a self-perpetuating community, provided drastic climatic changes or catastrophic factors do not ensue. Shrubs and vines appearing most commonly in the typical white oak-hickory climax forest are arrowwood (*Viburnum affine*), maple-leaved viburnum (*V. aceri-folium*), sugarplum (*Amelanchier canadensis*), American holly (*Ilex opaca*), summer grape (*Vitus aestivalis*), and horse brier (*Smilax rotundi-folia*). Herbs, aside from bedstraw, pipsissewa, and bush clover, include tick clover (*Desmodium nudiflorum*), hawkweed (*Hieracium gronovii, H. venosum*), panic grass (*Panicum* sp.), and cocklebur (*Agrimonia gryposepala*).

As the forest type seral stages become established in an old field area, the fauna will change because the amount of wind, humidity, evapora-tion, insolation, soil moisture, litter depth, and temperatures will all differ from the surrounding open field areas. In general, wind speed, evaporation rate, insolation, and thermal variability are notably reduced when compared with those prevailing in adjacent open field communi-ties. Humidity and soil moisture within a heavily wooded area will vary, depending on the thermal conditions, rate of transpiration, the amount and distribution of precipitation, and so on. The increased litter depth in pine and deciduous forest types will serve as a most suitable environ-ment for a large number of invertebrates because moisture conditions, food availability, and minimal thermal variation provide a more suitable habitat than do the earlier successional stages of open field stands. The fact that far less variation ensues in the general environment and various microenvironments of pine and deciduous stands accounts for the greater similarity of the faunal components of these areas. Table 10–2 lists the most common vertebrates that inhabit pine and deciduous forest com-munities in the course of old field succession in the southeastern United States. The most common type of habitat for each species is listed; in many cases, however, the species may be found in several types of com-munities. Generally, the species will spend more resident time in the community containing its nest site or homesite; therefore, this is the area listed as the most common habitat.

TABLE 10-2. *Common Vertebrates Inhabiting Coniferous and Deciduous Stands of the Southeastern United States, Indicating the Successional Sequence of These Organisms*

NAME	COMMON HABITAT
Class Mammalia:	
Deer and white-footed mouse (*Peromyscus* spp.)	Forests and old fields
Pine voles (*Pitymys pinetorum*)	Pine forests (in leaf mold of forest floor)
Southern flying squirrel (*Glaucomys volans*)	Pine and hardwood forests (nocturnal)
Short-tailed shrew (*Blarina brevicauda*)	Pine and hardwood forests (leaf mold)
Bobcat (*Lynx rufus*)	Large forests (in tree stratum)
Eastern spotted skunk (*Spilogale putorius*)	Hardwood forest borders
Striped skunk (*Mephitus mephitus*)	Hardwood forest borders
Long-tailed weasels (*Mustela frenata*)	Hardwood forest borders
Fox squirrels (*Sciurus niger*)	Hardwood forest borders
Gray fox (*Urocyon cinereoargenteus*)	Hardwood forests
Eastern chipmunk (*Tamias striatus*)	Hardwood forests
Class Aves:	
Horned owl (*Bubo virginianus*)	Pine forests
Common crow (*Corvus brachyrhynchos*)	Pine forests
Blue Jay (*Cyanocitta cristata*)	Pine forests
Hermit thrush (*Hylocichla guttata*)	Pine forests
Ruby-crowned kinglet (*Regulus calendula*)	Pine forests
Myrtle warbler (*Dendroica coronata*)	Pine forests and myrtle thickets, lowland areas
Cooper's hawk (*Accipiter cooperii*)	Pine and hardwood forests, nests in coniferous forests
Red-tailed hawk (*Buteo jamaicensis*)	Hardwood forests
Brown creeper (*Certhia familiaris*)	Hardwood forests
Wood thrush (*Hylocichla mustelina*)	Hardwood forests
Red-eyed vireo (*Vireo olivaceus*)	Hardwood forests
Cardinal (*Richmondena cardinalis*)	Hardwood forests
Reptilia:	
Eastern fence swift (*Sceloporus undulatus*)	Pine and hardwood forest borders, under debris or on rocks and trees
Blue-tailed skink (*Eumeces fasciatus*)	Pine and hardwood forests, under loose bark of rotting logs
Common chain king snake (*Lampropeltis getulus*)	Pine and hardwood forests, also in open old fields

TABLE 10–2 *(continued)*

NAME	COMMON HABITAT
Reptilia: *(continued)*	
deKay snake *(Storeria dekayi)*	Pine and hardwood forests, under debris
Ground lizard *(Leiolopisma unicolor)*	Hardwood forests
Ring-neck snake *(Diadophis punctatus)*	Hardwood forests, under rotting logs
Copperhead *(Ancistrodon contortrix)*	Hardwood forests
Box turtle *(Terrapene carolina)*	Hardwood forests
Amphibia:	
Pine-tree frog *(Hyla femoralis)*	Pine forests
Slimy salamander *(Plethodon glutinosus)*	Hardwood forests, under rotting logs
Narrow-mouthed toad *(Gastrophyne carolinensis)*	Hardwood forests, under rotting logs

Invertebrates located within the pine and hardwood forest communities are numerous in terms of numbers and species. One basic reason for the large populations found in these communities is the variety of environmental situations available for colonization. The soil strata, litter layer, the interior of rotting logs, the ecological niches below these logs, and small areas under rocks—all of these suitable microenvironments for many invertebrates—present a considerable spectrum of environmental situations. In addition, the surfaces of living plants (leaves, branches, vines, tree trunks) or the tiny spaces under loose bark or within living plant tissues provide a wealth of possible microhabitats, so that it is little wonder that some species reach fantastic numbers. Pearse (1946) stated that of the total number of microfauna collected and separated by a Berlese funnel apparatus from the forest floor (actually a Tullgren funnel was used in separation similar to the apparatus shown in Figure 10–14), 65 per cent of the fauna inhabited the forest litter, 30 per cent lived in the upper two inches of soil, and 5 per cent were isolated in the next three inches of soil (depth of two to five inches below the soil surface). Within limits, these figures give a general idea of the density of invertebrates and their general location in these strata.

Mites and collembolans (springtails) are the most common organisms residing in the forest litter and underlying soil. Nematodes, insect larvae (mostly beetle and fly larvae), thrips, ants, symphylids, spiders, japygids, millipedes, and at times, pseudoscorpions are recovered in considerable numbers. Other groups of invertebrates found living under stones, under fallen logs, or within logs include sowbugs, snails, slugs, beetles, termites,

FIGURE 10–14 A Tullgren funnel apparatus used to separate the soil microfauna from the surrounding detritus. Shown here are a battery of several funnels. *A* indicates the light source with reflector shade; *B* the container that holds the detritus; *C* the funnel rack holding plastic funnels; and *D* the collecting jar into which the microorganisms will fall.

centipedes, roaches, and millipedes. Forest foliage serves as a suitable habitat for leafhoppers, beetles, lacewings, walkingsticks, tree crickets, plant lice, stinkbugs, spiders, and katydids. True flies, sawflies, wasps, bees, beetles, lacewings, and true bugs fly from place to place within the forest or enter and leave the forest at times in search of food, shelter, or places to oviposit eggs during certain seasons of the year.

FRESHWATER SUCCESSION

Succession in freshwater areas will vary in rate and pattern, depending on the extent of the aquatic area and the net rate of water movement. In lentic areas, such as lakes, ponds, swamps, and bogs, where water does not exhibit any gross movement over long periods from one geographic locality to another, a **silting in** process will determine the rate of succession. Silting in refers to the soil which is introduced into a quiet body of water from outlying areas by rivers, brooks, and small streams. This continual accumulation of soil, rock, and assorted detritus causes considerable problems in man-made lakes formed by dams because such impoundments will become shallower, causing flooding in surrounding areas and considerable pressure on structural elements of the dam. The rate at which this process occurs depends upon the amount of erosion that will occur in the area's neighboring streams, the types of soils in surrounding areas (soil particles vary in size depending on soil type), the amount of precipitation, and the type of precipitation (snow, sleet, or rain). The number, size, and rate of flow of streams introducing this soil into a pond, lake, or bog will also affect the rate of silting in. As this buildup of soil material continues uninterrupted over a period of years, the entire lake or pond will accumulate so much soil that the body of water becomes shallower. Eventually a bog or swamp type of habitat will appear, and finally a mesic forest becomes established in the area. Around the shoreline of any natural lake or pond, there will be zones of vegetation (as has been mentioned in "Freshwater Zonation," Chapter II). These concentric rings of vegetation change position relative to the original shoreline as silt accumulation continues and the water gradually becomes shallower. As the shoreline moves toward the center of the pond or lake, the vegetation (emergent and submergent hydrophytes) move in the same direction over a period of time.

It is not inconceivable that over a long time period a relatively large lake may become smaller as silt and organic debris build up, gradually decreasing the water depth and supporting a marginal vegetation that slowly encroaches on portions of the lake where the bottom is undergoing a continual buildup. With continued decrease in the size of an open water community, a pond materializes, followed by a marsh, a marsh thicket, and finally a climax forest. During this sequential development of communities, the floral and faunal components change as the surrounding environment changes.

In drier climates, the successional sequence may follow the general pattern until a marsh develops. The marsh becomes a low prairie, rather than a marsh thicket, and finally a climax or true prairie vegetation develops (Figure 10–15). Vegetational succession begins with submerged hydrophytes such as waterweed, pondweed, milfoil, hornwort, bladder-

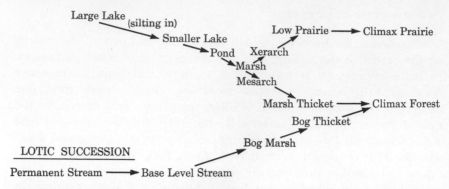

LENTIC SUCCESSION

Large Lake
(silting in)
Smaller Lake
Pond   Xerarch
Marsh
Mesarch

Low Prairie ⟶ Climax Prairie

Marsh Thicket ⟶ Climax Forest
Bog Thicket
Bog Marsh

LOTIC SUCCESSION

Permanent Stream ⟶ Base Level Stream

FIGURE 10–15 Freshwater succession, from a lotic or lentic type of environment to a climax terrestrial community. Climax prairies evolve in drier regions, while forest communities appear in regions with greater quantities of precipitation.

wort, and tape grass. Following this stage is the establishment of floating hydrophytes such as water lily, pondweed, smartweed, duckweed, and water hyacinth. Finally, as the edge of the pond gradually changes into a marshtype pattern of succession, cattail, bulrush, wild rice, and saw grass appear. As the substrate builds up and excessive moisture is reduced, a marsh thicket with buttonbush (*Cephalanthus occidentalis*), alder (*Alnus rugosa*), swamp rose (*Hibiscus palustris*), and cottonwood (*Populus heterophylla*) will appear. With a trend from hydric toward more mesic conditions, a swamp forest develops with red maple (*Acer rubrum*), silver maple (*A. saccharinum*), and swamp white oak (*Quercus bicolor*) as the major dominants; but white elm (*Ulmus americana*) and white ash (*Fraxinus americana*) may become codominants in the area. In the Midwest, basswood (*Tilia americana*) is followed by the tulip tree (*Liriodendron tulipifera*). The climax forest for the area, a beech-sugar maple community (*Fagus grandifolia-Acer saccharum*), develops later. In cooler temperate regions, a bog and subsequent bog thicket (Figure 10–16) develop in open lakes, with sedges, grasses, and sphagnum mosses forming floating mats of vegetation and concentric rings of plant growth that gradually advances toward the center of the lake. These floating rafts of vegetation build up from the top downward, gradually adding debris and rootlets that can support a bog forest dominated by larch (*Larix laricina*), spruce (*Picea mariana*), and arbor vitae (*Thuja occidentalis*). Bogs are usually far more acidic than are the typical pond-marsh communities previously discussed. Though the bog communities have evolved and matured in a different manner than have the lake-pond-marsh stages, the often long-lived bog forest (which can be considered an edaphic climax) is eventually replaced by a climax forest community.

As the vegetation has changed with the aging of a pond and the de-

FIGURE 10–16 A northern bog thicket covered with leatherleaf, along with isolated clusters of red pine, in Upper Michigan National Forest. Courtesy of the U.S. Forest Service.

velopment of marshes, the animal life has also changed. Pioneer species of fish found in young ponds include the black bass (*Micropterus*), sunfish (*Lepomis*), and pumpkinseed (*Eupomotis*). Perch (*Perca*) chub suckers (*Erimyzon*), and speckled bullhead (*Ameiurus nebulosus*) may also have been present during the early stages of pond development, but unlike the black bass, sunfish, and pumpkinseed that are gradually replaced as their breeding areas disappear owing to the rapid growth of vegetation, these fish increase in numbers as vegetation and food sources increase. With the increase in emergent and floating vegetation, the water becomes choked and serves as a suitable habitat for the black bullhead (*Ameiurus melas*), one of the last fishes to disappear before the area becomes a marshy environment. The mudminnow (*Umbra*) and pickerel (*Esox*) are often found in all of the seral stages of pond development, and along with the black bullhead they are often the last to disappear before the marsh finally encroaches on all open water areas and reduces the water level and oxygen concentration to the point that fish can no longer survive in the area.

Vertebrates commonly associated with lakes, ponds, marshes, and marsh forests are listed in Table 10–3. Some of these organisms that have

TABLE 10–3. *Vertebrates Commonly Associated with Aquatic Environments, Indicating Affinities for Particular Successional Stages of These Communities*

NAME	LAKE OR POND	MARSH	DISTRIBUTION*
Class Mammalia:			
Moose (*Alces alces*)	X		Extreme northern parts of U.S.
River otter (*Lutra canadensis*)	X	X	Cosmopolitan
Beaver (*Castor canadensis*)	X	X	Cosmopolitan
Florida water rat (*Neofiber alleni*)	X	X	Florida, southern Georgia
Muskrat (*Ondatra zibethicus*)	X	X	Cosmopolitan
Water shrew (*Sorex palustris*)		X	Northwestern, northeastern U.S.
Raccoon (*Procyon lotor*)		X	Cosmopolitan
Mink (*Mustela vison*)		X	Everywhere except southwestern U.S.
Rice rat (*Oryzomys palustris*)		X	Southeastern U.S.
Bog lemming (*Synaptomys cooperi*)		X	Northeastern U.S.
Nutria (*Myocastor coypus*)		X	Gulf Coast
Marsh rabbit (*Sylvilagus palustris*)		X	Southeastern U.S.
Class Aves:†			
Loon (*Gavia immer*)	X		Northern U.S.
Pied-billed grebe (*Podilymbus podiceps*)	X		Northern U.S., Pacific Coast
Belted kingfisher (*Magaceryle alcyon*)	X		Cosmopolitan
Great blue heron (*Ardea herodias*)	X	X	Eastern half of U.S.
Green heron (*Butorides virescens*)	X	X	Eastern half of U.S.
Red-winged blackbird (*Agelaius phoeniceus*)		X	Cosmopolitan
Swamp sparrow (*Melospiza georgiana*)		X	Northeastern U.S.
Virginia rail (*Rallus limicola*)		X	Everywhere except West Coast
American bittern (*Botaurus lentiginosus*)		X	Northern U.S.
Mallard (*Anas platyrhynchos*)		X	Great Lakes, western U.S.
Common snipe (*Capella gallinago*)		X	Northern U.S.

TABLE 10–3 (*continued*)

NAME	LAKE OR POND	MARSH	DISTRIBUTION*
Class Reptilia:			
Musk turtle (*Sternotherus odoratus*)	X		Eastern U.S.
Common mud turtle (*Kinosternon subrubrum*)	X		Southern U.S.
Common snapping turtle (*Chelydra serpentina*)	X		Eastern U.S.
Elegant slider (*Psudemys scripta*)	X		Southeastern U.S.
Spotted turtle (*Clemmys guttata*)	X		Atlantic Coast
Common water snake (*Natrix sipedon*)	X		Eastern U.S.
Painted water snake (*Natrix erythrogaster*)	X		Eastern U.S.
Green water snake (*Natrix cyclopion*)	X		Eastern U.S.
Diamond-backed water snake (*Natrix rhombifera*)	X		Eastern U.S.
Map turtle (*Graptemys geographica*)	X	X	Southeastern U.S.
Painted turtle (*Chrysemys picta*)		X	Northern U.S.
Blanding turtle (*Emydoidea blandingi*)		X	Great Lakes area
Muhlenberg turtle (*Clemmys muhlenbergi*)		X	From northern Pennsylvania to Virginia
Rainbow snake (*Abastor erythrogrammus*)		X	Southeastern U.S.
Mud snake (*Farancia abacura*)		X	Southeastern U.S.
Black swamp snake (*Seminatrix pygaea*)		X	Southeastern U.S.
Striped swamp snake (*Liodytes alleni*)		X	Florida
Yellow-lipped snake (*Rhadinaea flavilata*)		X	Southeastern U.S.
Cottonmouth (*Agkistrodon piscivorus*)		X	Southeastern U.S.
Alligator (*Alligator mississippiensis*)		X	Southern Florida, Gulf Coast

TABLE 10-3 (*continued*)

NAME	LAKE OR POND	MARSH	DISTRIBUTION*
Class Amphibia:			
Tiger salamander (*Ambystoma tigrinum*)	X		Central and southeastern U.S.
Mudpuppy (*Necturus maculosus*)	X		Eastern U.S.
Green frog (*Rana clamitans*)	X	X	Eastern U.S.
Bullfrog (*Rana catesbeiana*)	X	X	Cosmopolitan
Siren (*Siren lacertina*)	X	X	Southeastern U.S., Mississippi Valley
Mud siren (*Pseudobranchus striatus*)	X	X	Southeastern U.S.
Swamp chorus frog (*Pseudacris nigrita*)		X	Eastern, Midwest U.S.
Congo-eel (*Amphiuma means*)		X	Southeastern U.S.
Four-toed salamander (*Hemidactylium scutatum*)		X	Northeastern U.S.
Class Osteichthyes:			
Rainbow trout (*Salmo gairdneri*)	X		Pacific Coast
Lake trout (*Salvelinus namaycush*)	X		Great Lakes area
Lake whitefish (*Coregonus clupeaformis*)	X		Great Lakes area, New England
Shallow water cisco (*Coregonus artedi*)	X		Great Lakes, Hudson River Valley
Bigmouth buffalo (*Ictiobus cyprinella*)	X		Mississippi Valley, Gulf Coast
Creek chub (*Semotelus atromaculatus*)	X		Eastern three fourths of U.S.
Emerald shiner (*Notropis atherinoides*)	X		Great Lakes, Mississippi Valley
Northern pike (*Esox lucius*)	X		Great Lakes, New England
Muskellunge (*Esox masquinongy*)	X		Mississippi River System
Brook stickleback (*Eucalia inconstans*)	X		Northern U.S., Ohio, Missouri Rivers
Largemouth bass (*Micropterus salmoides*)	X		Great Lakes, Mississippi Valley, southeastern Atlantic Coast

TABLE 10-3 *(continued)*

NAME	LAKE OR POND	MARSH	DISTRIBUTION*
Class Osteichthyes: *(continued)*			
Smallmouth bass (*Micropterus dolomieu*)	X		Mississippi Valley
Bluegill sunfish (*Lepomis macrochiurus*)	X		Great Lakes, Mississippi Valley
Pumpkinseed (*Lepomis gibbosus*)	X		Mississippi Valley, Atlantic Coast
Redear sunfish (*Lepomis microlophus*)	X		Mississippi Valley
Warmouth sunfish (*Chaenobryttus coronarius*)	X		Mississippi Valley, Atlantic Coast
Black crappie (*Pomoxis nigromaculatus*)	X		Great Lakes, Mississippi Valley
Yellow bass (*Morone interrupta*)	X		Throughout central U.S.
Flathead catfish (*Pylodictis olivaris*)	X		Mississippi Valley
Stonecat (*Noturus flavus*)	X		Throughout central U.S.
Yellow bullhead (*Ictalurus natilis*)	X	X	Cosmopolitan (muddy ponds)
Brown bullhead (*Ictalurus nebulosus*)	X	X	Cosmopolitan (muddy ponds)
Common killifish (*Fundulus heteroclitus*)	X	X	Atlantic Coast (small ponds)
Banded killifish (*Fundulus diaphanus*)	X	X	Great Lakes, eastern U.S. (small ponds)
Grass pickerel (*Esox americanus*)	X	X	Eastern U.S.
Smallmouth buffalo (*Ictiobus bubalus*)		X	Ohio River System, Mississippi Valley
Black bullhead (*Ictalurus melas*)		X	Pacific Coast, Mississippi Valley, Great Lakes area
Golden shiner (*Notemigonus crysoleucas*)		X	Gulf Coast, Mississippi Valley

* Distribution in all cases refers to the continental United States.

† Distribution represented for the Class Aves refers to summer nesting sites only.

evolved from terrestrial forms are remarkably well adapted to an aquatic or semiaquatic existence. The water shrew can walk on the water surface with its broad hairy feet as well as swim and dive. The soft-shelled turtle is able to utilize dissolved oxygen in the water and hence does not depend on the terrestrial environment except for reproduction.

The invertebrate fauna found in freshwater phases of succession varies quantitatively in direct proportion with the amount of vegetation present in the area. Thus one finds a larger number of organisms and often a greater number of species in the older seral stages of aquatic succession. Younger communities with very little vegetation may support immature stages of midge flies, damselflies and caddisflies. Some adults of the back-swimmer (*Notonecta*) and whirligig beetles (Gyrinidae) are common, but all of these organisms tend to become more numerous as the pond becomes more mature. The alderfly (*Sialis*), the water boatman (*Corixa*), water striders (*Gerris*), giant waterbugs (*Lethocerus americanus*), the naiads of common dragonflies (*Anax junius, Libellula pulchella*), water scavenger beetles (*Hydrophilus triangularis*), and the diving beetles (*Dytiscus*) are other insects common in middle-aged ponds but often are more abundant in older, more mature ponds having submergent and emergent hydrophytes. A large number of mollusks attain a high population density with the increase in vegetation, and many remain until the latter stages of swamp succession. Gastropods including the genera *Lymnaea, Physa, Helisoma, Gyraulus, Amnicola,* and *Valvata*—all are common in mature ponds and swamps. Several species of snail, *Succinea ovalis, S. retusa,* and *S. avara* are common in swamp forests and may occasionally be collected from emergent tufts of swamp grasses in some areas of the temperate zone. *Anodonta, Pisidium* (particularly *P. compressum* and *P. abditum*), and *Sphaerium* (*S. striatinum, S. occidentale*) are freshwater bivalves most common in mature ponds and swampy areas. Other invertebrates including the coelenterate, *Hydra,* flatworms (*Dugesia*), water scorpions (*Ranatra*), isopods (*Asellus communis*), and amphipods (*Gammarus limnaeus, G. fasciatus, Hyalella knickerbocki*), are common in older ponds and may well be found in swampy regions.

Some vertebrates and invertebrates exhibit a high **seral adaptability**— that is, they are relatively tolerant of the changing ecological conditions that transpire during succession. An example of such adaptability is apparent among fishes when we compare the black bass or sunfish with the mudminnow or pickerel. The former individuals are limited to a single seral stage, but the mudminnow and pickerel are found throughout a number of successional communities in pond succession and exhibit considerable seral adaptability. The black bass and sunfish are termed **seral index** forms. In other words, if these fish are present in a freshwater area, the seral age of the community can be determined. Kennedy's work (1922) on the succession of dragonfly and damselfly naiads of western Lake Erie demonstrates seral adaptability and seral index forms in a group of invertebrates. Several species of damselflies (*Enallagma carunculatum, E. ebrium, E. exsulans*) were found as immature forms, inhabiting the margins containing submergent vegetation, lake margins with emergent and floating vegetation, young ponds, and mature ponds. Another species of damselfly, *Ischnura verticalis,* was found in all of the seral communities, from a lake margin environment with submerged vegetation to an old marsh with invading trees and shrubs (marsh forest community). Such species are excellent examples of seral tolerance, for a number of environmental factors in a lake margin area are quite different from those in a young marsh forest community. The dragonfly (*Gomphus plagiatus*), found only in the early seral communities (open lake devoid of macroscopic vegetation and lake margins with submerged hydrophytes), the damselfly (*Lestes forcipatus*), found in mature ponds and young marsh forest communities, and *L. uncates* and *L. unguiculatus,* found only in the latter type of community, are good seral index species.

In lotic environments (rivers, brooks), where water moves from one geographic area to another, the successional pattern is more variable because of the many factors which may instigate a change in the sequence. The speed of the current, the depth of the stream, the type of substrate, and the general topography of the area—all will cause variability in the successional pattern. As the stream ages, the rate of the current may change (slow down), forming numerous pools along its length. As the current undergoes a gradual deacceleration, a silting in takes place. The type of substrate underlying any portion of the stream will change from time to time as the stream cuts deeper into underlying strata of soil and rock material. To compound the situation, a stream may change its natural course, leaving behind isolated ponds or swamps that in time may become mesic forest areas.

MARINE SUCCESSION

Undoubtedly, less is known about succession in marine areas than in terrestrial or freshwater regions, even though the marine area seems to be a fruitful one in which to work. Primary difficulties encountered in studying such an environment are the tremendous depth of water in certain areas and the expensive equipment, crew, and operating expenses necessary to carry on work in some of the more remote areas. In addition, the tides, shifting substrate, dangerous currents, storms, dangerous organisms inhabiting some of these areas, and the comparative handful of qualified investigators—all give some idea why little work has been accomplished in some of the deeper waters. Intertidal communities have received more attention than have other regions because working conditions in these communities are more ideal. Hewatt's work (1935, 1937), some twenty-five years ago in Monterey Bay, California, indicated that a succession occurred on clean surfaces. Algae comprised the pioneer community, followed by limpets (algal eaters), then by mussels and barnacles during the spawning season.

Shelford at first concluded that succession in the terrestrial sense, involving the succession of communities that depend for their initial appearance upon conditions established by preexisting entities, did not apply in marine areas. Instead, it appeared there was a direct development of climax communities with seasonal changes, referred to as **aspection.** However, on the basis of Hewatt's work, Shelford stated that succession did occur in marine environments. Considerable work has been published in recent years on succession in fouling communities along coastal areas (Scheer, 1952) in different parts of the world. Redfield and Deevey (1952) have presented a critical review of the establishment of fouling communities on new or denuded surfaces. According to most such investigations, we find that a film of microorganisms precede the settlement of larger organisms. Thus, in a typical sequence of communities on a clean surface in an intertidal community, we might find the following succession: clean surface—bacteria—diatoms—algae and hydroids—bryozoans and serpulids—bivalve molluscs (*Mytilus*). The period of time that elapses during the sequence of these salt water communities is extremely short in comparison to the period of time that elapses during the sequence of a typical terrestrial sere. An estimate of approximately three years for the attainment of a climax community of bivalves on piling along the coast of New Zealand has been advanced by Ralph and Hurley (1952).

Coral reef communities and oyster bed aggregates display successional patterns as different organisms appear, settle, and gradually disappear from time to time. These reef communities exhibit a succession on submerged coral surfaces. As the calcareous substrate is built up, a variety of organisms settle on the surface; algae are generally pioneers. As temperatures change, they may be replaced by hydroids, snails (limpets), and echinoderms, particularly the echinoids. Oyster reefs will serve as ideal places for attachment of successional stages of marine life, particularly in the relatively shallow waters of bays and estuaries. In many of these intertidal regions, a firm surface of attachment for sessile invertebrates and vegetation is scarce. Consequently, a firm shell surface acts as a perfect substrate for colonization. Portions of the oyster bar will eventually grow to the point that emergence will gradually kill off some of the members of the aggregation from time to time, or silt will cover portions of the reef, necessitating establishment in some other portion of the estuary. Coral atolls and reefs represent some of the oldest living communities in marine areas. The Great Barrier Reef along the northeastern coast of Australia is as much a climax community as any terrestrial forest or prairie climax.

If reef coral are killed or die and water is extremely shallow, sand may be washed up over the reef by wave and tidal action. This sand surface may emerge above water level, forming an island or atoll. Wave action may pulverize the coral and produce a coral sand, and floating seeds may be washed ashore from neighboring islands or continental areas and produce a lush tropical vegetation. Birds and other animals may eventually be transported or fly to the island, which will foster a rather diverse fauna within a period of a few years.

ADDITIONAL CONSIDERATIONS RELATIVE TO SUCCESSION

MICROSUCCESSION

The sequence of **microcommunities (microsuccession)** that occurs within a **microhabitat** has recently attracted considerable attention among ecologists. The prefix *micro-* means "very small." Hence the words *microcommunity* and *microhabitat* indicate "a very small community" and "a very small habitat." The size, here, applies to spacial dimensions, and not to the population; the latter, particularly if we are concerned with bacteria and protozoa, may be exceedingly large in terms of number. Students can easily observe microsuccession in the laboratory with the aid of suitable cultures. Woodruff (1912) found that if pond water containing a mixture of protozoa is added to a medium of boiled hay water (containing large numbers of bacteria), microsuccession of protozoans will occur, with *Paramecium, Amoeba,* and *Vorticella* reaching population peaks in that order.

Another example of microsuccession are the gradual changes which occur in a fallen log on the floor of a forest stand. As time passes, the log will be invaded by successive populations, and as each population alters the wood it becomes more susceptible to invasion by a different group of organisms. Thus fungi, algae, insects, nematodes, millipedes, centipedes, pill bugs, snails, and beetles of several types will enter the gradually decaying mass of wood. Shelford (1913), Ingles (1931), and Savely (1939) have contributed valuable information regarding microsuccession in this type of environment. Microsuccession also occurs in cattle droppings in open grassland regions of Illinois, as Mohr (1943) has shown. Physical factors of greatest importance, according to Mohr, were the progressive losses of moisture. The microhabitat exhibited changes from a pioneer stage in which the freshly deposited dung was greenish brown in color, with a high moisture content. Following this initial stage the dung progresses through the following phases: uniformly brown and moist, blackish-brown with moist surface depressions, brown with a gradually thickening crust, and finally a light brown microhabitat that is entirely dry. During the time these physical changes are transpiring, a succession of living organisms make use of this microenvironment. Dipterans that utilize such a habitat during the early stages are the hornfly (*Haematobia*), the blowfly (*Sarcophaga*), and the root maggot (*Paregle*). These insects invade the dung very soon after it is deposited, utilizing this material for oviposition and subsequent larval development. The root maggot will remain in cattle droppings to pupate. The pupal stages of this insect have been isolated from this microhabitat after the sixth day and are present until the fourteenth day. Three other genera of flies use cattle droppings as suitable sites for oviposition, larval development, and pupation: *Sepsis, Leptocera* and, *Geosargus*. Mohr has referred to the successional stages that appear within cattle droppings as a **microsere** because they may be considered comparable to the seral communities that transpire in the macroenvironment. As is true of many other types of microsuccession, such as that occurring in carrion, there is no climax community because the final community is incorporated into a portion of the microenvironment and disappears as a distinct entity. In this respect, microsuccession in many instances differs radically from macrosuccession.

A microsuccession, of a type, occurs in areas where intermittent streams flow only during those portions of the year when precipitation or thawing of winter snows is greatest. During these moist portions of the year, aquatic communities flourish, teeming with aquatic bacteria, algae, hydra, flatworms, protozoans, snails, aquatic insect larvae, and so on. As the amount of water decreases and the stream bed gradually dries up, the aquatic community will be replaced by germinating mesophytes and terrestrial organisms—nematodes, terrestrial snails, slugs, annelids, and insects. Many of the aquatic forms will form drought-resistant cysts and remain quiescent until the next wet period arrives.

It must be kept in mind that succession is continuous in nature until the climax stage has been reached. Furthermore, it is unidirectional—that is, it progresses from one type of community to another without regression. Provided that climatic and biotic conditions are similar, the next stage or the rest of the successional series can be predicted if one is familiar with this particular type of succession. The rate of succession will depend upon a vast complex of conditions. Climate, moisture, and edaphic factors are a few of the important regulating conditions. The proximity of other communities will sometimes alter the successional rate: availability of a seed source and the fact that animals migrate and transport flora and fauna from surrounding communities must not be overlooked.

Historically, the value of successional studies and the important relationships involved were first recognized by botanists. In 1885, a paper on vegetational analysis in Finland first dealt with the problem of botanical succession. Henry Cowles and F. E. Clements contributed much valuable information with regard to botanical succession. Cowles (1899) is known for his classical work conducted in the Lake Michigan area, particularly his research on sand dune succession. Clements worked and wrote prolifically about succession in the Far West (prairie vegetation). V. E. Shelford pioneered some of the early studies on animal succession in the Midwest.

Selected References

Beckwith, S. L. 1954. Ecological succession on abandoned farm lands and its relation to wildlife management. Ecol. Monogr., 24:349–376.

Bond, R. M. 1945. Range rodents and plant succession. Trans. 10th No. Amer. Wildlife Conf., 229–234.

Cain, S. A. 1939. The climax and its complexities. Amer. Midl. Nat., 21:146–181.

Chapman, H. H. 1932. Is the longleaf type a climax? Ecology, 8:328–334.

Clements, F. E. 1916. Plant succession. Carnegie Inst. Washington Publ., 242:1–512.

Cowles, H. C. 1899. The ecological relations of the vegetation on the sand dunes of Lake Michigan. Bot. Gaz., 27:95–117, 167–202, 281–308, 361–391.

Hedgpeth, J. W. *Treatise on Marine Ecology and Paleoecology.* Geol. Soc. of America. Memoir 67, 1:1–1296.

Hewatt, W. G. 1935. Ecological succession in the *Mytilus californianus* habitat as observed in Monterey Bay, California. Ecology, 16:244–251.

———. 1937. Ecological studies on selected marine intertidal communities of Monterey Bay, California. Amer. Midl. Nat., 18:161–206.

Hills, G. A. 1952. The classification and evaluation of site for forestry. Res. Rept. No. 24, Ontario Dept. of Lands and Forests.

Ingles, L. G. 1931. The succession of insects in tree trunks as shown by the collections from the various stages of decay. Jour. Ent. Zool., 23:57–59.

Keever, Catherine, H. J. Oosting, and L. E. Anderson. 1951. Plant succession on exposed granite of Rocky Face Mountain, Alexander County, North Carolina. Bull. Torrey Bot. Club, 78:401–421.

Kennedy, C. H. 1922. The ecological relationships of the dragonflies of the Bass Islands of Lake Erie. Ecology, 3:325–336.

Maturo, F. J. S., Jr. 1959. Seasonal distribution and settling rates of estuarine Bryozoa. Ecology, 40:116–127.

McDougall, K. D. 1943. Sessile marine invertebrates at Beaufort, North Carolina. Ecol. Monogr., 13:321–374.

Mohr, C. O. 1943. Cattle droppings as ecological units. Ecol. Monogr., 13:275–298.

Muller, C. H. 1940. Plant succession in the *Larrea-Flourensia* climax. Ecology, 21:206–212.

Oosting, H. J. 1942. An ecological analysis of the plant communities of Piedmont, North Carolina. Amer. Midl. Nat., 28:1–126.

Pearse, A. S. 1946. Observations on the microfauna of the Duke Forest. Ecol. Monogr., 16:127–150.

Peterson, W. 1926. Seasonal succession of animals in a chara-cattail pond. Ecology, 7:371–377.

Phillips, J. 1934. Succession, development, the climax, and the complex organism: an analysis of concepts. Jour. Ecol., 22:554–571.

———. 1935. Succession, development, the climax, and the complex organism: an analysis of concepts. Jour. Ecol., 23:210–246, 488–508.

Ralph, P. M., and D. E. Hurley. 1952. The settling and growth of wharf-pile fauna in Port Nicholson, Wellington, New Zealand. Zool. Publ., Victoria Univ. Coll., 19:1–22.

Redfield, A. C., and E. S. Deevey. Temporal sequences and biotic successions. U.S. Naval Institute, Annapolis, 1952.

Savely, H. E. 1939. Ecological relations of certain animals in dead pine and oak logs. Ecol. Monogr. 9:321–385.

Scheer, B. T. 1952. The development of marine fouling communities. Biol. Bull., 89:103–121.

Sears, P. B. 1948. Forest sequence and climatic change in northeastern North America since early Wisconsin time. Ecology, 29:326–333.

Shelford, V. E. 1911. Ecological succession. Biol. Bull., 21:127–151.

———. 1911. Ecological succession. Biol. Bull., 22:1–38.

———. *Animal Communities in Temperate America* (Chicago: Univ. of Chicago Press, 1913), pp. i–xiii, 1–368.

Smith, C. C. 1940. Biotic and physiographic succession on abandoned eroded farmland. Ecol. Monogr., 10:421–484.

Smith, V. G. 1928. Animal communities of a deciduous forest succession. Ecology, 9:479–500.

Vesey-Fitzgerald, D. F. 1960. Grazing succession among East African game animals. Jour. Mamm., 41:161–172.

Weaver, J. E., and F. E. Clements. *Plant Ecology* (New York: McGraw-Hill, 1938), pp. i–xx, 1–520.

Wetzel, R. M. 1958. Mammalian succession on midwestern floodplains. Ecology, 39:262–271.

Whittaker, R. H. 1951. A criticism of the plant association and climatic climax concept. Northwest Sci., 25:17–31.

———. 1953. A consideration of climax theory: the climax as a population and pattern. Ecol. Monogr., 23:41–78.

Woodruff, L. L. 1912. Observations on the origin and sequence of the protozoan fauna of hay infusions. Jour. Exp. Zool., 12:205–264.

XI. The Basic
Environments—
Terrestrial Areas

The basic and radically different environments encountered throughout the world are three in number: terrestrial, freshwater, and marine. The terrestrial environment, in an ecological sense, is the most complex type of all, for in this environment there is a greater fluctuation and interaction of environmental factors than there is in an aquatic medium.

COMPARISON OF TERRESTRIAL REGIONS WITH AQUATIC AREAS

MOISTURE

One of the most obvious limiting factors on land is the amount of moisture available within a specific environmental area. The physical state of such moisture is also of considerable importance, for whether it is present as a vapor (invisible vapor—humidity), liquid (rain, mist, fog), or solid (ice, sleet, snow, hail), it is of considerable importance to the plant or animal. Many plants and animals are limited, in regard to terrestrial distribution, by the amount of water vapor (humidity) present in the atmosphere. In some localities, the humidity is so low that the rate of water loss from the stem and leaf surfaces of plants (transpiration) is so great that only the most xerophytic plants, adapted to such dry environments, can exist there. Many animals are limited in distribution by the loss of moisture from the body surface. This is particularly so of the invertebrates such as the earthworm. This organism is normally found in the soil or damp leaf mold during the warmer, drier portion of the day; it emerges from its subterranean lair only after a shower or when the humidity is high, after darkness. This organism and many other subterranean plants and animals would die within a short period if exposed to dry air. Terrestrial organisms must be able to effectively balance water loss with water intake to prevent the dehydration of tissues, which may be lethal if allowed to progress for any extended period of time.

Individuals living in xeric areas must be able to cope with adverse moisture conditions by means of structural or physiological adaptations. Plants in such environments will have fewer stomata per unit surface of leaf area, thereby reducing the transpiration rate. Usually the few stomata that are present are nearly always closed, so that water loss by transpiration is exceedingly slow. Other plants commonly referred to as sclerophyllous species, including such common genera of prairie grasses as *Stipa* and *Festuca,* have rigid leathery leaves with few stomata. The thickness of the cuticle and epidermis impedes the passage of water through these areas. Other xerophytes have, in contrast, very thin leaves and lose considerable quantities of water during dry spells. *Artemisia,* the common sagebrush, is an example. The plants often have extensive root systems. Some root systems grow deep enough to come in contact with a water table or capillary fringe; others are broad and extensive and lie just below the soil surface, so that all of the available rainwater may be used as effectively and rapidly as possible (Figure 11–1). Some of the succulent plants (*Sedum* and *Sempervivum* and many cacti) have extensive water storage tissues that will supply the plant with adequate amounts of moisture during unfavorable climatic periods.

Animals must also be specially adapted to withstand the rigors of dry environments. Many of the animals living in regions with limited amounts of water will rarely have access to streams, ponds, lakes, or watering holes. These individuals often curtail their movements during periods in which the humidity is low; they are nocturnal, hunting and feeding during the cool, more humid periods. They obtain adequate quantities of water from their foods, tissue fluids, and blood (in the case of carnivorous species), or they have a tendency to consume succulent vegetation. Still others are physiologically adapted to such an extent that they are able to obtain metabolic water from air-dry foods (as mentioned in "Food Sources" of Chapter VII). Wastes of many of these xerophilic organisms are in the form of uric acid crystals. Uric acid is insoluble in water, hence wastes can be concentrated within the

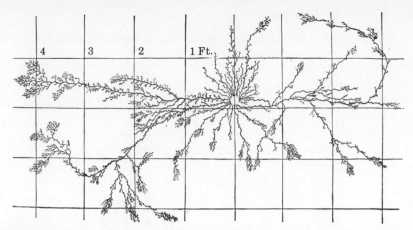

FIGURE 11-1 The surface roots of a small common cactus (*Opuntia camanchiae*) as seen from above. Most of the absorbing roots occur in the upper four inches of soil; only three to five roots extend to depths of two or three feet. From *Plant Ecology* by John E. Weaver and Frederic E. Clements. Copyright 1938. McGraw-Hill Book Company. Used by permission.

organism and released without the loss of large quantities of water that are necessary when urea is the end product of metabolism. Urea must be diluted by the addition of considerable amounts of water in order to prevent self-poisoning because urea, unlike uric acid, is soluble in water. Wastes of many birds, reptiles, and arthropods are in the form of uric acid crystals. These organisms release large quantities of wastes in the form of dry pellets. Structural adaptations in the form of chitinous exoskeletons (spiders and insects), mesodermal scales (snakes and lizards), and a fewer number and smaller size of sweat glands in many mammals drastically reduce the amount of water lost from the body surface. It must be emphasized, however, that a much larger group of plants and animals lack many of the adaptations, both physiological and anatomical, that have been mentioned and are therefore limited in their terrestrial distribution.

TEMPERATURE

Thermal values fluctuate over wide ranges in terrestrial areas. A drop or increase of 20° C. or 30° C. within a twenty-four-hour period is not unusual in many areas. In aquatic communities, such radical changes do not transpire. The high specific heat of water, in comparison to many other substances, as shown in Table 11-1, prevents these drastic thermal changes from ever occurring, despite such changes in overlying masses of air. Of all the common substances, water has the highest specific heat. Much larger amounts of heat and heat loss, respectively, are needed to raise and lower the temperature of water than are needed to raise and lower the temperature of any one of the other common substances.

T A B L E   1 1 – 1 . *Specific Heat of Some Common Chemical Substances*

SUBSTANCE	SPECIFIC HEAT
Lead*	0.031
Mercury*	0.033
Silver*	0.056
Copper*	0.092
Aluminum*	0.214
Olive oil**	0.470
Steam**	0.470
Ice**	0.502
Water**	1.000

* Extracted from L. D. Weld, *A Textbook of Heat* (New York: Macmillan, 1948), pp. i–x, 1–436. Used by permission.
** Extracted from P. McCorkle, *The Physical World* (New York: McGraw-Hill, 1950), pp. i–vii, 1–450. Used by permission.

Substances such as mercury and lead change temperatures so rapidly that only a small amount of time is required to increase or decrease their temperatures to conform with surrounding environmental values. Thermal changes are not as severe in terrestrial regions located in the vicinity of large lakes or marine areas. The loss or gain of large amounts of heat from aquatic surfaces without extreme temperature changes helps to modify the thermal variability that would ensue in the absence of these aquatic environments.

SUPPORT

The atmosphere provides little support for the body of any organism. For this reason, body size of terrestrial organisms is limited with regard to the extent of the skeleton or, in the case of plants, the strength of the cell wall of plant tissues. Strong skeletons or internal fluid pressure is necessary if body cavities are to exist. This extreme degree of support is not required in aquatic areas because the buoyancy of the water precludes the need for a bulky skeleton or exoskeleton. In marine areas, where the buoyancy of the water is more pronounced than it is in freshwater habitats, this is even less of a problem. The comparative sizes of terrestrial organisms as compared with aquatic flora and fauna is undeniable evidence of the forementioned facts. The largest known invertebrates are the marine mollusks, the giant squid of the North Atlantic; the largest vertebrate is the mammoth whale, whose relatively well-developed skeleton would never support the tremendous weight of its body on land.

DISTRIBUTIONAL BARRIERS

In terrestrial areas, a number of physical and climatic barriers exist that prevent the unlimited distribution of a large number of species into suitable environmental areas. Occasionally, birds and other wild animals have transported seed, cysts, and small invertebrates over existing barriers and introduced these organisms into previously uncolonized territories. However, man in the past few centuries has probably been a far more effective agent of transport than have most wild animals, for he has consciously or unknowingly carried plants and animals over and across some of the most formidable barriers, including oceanic ranges, mountain ranges, and deserts. The transport of organisms has increased in relation to the increase in international transportation of materials and travelers. As transportation increases in frequency and quantity, the likelihood of purposeful or accidental transport of other organisms, plant and animal, will also increase. One of the most effective barriers that tend to prevent the successful dissemination of any species are the aquatic regions such as oceans, seas, rivers, and large lakes. Some plants, but few terrestrial animals, are able to survive any extensive period of submersion or partial submersion in water, particularly saline waters. Mountain ranges and deserts may be nearly as effective as water barriers. The great extent of these obstacles, usually hundreds of miles, block the migration of a species. To cross a mountain range short of direct flight is a feat few wild animals can accomplish with any degree of success. Variability in oxygen concentration and altitudinal variability in thermal values are formidable obstacles. The thermal variability encountered in desert areas, where temperatures may drop below 0° C. (32° F.) at night and exceed 40° C. (104° F.) during the day, coupled with lack of water and low humidity, prevents unaided travel of nondesert animals across this type of environment.

The barriers encountered in most aquatic areas are usually not as abrupt, nor are they as severe as compared with terrestrial regions. Usually, fewer physical barriers are present in freshwater and marine areas. Slight, and often gradual thermal differences, as well as occasional dams and rapids are the most common obstacles encountered by submerged organisms. Chemical factors are usually of greater importance in aquatic distribution. Dissolved gases like oxygen, carbon dioxide, and hydrogen sulfide concentrations as well as salinity are the most effective inhibiting agents aside from temperature. Aquatic regions are often interconnected, so that it is not unusual for one species to be located throughout an entire stream system, including many of the tributaries, an area sometimes covering many hundreds of miles. Such broad, continuous distribution of terrestrial species is uncommon, except in the largest forest and grassland regions of the world, because the discontinuity of various habitats precludes such a possibility. The increase in salinity as one approaches oceanic areas by way of stream systems may effectively prevent the entry of some freshwater species into estuaries or coastal waters and the possible colonization of neighboring or distant drainage systems, just as the gradual reduction of salinity in estuaries and up-stream areas eliminates the stenohaline fauna and flora of oceanic areas. However, some fishes such as the lampreys (*Petromyzon marinus*), the alewife (*Alosa pseudoharengus*), American shad (*A. sapidissima*), and chinook, or king salmon (*Oncorhynchus tshawytscha*) that spawn in freshwater streams after maturing in a marine environment, have in the course of evolution become morphologically or physiologically adapted to cope with the osmotic variability encountered while moving through waters of varying salinity. Thus we find differences of a chemical and physical nature in aquatic environments, although such variability is usually more gradual than that encountered on land. Consequently, the flora and fauna exhibit a more contiguous distribution rather than the often abrupt discontinuity evidenced in the latter type of environment.

BIOGEOGRAPHY

No plant or animal species occurs uniformly throughout the entire world, for each is restricted to a definite range or area of distribution. The field of study concerned with the distribution on a worldwide basis as well as the factors controlling its ability to populate these areas is known as **biogeography.** The term *range* in biogeography may imply any one of several different types and often must be designated as to type if the meaning is not clear in the context. In referring to the **geographic range,** the biogeographer means the entire extent of land or water over which a particular species may be found. The black bullhead (*Ictalurus melas*) has a geographic range extending from southeastern Canada through the Great Lakes and the Mississippi Valley to the Gulf of Mexico and westward to the Rocky Mountains. Recently, it has been introduced into the Pacific Coast area in drainage systems of Idaho and Oregon. The marsh rabbit (*Sylvilagus palustris*) is found from the Mobile Bay area, throughout Florida to southeastern Virginia in the coastal plain area.

The **ecological range** refers to the particular type of environment normally inhabited by the organism. The black bullhead is most commonly found in shallow, muddy pools along rivers and in the shallow water in the zone of submergent and emergent vegetation of ponds and lakes. In fact, as was mentioned in our discussion of freshwater succession, it is not uncommon for these fish to inhabit shallow marshes where they are able to contend with the reduced oxygen concentration of the water. The common name "marsh rabbit" is fairly descriptive of the ecological range of this mammal. It is common in thickets and marshes along the southeastern Atlantic and Gulf coasts. The young are born and raised in dense, almost impenetrable thickets that offer excellent protection from predators until the offspring are able to explore surrounding, more vulnerable areas of marshland regions. The **geological range** of any species or group of organisms refers to the occurrence and abundance of a species in past epochs as well as the present. The bullhead had its origin in the early Tertiary period, probably during the late Paleocene about sixty million years ago. The marsh rabbit has evolved from the more primitive rabbit ancestors; these oldest lagomorphs (*Eurymylus*) have been recovered from the upper Paleocene of Asia. The marsh rabbit has a geological range extending back into the Miocene epoch.

METHODS OF DISTRIBUTION

The distribution of animal and plant life throughout the world has materialized by means of a number of biotic and abiotic agents. Some of the more important agencies of distribution are described below. One of the most obvious means is by the animal's own efforts. Most animals possess some means of locomotion, and provided the surrounding environmental conditions do not become too adverse, they will tend to move away from population centers where competition for life's essential materials may become increasingly more acute. Birds, bats, and insects may move across harsh or unfavorable environmental areas and become established some distance from their former abode, while other animals may be limited to more likely avenues of escape, if any exist. Some of the smaller invertebrates and plants as well as reproductive products may be transported by other animals considerable distances and become established in a suitable habitat some distance away after becoming detached from the plumage, pelt, or body of the transporting agent. Man has transported many species accidentally or purposely from one geographic region to another on his person or by some means of transportation, such as autos, trucks, boats, planes, and so on.

Wind. Two abiotic agents, wind and water, have also transported the world's flora and fauna great distances. Wind can transport small organisms and is probably a more effective agent of dispersal than most people realize. Man is often inclined to disregard the lifting force of winds because of the negligible effect moderate winds have on his own body. We find that the lifting force of any body of air will depend on a ratio of body mass to surface area. Surface area will vary in proportion to the square of the size of an organism, but the mass will vary with the cube of the size (Figure 11–2). Thus, when we compare different types of organisms, we find that a decrease in size will bring about a more pro-

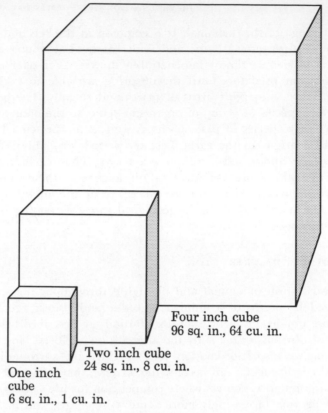

Four inch cube
96 sq. in., 64 cu. in.

Two inch cube
24 sq. in., 8 cu. in.

One inch
cube
6 sq. in., 1 cu. in.

FIGURE 11–2 Surface areas of cubes increase as the size increases, but not in proportion to the increase in mass (volume). Ratios of surface area to volume vary from
6 to 1 for a one-inch cube, 3 to 1 for a two-inch cube, and only 1½ to 1 for a four-
inch cube.

nounced decrease in weight than it will in surface area. This, in turn,
means that smaller animals will have a greater surface area exposed to
wind action in proportion to their mass than will larger animals. The
force and carrying capacity of any volume of air will increase according
to the square of the wind's velocity (approximately). According to
Darlington (1957), the effect of a 100 mile per hour wind on an animal
with a mass of one ounce (such as an adult house mouse) is about 224
times as great as a 25 mile per hour wind on a man of average mass! It
is not inconceivable, in the light of this, that surface winds may lift and
carry small organisms long distances, especially when they act in concert
with thermal updrafts. These updrafts may carry the organism several
thousand feet into the atmosphere where it may be moved by winds of
far greater intensity than those to which it was subjected on the earth's
surface. Hurricanes, tornadoes, and typhoons (Figure 11–3) may at times
transport plant and animal life to suitable areas where colonization may
occur.

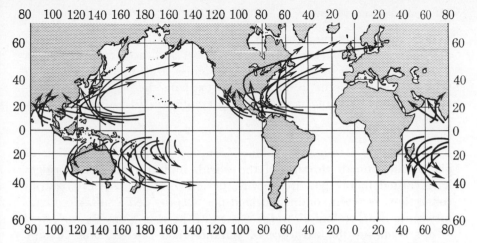

FIGURE 11–3 Storm tracks of destructive storms (hurricanes and typhoons) throughout the world, showing the most frequent paths and directions of such storm centers. Reprinted from *Weather Around the World* by I. R. Tannehill by permission of Princeton University Press, 1952.

Water. Bodies of water can and do transport plant and animal life along drainage systems and across bodies of salt water. Seeds, spores, and invertebrates are undoubtedly transported in this fashion. The main Equatorial Current of the mid-Atlantic is an intercontinental current that carries vast quantities of water and included materials across the tropical Atlantic from the shores and rivers of West Africa to South America. Guppy (1917), using marked drift bottles, estimated that it took approximately twelve weeks for these bottles to cross the Atlantic from the Gulf of Guinea along the western shores of Africa to the coast of Brazil by way of the South Equatorial Current, (Figure 12–15, Chapter XII). It is a known fact that much floating driftwood comes from the Niger and Congo rivers of Africa and lands along the shores of Brazil, while some is swept northwestward and lands on the shores of the Guianas, Venezuela, or the West Indies. It is not inconceivable that encysted organisms, marine invertebrates, or resistant reproductive botanical material has crossed and will continue to cross this formidable oceanic barrier in this fashion. Of course, chances of survival are slim, if not overwhelmingly so, but given enough time, say several million years, some organisms could conceivably surmount the odds.

Rafts of trees, soil, and other debris with root systems forming such a tangled mass that the entire chunk of vegetation and associated soil forms a floating raft, have been seen. These floating units that have been dislodged from their former positions by storms or continual long-termed erosive activity are suitable transport media, carrying vegetation and animal life across ponds, lakes, along drainage streams, and even out to sea. In some instances, this may very possibly explain the populations of oceanic islands. A raft of considerable size, 100 feet square and with trees 30 feet high, bound together by the roots of living plants, was seen off the east coast of North America in 1892 and, according to Powers (1911), was known to have drifted 1,000 miles. Rafting has occurred in the past and will occur in the future; it explains the mysterious appearance at times, of faunal and floral representatives in hitherto unlikely areas.

Land Bridges. Geological evidence, coupled with the distribution of plants and animals throughout the world, indicates that **land bridges** have existed in the past for varying periods of time. These terrestrial connections between continental land masses provided a suitable migratory route if an **ecological bridge** existed at the same time. By *ecological bridge* is meant the existence of suitable food, shelter, and climatic conditions along the entire length of these terrestrial connections. Many possible land bridges, it has been proposed by geologists and biogeographers, have existed in the past; however, on the basis of information gathered from investigations of fossils and present distribution of different groups of organisms, it is doubtful that some ever existed. The Bering Land Bridge, however, that is believed at one time to have connected Eurasia with the North American continent existed, in all probability, as a result of a lower sea level in the region of the Bering Strait. This bridge of land was probably a broad plain covered with tall grasses similar to the type found on the Alaskan Peninsula at the present time. The reason for this conclusion is that it is known that the climate was warmer during the Tertiary Period, when this land bridge was in existence. Furthermore, this area was exposed to the warm Japan Current. This connection that existed during the Tertiary was interrupted by submergence from time to time—during the Paleocene, middle Eocene, midde to late Oligocene, and for a short interval during the first part of the Pliocene. (See Table 11–2.) The fossil record, particularly in the mammalian groups, indicates a Eurasian-North American bridge after the early Eocene Epoch. There is a strong indication that only one such connection existed, a North Pacific bridge.

During the early Eocene, there were wholesale, mutual exchanges of continental faunas between Eurasia and the New World, but following this epoch, the amount of passage was quantitatively and qualitatively reduced in relation to the increased severity of the climate (cooler epochs), ending with glaciation in the Pleistocene Epoch. Although the Bering Land Bridge was warmer during the Tertiary period, tropical and semitropical animals of the Old World, such as true pigs, civet cats, giraffes, mongooses, fruit bats, and Old World primates (except man), never left the Eurasian tropics or semitropics. Ecological incompatibility was obviously the reason for geomyoid rodents (burrowing rodents—that is, pocket gophers) and pronghorns remaining in the relatively dry western parts of North America. There was a movement in both direc-

TABLE 11-2. *Geological Time Chart Showing Only the Cenozoic and Mesozoic Eras with Included Systems and Series in North America**

ERAS	PERCENT OF GEOLOGICAL TIME**	SYSTEM	SERIES (NORTH AMERICA)
		Quarternary	Recent
			Pleistocene
Cenozoic (60 million yrs.)	3%		Pliocene
			Miocene
		Tertiary	Oligocene
			Eocene
			Paleocene
			Upper Cretaceous
		Cretaceous	
			Lower Cretaceous
Mesozoic (130 million yrs.)	6½%		Upper Jurassic
		Jurassic	Middle Jurassic
			Lower Jurassic
			Upper Triassic
		Triassic	Middle Triassic
			Lower Triassic

* Adapted from (1) R. R. Shrock, and W. H. Twenhofel. *Principles of Invertebrate Paleontology* (New York: McGraw-Hill, 1953), Table 1–4, pp. 24–25. Used by permission.
And (2) W. H. Emmons, G. A. Thiel, C. R. Stauffer, and I. S. Allison, *Geology: Principles and Processes* (New York: McGraw-Hill, 1955), Appendix C, p. 621. Used by permission.
** Percent of geological time is based on the total time that living organisms have been estimated to exist on earth. Such percentages are approximations at best and are not to be considered as exact computations.

tions across the Bering Land Bridge, but it is apparent that more animals crossed from Eurasia to North America, rather than in the reverse direction.

A North Atlantic Land Bridge linking Europe and North America has been postulated, particularly by botanists, but there is no direct evidence at the present time that would support or favor such a theory. Most certainly, all of the known living and fossil forms could have arrived by way of the Bering connection. After the early Eocene Epoch, evidence is definitely in favor of a single North Pacific Bridge. Certainly mammalian distribution does not support the idea of a dual connection since the early Tertiary, if ever. On the other hand, a land connection between North and South America has existed from the late Tertiary Period (late Pliocene Epoch) to the present time. Several genera of freshwater fish, including a genus of catfish, and several saline-tolerant cyprinodont fishes (soft-finned fishes, killifishes, and minnows) have crossed the entire bridge, and gar pikes have moved a little over halfway across this connection. There has been no southern movement of northern fishes.

There has been a mutual exchange of mammalian groups. Marsupials, edentates (sloths, armadillos, and anteaters), and one or more ungulates evidently reached South America from North America, along with many of the plantigrade, carnivorous mammals. Mammals reaching South America during the Tertiary apparently arrived from its northern neighbor. After a land connection was established in the Pliocene epoch, there was a rapid exchange in both directions, as is evidenced by the fact that in the following epoch (Pleistocene) the two continents had twenty-two families of mammals in common. Following this initial exchange there were many withdrawals and extinctions as ecological factors took their toll. The end result was that the North American fauna did not exhibit much change. The South American biota, on the other hand, was radically changed; many of the native mammals became extinct and were replaced by North American types that attained considerable dominance in many communities of South America. Northern placental carnivores and ungulates have replaced marsupial carnivores and ungulates that formerly inhabited the South American continent. A shrew, tapirs, peccaries, camels, deer, a bear, a genus of rabbit and pocket mice, squirrels, two types of horses, three or more types of cats, three or four types of elephants, several cricetid rodents (small rodents—that is, hamsters) and four types of mustelids (carnivorous mammals, a group including weasels, mink, otters, badgers) invaded South America. Of all these groups, only elephants, camels, horses, and sabertooth cats have failed to establish themselves and survive in South America. Other typical North American forms such as moles, pikas, sciurids (other than squirrels), beavers, jumping mice, pronghorns, and bovids have never invaded South America.

Movement in the opposite direction, which was less successful, included opossums, three families of ground sloths, porcupines, two types of armadillos, two types of glyptodonts (an extinct group of mammals belonging to the order Edentata), and two species of capybaras (largest known living rodent, often four feet long and two feet high). Only the opossum and porcupine have become widely distributed throughout the North American continent. The extinct glyptodonts occurred only in New Mexico and Texas and the armadillo is native to Texas only. The carnivorous marsupials and South American ungulates that were replaced by North American forms in South America never entered this continent. Other groups such as monkeys, anteaters, and tree sloths never entered North America, though some have invaded the southern parts of Central America.

The possibility that a land bridge at one time existed between South

America and Africa has been debated for some time. An alternative is that Africa and South America were in contact at one time in the geological past—just as other continental masses were (Mayr, 1952), and then shortly before and during the Mesozoic period the single land mass broke apart and the continents drifted apart—**continental drift**— (Wegener, 1924) and finally became located in their present positions.

In recent years, geologists and biogeographars have made two diametrically opposed proposals relative to the formation of continents and ocean basins. One group contends that the earth has been gradually cooling and that the gradual contraction has created compressive forces that have produced mountain ranges along the weaker regions of the earth's crust. The granitic formations of the continents have remained in place since the close of the initial molten stage of the planet's history. The time required for cooling of the earth to its present temperature would have required about one hundred million years. Another rather small group of geologists and some biogeographers believe that the earth is slightly plastic, thereby allowing continents to drift slowly (continental drift) over the surface. Studies based on radioactivity, on terrestrial magnetism and, in the past few years, on submarine geology have lent considerable support to the hypothesis. Radioactive dating of rock strata has shown that the earth is about four and one-half billion years old. Radioactive decay of uranium and thorium have probably generated a supply of internal heat that has slowed the cooling process of the earth's interior. Adherents of continental drift believe that the earth's interior possesses convection currents that carry heat from the earth's core toward the mantle layer. These convection currents move too slowly, about a few centimeters per year, and are too deep within the earth's interior to measure directly. However, it is believed, that in areas where ridges are present, these convection currents are flowing upward toward the earth's crust, and in areas where oceanic trenches are present, the convection currents are moving toward the earth's interior. Indirect evidence seems to substantiate this assumption. Sir Edward Bullard of the University of Cambridge has found that the flow of heat exceeds the average heat flow of a millionth of a calorie per square centimeter per second recorded in other areas by two to eight times this value. Heat flow in the oceanic trenches is about one tenth of the average value cited. Between the regions of vertical movement of molten materials (between the ridges and trenches), it is assumed that these currents are moving horizontally in a region several hundred kilometers thick, known as the **asthenosphere.** The speed of sound through this layer is slower than it is through other portions of the earth's interior, which indicates that a less dense, more fluid region exists in this stratum. The sinking of convection currents produces trenches in the ocean floor, but in continental areas mountains are formed where these currents descend owing to a pileup of more brittle material in the earth's crust.

Assuming that the theory of continental drift is a plausible explana-

tion for past geological activity, let us examine the main events that have
transpired since mesozoic time. The supercontinent developed a rift
shortly before the Cretaceous period forming the Atlantic Ocean. The
fact that convection currents, despite their constant direction, have varied
in activity opened a rift in the southern extreme. This rotational movement, with less rotation occurring in Siberia, may have caused the
compression and uplift that produced the Verkhoyansk Mountains in
eastern Siberia. This same rift separated Africa from Antarctica. A new
rift came into existence at the beginning of the Tertiary period that
separated Africa from India and Australia, and Australia from the Antarctic land mass.

A quote from one of Wilson's recent articles on continental drift (1963)
summarizes rather succinctly our current views relative to the theory and
offers a hint of future promise. "Some physicists and biologists are now
prepared to accept continental drift, but many geologists still have no
use for the hypothesis. This is to be expected. Continents are so large
that much geology would be the same whether drift had occurred or not.
It is the geology of the ocean floors that promises to settle the question,
but the real study of that two thirds of the earth's surface has just begun."
Whether one adheres to the theory of fixed continents or that of continental drift, as is true of many events dealing with the earth's past, both
theories are speculative. There are arguments that may be advanced by
either group, and as yet the issue is undecided. Animal distribution is of
no value as evidence to support either theory because distribution could
have occurred by means of land bridges on a fixed continent basis or by
means of continental drift with few or no land bridges. It is my belief,
however, that current evidence definitely indicates the previous existence
of land bridges across the Bering Strait and in the Panama area, with
the probable rifting and subsequent movement of land masses in the
geological past. However, since I have discussed the possibility of continental drift and pointed out that it is gaining wider acceptance among
physicists and biologists, let us continue our discussion of land bridges,
rejecting the plausibility of drift as a reason for animal distribution.

Some zoogeographers still agree with the following statement made by
Darlington (1957, p. 606): "So far as I can see, animal distribution now
is fundamentally a product of movement of animals, not movement of
land." Furthermore, Darlington feels that nowhere in the world does the
distribution of freshwater fish agree with the theory of continental drift.
The results of a comparison between the types of fish found in South
America and African species with respect to close relationships are not
overly impressive. In fact, any affinities that do exist would suggest movement along a land bridge between North and South America. In the
latter case, freshwater fishes moved from the Isthmus of Panama to the
Isthmus of Tehuantepec, a distance of thirteen hundred miles, or roughly
about two-thirds the distance from Africa to South America. There is a

remote possibility that a land bridge existed between Africa and South America at some time during the Cretaceous Period, but any relationships between freshwater fish of the two continents could also be explained by assuming a movement along the warm margins of northern continents. If future research establishes any link between African and South American hystricomorphs (a suborder of rodents including porcupines, cavies, agoutis, and chinchillas) the probability is that these organisms could have arrived by means of rafts.

Every known factor indicates that South America (and many other continents) was completely isolated during most of the Tertiary Period. The plausibility of a possible link between Australia and South America has been discussed. One of the stronger points favoring such a possibility, namely the presence of marsupials in both areas, has been questioned. It is believed that the marsupials reached both areas separately in the geological past and in the course of evolution they developed similar structures. A connection between Australia and South America by way of New Zealand and Antarctica in all probability existed before the Tertiary Period, if at all. In any case, there is no indication that any vertebrate made use of such a land bridge; although it could have existed before the appearance of vertebrates, as is evidenced by some plants and invertebrates that show convincing affinities. If such a land

FIGURE 11-4 The hypothetical location of Lemuria, an interconnecting land bridge that has been suggested as having once existed between the east coast of Africa and Madagascar. Terrestrial areas that once existed along the coasts of the Indo-African area and the island chain located across the Arabian Sea are represented by diagonal lines.

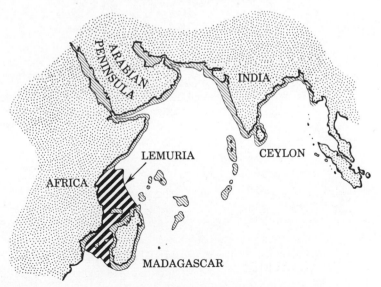

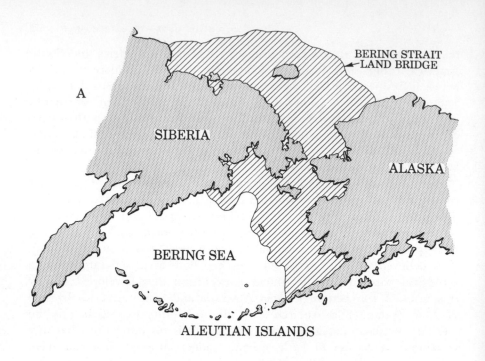

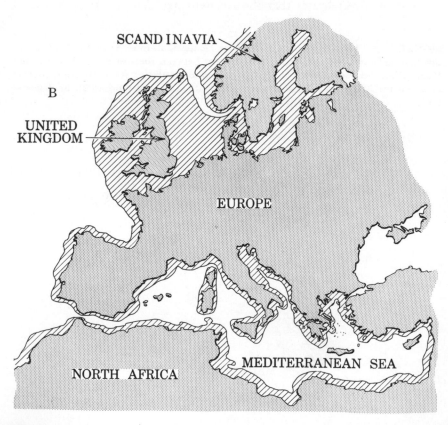

C

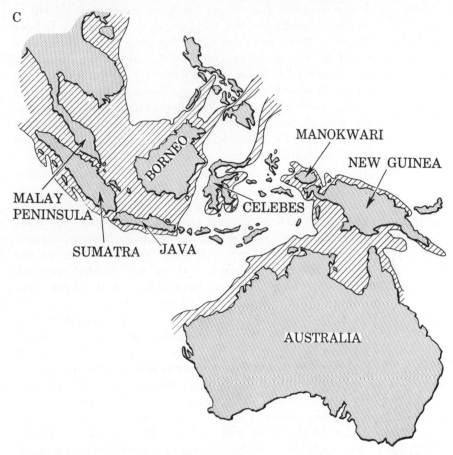

MALAY PENINSULA

SUMATRA JAVA

BORNEO

CELEBES

MANOKWARI

NEW GUINEA

AUSTRALIA

FIGURE 11–5 Land bridges believed to exist in the geological past are represented on the three maps. Map *A* indicates the location of the Bering Strait land bridge (diagonal lines); Map *B*, the land bridge that once existed between Europe, Scandinavia, and the British Isles; and Map *C*, the land bridges between southeastern Asia and part of the East Indies and between Australia and New Guinea.

bridge did exist, only the plants and invertebrates have managed to survive on the remnants of such a terrestrial connection. Opponents to the theory that such a connection existed state that it is possible that insects could have flown the gaps and that many of the plants (particularly seed and spores) and invertebrates could have been carried by wind across many of the aquatic barriers and that these transported organisms colonized successive landmasses and finally completed the movement by reaching one or the other of the continents. Such views merit consideration, for it is possible for wind to carry invertebrates and light plant seeds and spores great distances, and if climatic factors were suitable in the geological past, this successive hopping of aquatic barriers and repeated colonization could have occurred.

The theory that a continuous Australian-Asian connection existed at any time is without foundation, for it is assumed that mammals have arrived by crossing water barriers and island hopping. If this assumption is true, it would be logical to expect that the Australian fauna has evolved from comparatively few ancestral forms (that have managed to complete the hazardous journey by crossing a series of aquatic barriers) and that these organisms have arrived at different times during the past. All the known evidence seems to support such an assumption. There are no clues as to the origin of the monotremes and marsupials, but rodents and bats have undoubtedly come from Asia.

One final connection might be discussed before we conclude our discussion of land bridges and the dispersal of organisms along these terrestrial routes. There is little doubt that a land bridge has existed, at intervals, between eastern Africa and India. A dispersal of land vertebrates has occurred between these two areas. Mammalian records indicate that the two landmasses were separated before the end of the Eocene epoch, but a connection has been reestablished periodically since this time. In the past, some biogeographers have claimed that a broad connection, which they call Lemuria, existed between Africa, Madagascar, and India (Figure 11–4) during the Tertiary period. This possibility has been refuted for two reasons, both based on distribution of vertebrates. It is unreasonable to assume that such a connection ever existed between Madagascar and Africa when we note the absence of a freshwater fish fauna on Madagascar. The failure of fishes to move along a terrestrial connection over the relatively short distance between Madagascar and the east coast of Africa makes it hard to justify the existence of such a connection in view of the movement of fishes that has taken place between North and South America (a far greater distance by comparison). Even the lemurs, for whom Lemuria was named, contradict the hypothesis. The lemurs of Africa and tropical Eurasia are related, but those on Madagascar belong to a distinctly separate evolutionary offshoot. All known evidence contradicts the existence of an expansive land bridge referred to in the literature as Lemuria.

That some of the proposed land bridges (Figure 11–5) did exist during past geological epochs is, as far as we know at present, an absolute fact. On the basis of fossil evidence, records of distribution, and geological evidence, it is fairly certain that a land bridge did exist across the Bering Strait. Another existed between Africa and India, and a third one allowed for dispersal between North and South America. It is more doubtful that a terrestrial link connected Australia and South America, but it is even more unlikely that any trans-Atlantic bridges have ever materialized in the past or that any substantial connection ever linked Australia with Asia or Madagascar with Africa. We have been concerned with intercontinental connections, with one exception, Africa-Madagascar. It must be realized, however, that more limited connections have existed in the past between continents and islands (Europe and the British Isles, for example).

SPECIATION

It is apparent that the number of species varies over a wide range of latitude on the earth's surface. The earliest biogeographers noted that the number of species was far greater in tropical areas as compared with quantitative data in more northern (or more southern) areas. But we find that the number of species in specific groups does not always increase as we approach the equatorial areas. There is a decrease in the number of subterranean mammals in more tropical areas compared to temperate localities, and the passerine avifauna (perching birds) also decreases with respect to species southward. Plausible explanations advanced by Darlington (1957) are that tropical areas foster more ideal conditions for speciation—higher mutation rates, more intense selection pressures, and shorter reproductive periods. In addition, in northern areas, frequent climatic disasters that tend to eradicate some of the species in these areas have been more common. Although such arguments may be perfectly valid, many biogeographers are convinced that other factors are involved.

One obvious factor is the increased floral complexity encountered in tropical areas, as compared to that found in temperate climes. There is increased stratification of vegetation and an increased number of species in a tropical rain forest. This, in turn, yields a greater number of microhabitats and a greater likelihood of adaptive radiation, genetic drift, and subsequent speciation. For many species of vertebrates, the breeding season is a period of greatest competition between species for available food, breeding sites, and shelter. If there is a relatively long period of time each year during which weather conditions are suitable for breeding, a greater number of species may be accommodated by a staggering of breeding cycles among the competing sympatric species. (Sympatric species occupy the same geographic area in at least some part of their range.) According to Klopfer (1962), species diversity in tropical areas is due, in part, to a reduction in the place niche of a species or in the area normally used in the course of daily activity, whereas more northern species have a wider range of movement. If this is so, the behavior of the organism would be more stereotyped, or there would be a reduction in the number of objects in the environment that would elicit a response. Klopfer's argument centers around the fact that nonpasserine birds are characteristic of tropical areas, and their behavioral response indicates a definite orientation toward stereotyped activity. However, the passerine fauna, which is more common in the extratropical areas, displays a more plastic behavior that conforms with the demands of the continuous seasonal changes—changes in feeding habits, predators, and competing organisms that continue to appear or disappear as the climate dictates. There is some evidence that other vertebrates, besides the avifauna, display a greater diversity of response relative to the environment in northern areas than do the tropical species.

ZOOGEOGRAPHIC REALMS

The entire world can be subdivided into a number of terrestrial areas of considerable extent, harboring an endemic fauna and flora peculiar to that particular region (Figure 11–6). Some of the organisms that are characteristic of a particular realm may be restricted to a very small portion of the realm, as is the case with the alpine flora and fauna or swamp organisms. On the other hand, some organisms may be widespread in distribution, existing throughout the entire geographic area. The establishment of realms by the biogeographer is based on worldwide climatic zones and the existence of barriers that would tend to prevent, or at least impede, the distribution of organisms. The dissemination of biota throughout a realm has included a population center where the species evolved in the geological past and all of the possible agents or innate locomotive ability of the species that have enabled it to colonize various habitats that meet the minimal ecological conditions necessary for survival. Six biogeographic realms, referred to as botanical and zoological realms, respectively, are recognized by plant and animal bio-

FIGURE 11–6 The six major biogeographical realms with diagonal lines representing boundaries and transitional areas between these regions. Reprinted from *Zoogeography: The Geographical Distribution of Animals* by Philip J. Darlington, Jr., by permission of John Wiley & Sons, Inc., 1957.

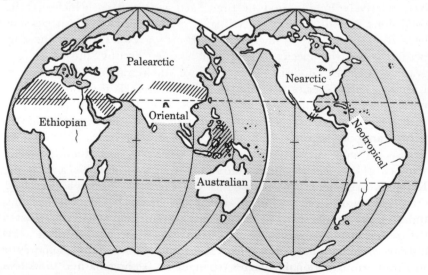

geographers (see Table 11–3). These faunal realms were first proposed by Sclater as a result of his work on the distribution of birds in a paper read before the Linnean Society in 1857 (Sclater, 1858). It is a tribute to Sclater's work that his regions stand to this day, with only minor modifications in terminology and boundaries.

TABLE 11-3. *Some of the Flora and Fauna Characteristic of Different Biogeographical Realms Throughout the World*

REALM	FLORA	FAUNA
Ethiopian	Baobab tree, traveler's tree, royal poinciana, acacia trees	Gorilla, chimpanzee, African elephant, lion, zebra, giraffe, ostrich, guinea fowl, rhinoceros
Oriental	Teakwood, camphor, ebony, bamboo	Tarsiers, gibbons, orangutan, Indian elephant, peacock, jungle fowl
Palearctic	Cork oak, rye, wheat, cottongrass, rockrose, heather, bog birch, live oak	Hedgehog, wild boar, fallow deer, lemmings
Nearctic	Sugar maple, dogwood, Labrador tea, sunflower, maize, gourds, tobacco, sagebrush, reindeer moss, pumpkin	Mountain goat, muskrat, caribou, pronghorn antelope, bison
Neotropical	Brazilnut tree, cashew, rubber plant, cassava, cacao, mimosa, century plant, balsa, cajiu	Llama, alpaca, peccaries, armadillos, anteater, rheas, arboreal sloths, vampire bats
Australian	Eucalyptus, mahogany, rosewood, sandalwood, Australian brushcherry, bottle brush, Queensland nut	Monotremes, most marsupials, brush turkeys, cockatoos, birds of paradise

The two northern regions, the Palearctic and Nearctic realms, are separated from the tropical areas primarily by climatic barriers, but the Neotropical and Australian realms have been segregated from other areas of the world by geographic barriers in the form of bodies of salt water. The Ethiopian and Oriental realms are not as completely separated. From paleontological, ecological, and biogeographical information it is apparent that in the past, faunal and floral representatives have radiated out from the latter two realms in a worldwide pattern of dispersal. The Ethiopian realm is a tropical region including most of Africa, except the northwestern corner (northern Algeria and Morocco), and southern

Arabia. The biota is more dense within the tropical belt and gradually becomes more sparse quantitatively and qualitatively toward the northern arid region and the southern temperate tip of Africa. Most of the typical plants and animals found in this realm are more nearly like those endemic to the Oriental realm; in fact, there are many taxonomic groups of vertebrates shared by both realms. Most of the vertebrates found in the Ethiopian realm are limited to the area south of the Sahara Desert or are confined to the Nile Valley. When the Ethiopian and Oriental fauna and flora are compared, it is quite obvious from the close relationships that exist that a considerable exchange has taken place in the past. Climatically, the Oriental realm is quite similar to the neighboring Ethiopian area, for some of the area is covered by tropical rain forest located in southeastern Asia and including the islands of Ceylon, Sumatra, Java, Borneo, and Formosa. The fauna and flora are more populous and varied in the wetter, southeastern portion of the realm, notably in southeastern China, Java, and Borneo. This part of the world is not as sharply separated from neighboring biogeographic areas; a number of transitional areas exist. From the evidence at hand, it appears that the Oriental realm has served as a center of dispersal in the past.

One of the most diverse realms is the Palearctic region, which contains a temperate European and far eastern (China and Japan) deciduous forest, but much of temperate Asia is a vast, arid area. North of these forementioned regions is an extensive northern coniferous forest above which is a frigid, barren tundra. This realm is of vast geographic extent—from Iceland to Japan. Although the fauna and flora are richest in the temperate deciduous forested areas, the variety of fauna does not compare with that of the Oriental and Ethiopian realms. A much reduced biota is characteristic of the arid and northern portions of the Palearctic realm, but we find a more diverse vertebrate fauna in China due, in all probability, to the invasion and success of some of the Oriental representatives. Another area of comparative diversity in biota is in the Mediterranean area because it has received organisms from the Ethiopian area. The biota, however, has not attained the richness that is characteristic of the Far East.

An area comparable in climate with the Palearctic realm is the Nearctic realm. It extends over North America above the tropics—from the Arctic through northern Mexico—and contains deciduous forests in the eastern temperate areas. Grasslands, desert, and mixed coniferous forests are encountered as one travels westward to the Pacific Coast. As is true in the northern Palearctic realm, extensive coniferous forests and tundra vegetation are located above these southern vegetational zones. The vertebrate fauna in this realm is not as rich as those in neighboring tropical areas. Evidence indicates that much of the fauna and flora have come from the Palearctic (across the Bering land bridge) and the southern more tropical areas (Neotropical realm). In general, vertebrates are more numerous in the southern regions and gradually diminish northward. There is some differentiation east and west throughout the Nearctic in a faunal sense, as is true botanically. According to Darlington (1957), more freshwater fishes and turtles are located east of the Rocky Mountains. Salamanders and snakes are also more numerous in the east, but lizards and some families of rodents (pocket gophers, pocket mice, most ground squirrels, prairie dogs, and kangaroo rats) are limited to the western half of the United States, where in many cases the arid conditions are more in keeping with their ecological requirements.

Central and South America are included within the Neotropical realm. Most of the area is climatically tropical, blanketed by extensive tracts of rain forest (Central America, Ecuador, Colombia, and much of Brazil and Bolivia), grassland and savanna vegetation, as well as scattered arid regions (particularly along the west coast of South America). This basically tropical realm gradually grades into a temperate region toward the southern tip of the continent, with a cool temperate forest of southern beech (*Nothofagus*) in the region of Tierra del Fuego. The biota, in general, comprise a remnant of the Tertiary flora and fauna when South America remained isolated from other biogeographical regions and some North American types, some of which have entered from other Old World areas. The richest biota is centered in the northern tropical regions of South America—areas that are covered by tropical rain forest. The Australian realm includes Tasmania and New Guinea and certain smaller islands in the area (Waigeo, Batanta, Salowati, Aru—off the New Guinea coast—and Kangaroo and King Islands off the south coast of Australia). New Guinea and the northern point of Australia are tropical, covered by tropical rain forest and grassland areas. Southern Australia is of a temperate climate, with forests of eucalyptus and mixed hardwoods. The Australian interior is arid. The fauna of the Australian area contains some remnants of ancient endemic groups as well as some additions that show affinities with organisms of the Oriental realm, but there is little to indicate derivation from either the Neotropical or Ethiopian areas.

TRANSITIONAL AREAS BETWEEN BIOGEOGRAPHICAL REALMS

Wherever regional faunal and floral groups come into contact or are incompletely separated (or poorly separated), a transition will occur that varies with the species and environmental conditions extant in the area. The degree of transition may vary from one extreme where entire families, genera and species may be **exclusive**—that is, they are found in only one realm—to the other extreme where taxonomic groups are shared, or in other words, are found as often in one realm as in another. Some of the biota may be transitional—that is, they extend into the neighboring realm some distance until ecological conditions become intolerable. The degree of transition, sharing, or exclusion can refer to entire families, genera, or species. The Ethiopian-Oriental transitional area contains many shared and exclusive groups, few of which are truly transitional. A few from the Ethiopian realm (chameleons, some birds, hyena, and lion), but only a few vertebrates (some fishes) are transitional from the Oriental area. A parallel situation exists in the region of the Ethiopian-Palearctic transition, where many groups are shared and many are exclusive, but few are truly transitional. Ethiopian animals (geckos, chameleons, birds, elephant shrews, a hyena) extend into the southern part of the Palearctic area, but few Palearctic forms (a turtle, a genus of voles) extend southward.

A transition between the Oriental and Palearctic realm occurs in eastern Asia, with a greater number of organisms extending northward (frogs, many reptiles, birds, and mammals) than are found extending in the opposite direction. The mole, wolf, and a few salamanders are the most common examples of northern invasions of the Oriental realm. A comparison of the Nearctic and Palearctic flora and fauna indicates an extensive transition in northern areas, that is, of the northern flora and fauna. In fact, many species as well as genera and families are common to both areas. But transition is limited to northern temperate areas, for we find that the tropical organisms in each realm show little or no signs of it. The main direction of transition is uncertain because, as regards present biotic distribution, the amount of extension of forms from both realms is difficult to assess from existing information.

An arbitrary point of division between the Nearctic and Neotropical realms occurs north of the isthmus of Tehuantepec (Mexico) with a transitional area extending throughout Mexico and Central America as well as projecting into areas adjacent to these broad transitional areas (United States and parts of northern South America). Nearctic forms extending into the Neotropical realm include *Rana* and plethodontid salamanders that have spread into the northern fringes of South America and occupy all of Central America. Birds including the evening grosbeak, titmice, crossbills, and crows extend into parts of Central America. In the opposite direction, Neotropical reptiles such as the caiman found in Mexico and the crocodile extending into parts of Florida and some of the other Gulf States are examples of a northern invasion from tropical areas. Birds including the cracids, trogons, ibises, and parrots have reached Texas and, in some instances, the southeastern United States. The main direction of transition varies within different classes of vertebrates, as we would expect in a complex intermingling of this type. Among the freshwater fish and amphibians, movement into transitional areas tends to be limited and equal in both directions, but there is a greater number of Nearctic reptiles that have invaded Central America. A greater number of Neotropical, nonmigratory birds extend into Nearctic regions. A greater number of Nearctic mammals occupy Neotropical areas than is true of Neotropical groups, except some of the bats.

The transition, limited as it is, between the Oriental and Australian realms is of considerable interest from the historical point of view. A number of biogeographers have attempted to unravel the complex problem of transition in this part of the world. Even the location of a line of division between the Oriental and Australian realms has aroused considerable controversy (Mayr, 1944), to say nothing of the transitional problem proper. Wallace's Line (Figure 11–7) as first proposed by Wallace (1860) included Bali, Borneo, and Mindanao in the Oriental realm and Lombok, Celebes, Sangi, and Talaud (which fell on the other side of the line) in the Australian realm. At present, the separation of the Oriental and Australian realms may be solved in two ways as suggested by Darlington. A line separating islands with a majority of Oriental forms from those islands with a greater number of Australian representa-

FIGURE 11–7 Islands of the Oriental Region are shown at the left; those of the Australian Region are shown at the right. The intervening group of islands (shaded) represent Wallacea. The western border of Wallacea is formed by Wallace's Line; the eastern boundary is shown by a dashed line to the right of Weber's Line. From *Zoogeography: The Geographical Distribution of Animals* by Philip J. Darlington, Jr., by permission of John Wiley & Sons, Inc., 1957.

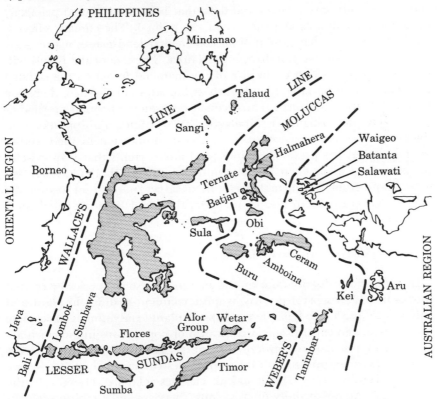

tives (a line of faunal balance, known as Weber's Line) would be one arbitrary solution. Possibly a more satisfactory way of solving the question of separation is the establishment of the Oriental boundary along or near Wallace's Line and the Australian boundary just west of New Guinea including the islands of Waigeo, Batanta, Misol and Aru. The area lying between these boundaries has been called "Wallacea" by Dickerson. It constitutes an important transition zone for many forms from both realms. The general direction of transition between the realms has been primarily from the Oriental realm to the Australian area, with the main area of transition on Celebes. Amphibians, reptiles, and birds display considerable transition from Bali and Celebes to Timor, New Guinea, and northern Australia. Mammals have not enjoyed the extent of transition described for lower vertebrates, which is understandable, because the distribution and subsequent transition are dependent on the availability of natural transport and the organism's ability to cross salt water barriers. For this reason, many of the lower, smaller, and often more tolerant vertebrates have been more successful than have the larger mammals.

The distribution of animals on continental islands (Sumatra, Borneo, Java, Ceylon, Formosa, Japan, Tasmania, Trinidad, Newfoundland, and Greenland) have a fauna and flora that have been limited primarily by climatic conditions and the size of the animal. The climatic effect is much the same as that exhibited on continental land masses mainly—the cooler the climate the less diverse the fauna. The size of the island will be in direct proportion to the size of the mammal found on the isolated land mass. Even on large islands such as Sumatra and Borneo, there is a loss of the larger mammals that becomes even more apparent on smaller islands. On the fringing archipelagos (West Indies, Philippines), continental representatives reach these areas in proportion to their ability to cross water, the prevailing winds, and any currents that may exist in the immediate area. There is evidence that many vertebrates have crossed water gaps from continental areas in a larger number of taxonomic groups (genera) and in greater numbers than had been supposed until recently.

DISCONTINUOUS DISTRIBUTION

Discontinuous distribution, or the presence of some species or related species in widely separated areas, is quite common in different plant and animal groups. These separated groups of plants and animals have come into being by an extinction or withdrawal of populations in intermediate areas for one or more of several reasons: (1) unfavorable ecological conditions (extreme predation, catastrophic destruction of habitats, severe climatic conditions); (2) geological changes (Figure 11–8); (3) the ability and the opportunity to cross water barriers and establish separate

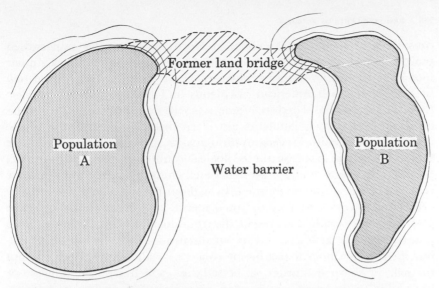

FIGURE 11–8 Two populations, *A* and *B*, isolated from one another owing to an existing water barrier and disappearance of a former land bridge. This has resulted in an extinction of an intermediate aggregation of the species.

population centers; (4) the destruction of a former land bridge that existed at one time in the geological past between the British Isles and Europe, between New Guinea and Australia, and between other areas mentioned previously. Many groups of animals and plants are found in the temperate regions of Eurasia and North America, but between which there is no interconnecting link. This is obviously explained, geologically, by the existence of the Bering land bridge and a warmer climate in the past. Magnolias, tulip trees, and witch hazels are examples of botanical discontinuities in temperate areas; some salamanders, skinks, alligators, and paddlefishes are faunal examples. A number of discontinuities are apparent in tropical regions—in such widely separated regions as tropical Africa, Asia, and South America.

BIOMES AND BIOME TYPES

A **biome** is a climatically controlled area including a number of different communities in various stages of succession. The entire region is dominated by a typical climax type (climatic climax), but it will include a number of diverse climax types (disclimax, edaphic climax, and so on) in accordance with existing ecological conditions. Biomes have been referred to in the literature as **biotic formations,** or **formations.** Although ecological terminology is often loosely applied to local situations, the former terms are in most instances synonymous with the term *biome.* When the biomes of the world are considered, we find that similar biomes have lost their operational or transitional connections and should be considered as **biome types.** Thus, in North America, the grassland or prairie regions are interconnected with few exceptions, just as a similar biome (grassland) in Africa is connected. However, there is no connection between the North American grasslands and those situated in Africa; they should be considered as biome types if we are treating such areas on a worldwide basis. Students are often prone to confuse the biome and biome type with biogeographical realms, previously discussed. The biome concept is based on the ecological conditions (primarily climate) prevalent in the area at the present time; whereas biogeography and the realms that have been established throughout the world are based on the geological history and patterns of dispersal that have occurred in the past, correlated with the present distribution and endemic forms. Two points should be kept in mind in our discussion of biome types throughout the world. One is that a biome concept is valuable until we attempt to make a sharp definition of boundaries, which is often difficult or impossible to do because of overlap, interdigitation of flora and fauna, and the transitional zones which inevitably appear nearly everywhere. The other point is that the faunal distribution discussed is limited to the vertebrates in most cases because the distribution and analysis of the invertebrate fauna is still incomplete in many areas.

TUNDRA

The northernmost biome recognized by ecologists is the **tundra,** a circumpolar formation situated below the polar ice cap in the Holarctic area (Nearctic and Palearctic realms). This region may be more clearly designated as the **arctic tundra** to differentiate it from similar communities situated at high altitudes in montane areas throughout the world, called **alpine tundra.** Arctic tundra covers an extensive area on a worldwide pattern of distribution, as shown in Figure 11–9. The soils in such areas are usually poorly drained and poorly aerated, with permafrost (a permanently frozen substrate) situated a few feet below the surface of the ground. The terrain (Figure 11–10) is of a gentle rolling type, with numerous depressions containing water or ice, depending upon the season of the year. Melting snow, fogs, and frequent rains keep much of the area very moist. Vegetation in these regions is dominated by grasses, sedges, rushes, and lichens, and large conspicuous flowering plants in the drier parts, along with scattered evergreen heaths of leatherleaf (*Chamaedaphne calyculata*), crowberry (*Empetrum nigrum*), and bearberry (*Arctostaphylos uva-ursi*). The large number of depressions that are filled with water much of the time are referred to as *muskegs;* they contain large quantities of *Sphagnum* and *Polytrichum* mosses. Vegetation is affected by the depth to which the soil thaws during the growing season as well as by the ability to survive freezing temperatures that prevail at night during the growing season. Most of the tundra flora will have only

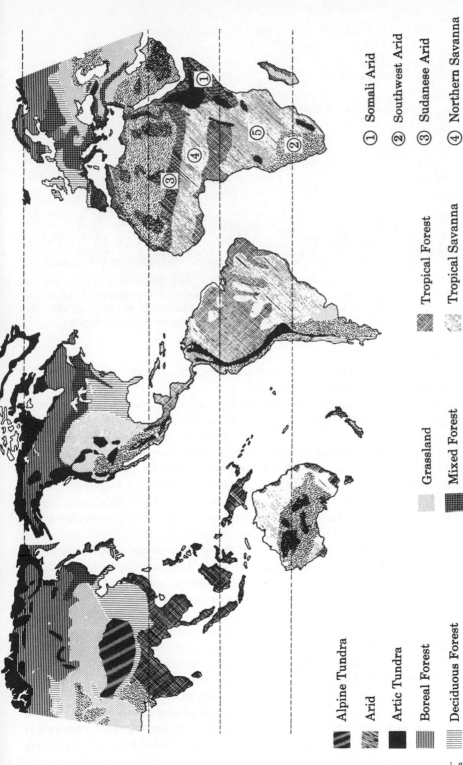

Alpine Tundra

Arid

Artic Tundra

Boreal Forest

Deciduous Forest

Desert (darker
patches = extreme desert)

Grassland

Mixed Forest

Montane Forest
and Alpine Tundra

Tropical Forest

Tropical Savanna

Woodland and Chaparral

① Somali Arid

② Southwest Arid

③ Sudanese Arid

④ Northern Savanna

⑤ Southern Savanna

FIGURE 11–9 Major biomes and their locations throughout the world. (Reprinted from *Animal Ecology* by S. C. Kendeigh by permission of Prentice-Hall, Inc, © 1961, and the author.)

FIGURE 11-10 Tundra biome of the subarctic regions. Photograph taken along the Colville River Delta in Alaska. Plants in blossom around the periphery of the tundra pond in foreground are marsh marigolds *(Coetha palustris)*. Courtesy of Fish and Wildlife Service, U.S. Department of the Interior. Photograph by Urban Nelson.

two or three months for growth and reproductive activity, followed by a long low temperature dormancy.

As might be expected, alpine tundra vegetation is related and often quite similar to the arctic type, because such isolated zones of vegetation represent relic areas that have survived owing to peculiar environmental conditions or situations following the last glacial period, when the tundra area was located much farther south throughout the entire world. These isolated stands of tundra growth are found in isolated bogs and toward the summits of mountains (above the tree line) of some of our higher mountain ranges. Table 11-4 shows the common fauna active in arctic and alpine tundra.

Homoiothermous animals of arctic regions have developed means of conserving body heat in a number of ways. The arctic fox, the hare, and the lemming have what amounts to a double pelt, a woolly undercoat covered by dense soft fur. The former two organisms have even the soles of the feet invested with fur. The snowy owl and ptarmigan have the feet covered by feathers. During the warmer portions of the year, much of the pelt or plumage is shed according to thermal conditions. Of course, some of the arctic fauna (particularly birds) retreat southward during the more adverse periods: the snow bunting, falcon, and raven are examples. The arctic ptarmigan digs tunnels in the snow to provide shelter and also to locate food. Many of the mammals do not retreat but remain in the tundra. Reindeer and musk oxen congregate together, exhaling a

TABLE 11-4. *Common Fauna Found in Arctic Tundra and Alpine Tundra Throughout the World*

NAME	ARCTIC TUNDRA	ALPINE TUNDRA
Snow flea (*Isotoma nivalis*)	X	
Bumblebee (*Bombus consobrinus*)	X	
Snow flea (*Isotoma saltans*)		X
Butterfly (*Maniola glacialis*)		X (Eurasia)
Butterfly (*Bombyx alpica*)		X (Eurasia)
Butterfly (*Lycaena orbitulus*)	X	X (Alps, Pyrenees, Himalayas)
Bumblebee (*Bombus kirbyellus*)	X	X
Land snail (*Helix harpa*)	X	X (Alps)
European wood frog (*Rana temporaria*)	X (Eurasia)	X (Eurasia)
American wood frog (*Rana sylvatica*)	X (North America)	X (North America)
Green toad (*Bufo viridis*)		X (Himalayas)
Andes lizard (*Liolaemus multiformis*)		X (South America)
Snowy owl (*Nyctea nyctea*)	X (North America)	
Willow grouse (*Lagopus saliceti*)	X (North America)	X (Norway)
White grouse (*Lagopus vulgaris*)		X (Europe)
Arctic hare (*Lepus timidus*)	X (Eurasia)	
Arctic hare (*Lepus arcticus*)	X (North America)	
Musk-ox (*Ovibos moschatus*)	X (North America)	
Reindeer (*Rangifer tarandus*)	X (Eurasia)	
Caribou (*Rangifer caribou*)	X (North America)	
Lemming (*Lemmus trimucronatus*)	X (North America)	
Collared lemming (*Dicrostonyx hudsonius*)	X (North America)	
Collared lemming (*Dicrostonyx torquatus*)	X (Eurasia)	
Lemming (*Lemmus lemmus*)		X (Norway)
Mountain goat (*Oreamnos americanus*)		X (North America)
Bighorn sheep (*Ovis canadensis*)		X (North America)

dense cloud of vapor that yields a "greenhouse effect," retaining much of the animal heat below this vaporous cloud. "Greenhouse effect" implies that there is a conservation of heat energy within a limited area as is true in a greenhouse. Just as glass is a barrier to heat transmission, so is the dense cloud of exhaled vapor. Smaller mammals—arctic fox, hare, and lemmings—will either burrow into the snow or locate sheltered areas such as small depressions, rock crevices, or small caves that will afford protection during frequent blizzards.

Low temperatures, lack of food, and low atmospheric pressure are limiting factors with regard to the distribution of animals in the alpine tundra. A number of vertebrates are known to inhabit regions at considerable altitudes. Yaks are found at altitudes exceeding 6,000 meters, and wolves roam at 5,600 meters. The timberline (beginning of alpine tundra) is found at different altitudes, varying from a maximum of 4,600 meters in Tibet to only 2,000 meters on Mount Rainier, in the western part of North America, and about 260 meters in arctic Norway. The lower limits of alpine tundra depend on latitude, slope exposure (south slope, north slope, and so on), and angle of the slope. One noticeable characteristic of much of the alpine fauna is the increased melanism, or dark colors, that predominate in many groups. Many of the beetles, lepidopterans, salamanders, reptiles, and mammals have darker colors at higher altitudes, which is believed to be correlated with increased humidity. Certainly this darker coloration will result in increased absorption of heat and may afford protection against the increased ultraviolet radiation that permeates the thinner atmosphere in much greater quantity at these alpine elevations.

Geographic limitations of the earth's tundra are difficult to establish, but areas with a permanently frozen subsoil and timber line would serve as satisfactory criteria. Extensive circumpolar areas, from Labrador to Alaska in North America and from Lapland to the Chukchi Sea in Eurasia, are blanketed with tundra type vegetation and fauna. Borders of Antarctica and the surrounding islands represent the southern counterpart of the tundra biome type. Alpine tundra may be present on any mountain or mountain range of sufficiently high altitude, but the areas with a considerable amount of alpine tundra are the Himalayas of southeastern Asia, the Andes in South America, the Rockies and coastal ranges of North America, and isolated mountains and mountain ranges in eastern and southeastern Africa.

TAIGA

Taiga, or northern boreal forest, is the most extensive continuous forest type in either the Eastern or Western Hemisphere. Stands of taiga forest are located south of the tundra or treeless biome and are limited to the Northern Hemisphere. Worldwide distribution of this biome extends from the western portions of central Alaska, across Canada, then sweeps along the northern shores of Lake Superior to Newfoundland. In Eurasia, this biome extends from the western shores of Norway across northern and central Sweden, all of Finland, and throughout northern and central parts of Russia to the Sea of Ohotsk and the Bering Strait.

Precipitation in the form of rainfall or snowfall in these areas will vary considerably, averaging from 30 to 150 inches per year throughout the biome. On the North American continent, the white spruce (*Picea glauca*) is the most common (dominant) tree, though black spruce (*Picea mariana*) and tamarack (*Larix laricina*) are frequently dominant species in boggy or poorly drained regions, replacing the sphagnum mosses that have thrived in these muskegs (Figure 11–11). The former species is often found at considerable altitudes on cliffs and mountains throughout the boreal forest. Associated with these species are balsam fir (*Abies balsamea*) in eastern stands and balsam poplar (*Populus balsamifera*) on extensive flood plains; jackpine (*Pinus banksiana*) is common on sandy or sandy gravel soils. During dry seasons, portions of this biome frequently burn because of careless hunters, campers, or lightning. These burnouts in different stages of development represent excellent examples of the successional sequence, as shown in Figure 11–12. All of the successional series terminate with white spruce as the climax forest.

Though boreal forests as shown in Figure 11–13 have a rigorous climate, with freezing temperatures occurring at any time of the year, the greater amount of snowfall moderates the depth of freezing temperatures in the soil. Winter temperatures seldom fall below −39° C. (−39° F.)

FIGURE 11–11 A typical northern muskeg community in the Tongas National Forest, Alaska. Courtesy of the U.S. Forest Service.

FIGURE 11-12 Burn-out succession occurring in an area formerly populated by a coniferous forest community in Clearwater National Forest, Idaho. Courtesy of the U.S. Forest Service.

and the soil freezes to a depth of six to eight feet. The growing season averages a month or two longer than do the tundra regions to the north. Seasons are represented by a definite spring and summer, but the autumnal interval is often brief, merging into a long, cold winter usually a month or so after the termination of summer. Extensions of the boreal forest continue southward along mountain ranges, particularly through the Rocky Mountain and Sierra ranges and the Appalachian chain. In these instances, the dominant species varies from the spruce-fir (*Picea-Abies* association) of more southern stands to the hemlock-pine (*Tsuga-Pinus* association) of the Sierras.

HEMLOCK-HARDWOOD FOREST BIOME

South of the boreal forest or taiga, is a complex plant formation extending from southern Manitoba through southern Ontario, Quebec, New Brunswick, and Nova Scotia. From this area it extends southward through New York, most of New England, and through much of the Appalachian range, reaching higher altitudes toward the southern limits. This biome contains a larger number of characteristic species than is true of the more northern taiga formation. Hemlock (*Tsuga* sp.), eastern

(A)

FIGURE 11–13 Photograph *A* shows a northern coniferous forest biome typical of vast expanses of Canada and Alaska. This photograph, taken along Ella Creek, Alaska, shows coniferous trees dominated by yellow cedar, hemlock, and Sitka spruce. Photograph *B* is an aerial view of Tongas National Forest, Alaska, dominated by western red cedar and Alaskan cedar. Courtesy of the U.S. Forest Service.

(B)

white pine *(Pinus strobus)*, red pine *(P. resinosa)*, red spruce *(Picea rubra,* the chief source of pulpwood in North America), sugar maple *(Acer saccharum)*, red maple *(A. rubrum)*, beech *(Fagus grandifolia)*, and yellow birch *(Betula alleghaniensis)* are common representatives of these stands. Scattered throughout this biome are isolated relics of the boreal forest located along some of the higher slopes and in cooler areas where climatic conditions support this vegetation that dominated these same areas during much cooler geological eras. On the other hand, there are scattered stands of deciduous forest trees along the lower slopes, in valleys, and along the margins of large lakes, where the climatic conditions are warmer than the average permeating the typical hemlock-hardwood biome type. Climatic conditions in this biome are not as harsh as those characteristic of the boreal forest; the growing season is a month or more longer in length (four to five months per year), and freezing temperatures seldom occur between June and August, although nocturnal temperatures may range from 4.4 to 7.2° C. (40° F. to 45° F.). Mixed coniferous-hardwood forest extends through considerable parts of the eastern portion of Europe, western Russia, coastal parts of northern China, and Korea, as well as the southern part of the Scandinavian peninsula.

WESTERN MONTANE BIOME

The higher slopes of mountainous regions of the southwest and the entire slopes of the more northern extremities of western ranges are covered by coniferous stands of varying composition. Englemann spruce *(Picea englemannii)* and several species of fir *(Abies* spp.), mountain hemlock *(Tsuga mertensiana)*, and alpine larch *(Larix lyallie)* are associated in different parts of western montane forests. Forests dominated by Englemann spruce are located on slopes 3,000 to 4,000 feet above sea level in British Columbia, but in the southwestern parts of the United States this forest type is located at 10,000 or 12,000 feet. Below this belt of Englemann spruce is a belt dominated by Douglas fir *(Pseudotsuga taxifolia)*, in the northern Rocky Mountain range; western larch *(Larix occidentalis)*, western white pine *(Pinus monticola)*, and lodgepole pine *(P. contorta)* may be associated with this dominant. Lodgepole pine invades burned-over areas at every elevation and is most common in cool, moist situations at the upper limit of the Douglas fir zone. The western yellow pine *(Pinus ponderosa)* occurs along the eastern slopes of the Cascades and Sierras and on the lower slopes of the more northern ranges in British Columbia. This conifer is commonly associated with Douglas fir and sugar pine *(Pinus lambertiana)* in the Sierras to an elevation of 5,500 feet, and from 6,000 to 9,000 feet in the central Rocky Mountain area. Western yellow pine is seldom found above 3,000 feet in British

Columbia, but it may extend up to 8,000 feet or more in Arizona, New Mexico, and Texas, where it inhabits regions of low rainfall (twenty to thirty inches per year). The spotted frog (*Rana pretiosa*) and the western newt (*Taricha torosa*) are two of the more common amphibians found in montane forests. The avifauna would include the red-breasted nuthatch (*Sitta canadensis*), mountain chickadee (*Parus gambeli*), ruby-crowned kinglet (*Regulus calendula*), golden-crowned kinglet (*R. satrapa*), Clark's nutcracker (*Nucifraga columbiana*), and Audubon's warbler (*Dendroica auduboni*) as typical species. The black bear (*Ursus americanus*), the more northern grizzly bear (*Ursus horribilis*)—one of the largest terrestrial carnivores—western marten (*Martes americana*), wolverines (*Gulo luscus*), gray wolf (*Canis lupus*), mountain lions—also known as cougars—pumas and panthers (*Felis concolor*), lynx (*Lynx canadensis*), and the elk, or wapiti (*Cervus canadensis*) are some of the larger mammals representative of western montane forests. The yellow-bellied marmot (*Marmota flaviventer*) inhabits lower slopes of western mountains, while the golden-mantled ground squirrel (*Citellus lateralis*) is found at different altitudes in coniferous forest areas. Other rodents found in these areas include the yellow pine chipmunk (*Eutamias amoenus*), found at high altitudes in more northern areas, the Colorado chipmunks (*E. quadrivittatus*), in the higher mountains of southern montane forests, and the mountain beaver (*Aplodontia rufa*), which, incidentally, is not a true beaver. Scattered stands of montane forests are located in the higher mountainous areas of eastern Africa (Ethiopia, Kenya, eastern part of the Congo, northern Rhodesia, and the eastern part of South Africa). In South America, montane forest as well as alpine tundra are located along the Andes Mountains, from Colombia to southern Chile.

PINON-JUNIPER BIOME

Below the western yellow pine forests, where a drier climate prevails (average annual rainfall of ten to twenty inches), there are vast stretches of open, savannalike woodland dominated by piñon pines (*Pinus edulis* and *P. monophylla*) and several species of juniper (*Juniperus* spp.). Stands of this vegetation type, similar to the type shown in Figure 11–14, extend throughout large portions of the Great Basin and down into Arizona and New Mexico. The mule deer (*Odocoileus hemionus*), coyote (*Canis latrans*), and mountain lion often descend into this open woodland biome during the winter. Several rodents spend the entire year in these areas, including the desert wood rat (*Neotoma lepida*), the dusky-footed wood rat (*N. fuscipes*), the piñon mouse (*Peromyscus truei*), the Great Basin pocket mouse (*Perognathus parvus*), and the rock squirrel (*Citellus variegatus*).

FIGURE 11–14 Typical open woodland of the pinon-juniper type shows oak *(Quercus emorii)* and juniper *(Juniperus psychyphloea)* in foreground in the Coronado National Forest, Arizona. Courtesy of the U.S. Forest Service.

PACIFIC COAST FOREST BIOME

In northern parts of this biome, along the Oregon coast, the combined precipitation totals in excess of 130 inches. Part of this total is in the form of rainfall and the remaining portion is due to condensation of fog as it moves in off the coast. There are few places where forest growth of this type (Figure 11–15) extends inland more than thirty miles, but in the Washington, Oregon, and northern California area, this precipitation is maximal, becoming somewhat less in the northern extreme along the Alaskan coast and much drier through central and southern California. In the northern portion of this biome type is Sitka spruce *(Picea sitchensis)*, which stretches along much of the rugged Alaskan coastline; in Washington the western hemlock *(Tsuga heterophylla)* becomes the more dominant species. Farther south, Douglas fir and finally the towering redwood *(Sequoia sempervirens)*, often reaching a height of 340 feet, form the southern limit of the larger luxuriant forest trees.

In these northern stands, the high humidity and plentiful precipitation produce thick undergrowth—shrubs such as salmonberry, rhododendron, and dogwood and a number of tall ferns. Farther south along the

T A B L E   1 1 – 5 .   *Common Fauna of the Pacific Coast Forest Biome Types*

NAME	HUMID FOREST	DRY CHAPARRAL
Class Mammalia:		
Fisher *(Neurotrichus gibbsii)*	X	
Coyote *(Canis latrans)*	X	
Hoary marmots *(Marmota caligata)*	X	
Townsend chipmunk *(Eutamias townsendii)*	X	
Chickarees *(Tamiasciurus douglasii)*	X	
Northern flying squirrels *(Glaucomys sabrinus)*	X	
Tree heather vole *(Phenacomys longicaudus)*	X	
Mountain beaver *(Aplodontia rufa)*	X	
Rock ground squirrel *(Citellus variegatus)*	X	X
Black rat *(Rattus rattus)*	X	X
Western harvest mouse *(Reithrodontomys megalotis)*		X
Brush rabbit *(Sylvilagus bachmani)*		X
Class Aves:		
Hairy woodpecker *(Dendrocopos villosus)*	X	
Hermit thrush *(Hylocichla guttata)*	X	
Western bluebird *(Sialia mexicana)*	X	
Ruby-crowned kinglet *(Regulus calendula)*	X	
Cedar waxwing *(Bombycilla cedrorum)*	X	
Solitary vireo *(Vireo solitarius)*	X	
Purple finch *(Carpodacus purpureus)*	X	
Mountain quail *(Oreortyx pictus)*		X
California quail *(Lophortyx californicus)*		X
Wrentit *(Chamaea fasciata)*		X
California thrasher *(Toxostoma redivivum)*		X
Brown towhee *(Pipilo fuscus)*		X
Black-chinned sparrow *(Spizella atrogularis)*		X
Class Reptilia:		
Whip snakes *(Masticophis taeniatus)*		X
Class Amphibia:		
Bell toad *(Ascaphus truei)*	X	
Red-legged frog *(Rana aurora)*	X	
Spotted frog *(Rana pretiosa)*	X	
Olympic salamander *(Rhyacotriton olympicus)*	X	
Western newt *(Taricha torosa)*	X	

lower California coast, a chaparral-like oak type of open forest prevails because of the more xeric conditions in these areas. Chaparral vegetation, as shown in Figure 11–16, consists of broad-leaved evergreen plants of scrubby appearance, exhibiting a stunted or shrubby growth form. This

FIGURE 11–15 Pacific Coast forest vegetation, the luxuriant growth so typical of the forest communities in Washington and Oregon, is owing to ideal moisture and thermal values that exist throughout the growing season. Courtesy of the National Park Service, U.S. Department of the Interior.

vegetation has become the predominant type in areas where extremely dry periods lasting a number of months alternate with a rainy season of variable duration. Chamise (*Adenostoma fasciculata*), coastal live oak (*Quercus agrifolia*), and manzanita (*Arctostaphylos glauca*) are common species of vegetation in these areas. Open dry woodland and chapparal type vegetation extend through areas of central and southern Mexico,

FIGURE 11–16 A chaparral-oak community typical of the southern California coastal area. Courtesy of the U.S. Forest Service.

along nearly the entire Mediterranean coastline, and along the southern border of the Black Sea. Some of the common fauna of the Pacific Coast forest area is in Table 11–5.

MIXED DECIDUOUS FOREST

South of the hemlock-hardwood forest and east of the grasslands of the Midwest are extensive areas of mixed deciduous forest. The species composition of climax stands vary with the geographic locality, but the oaks (*Quercus* spp.) are one of the most constant representatives, and the white oak (*Quercus alba*) was and still is the most widely distributed species. Upland hardwood communities consist of beech-maple (*Fagus-Acer*), oak-maple-linden (*Quercus-Acer-Tilia*), white oak (*Quercus alba*), and farther south, oak-hickory (*Quercus-Carya*). In lowland communities, where soil moisture is relatively high or drainage is poor, different hardwood communities appear. In the north, swamp white oak (*Quercus bicolor*) and hickory predominate as climax species, but as one goes southward these are replaced by communities of elm (*Ulmus*), ash (*Fraxinus*), and red maple (*Acer rubrum*). Further south these elm-ash-maple communities give way to eastern cottonwood (*Populus deltoides*), willow (*Salix*), and American sycamore (*Platanus occidentalis*). In order to support these vegetational communities, there must be an average annual rainfall of thirty to sixty inches. Therefore, an annual rainfall of thirty-five inches in Texas, and twenty-five inches in Minnesota, cou-

(A)

pled with frequent and long-term droughts, prevents the establishment of deciduous forests west of these states. The point of transition between deciduous forest and grassland is not abrupt, but changes gradually: as the soil moisture becomes less adequate the dense forest gives way to a savannalike woodland with scattered trees (often dwarfed), and intermediate areas containing stands of grasses or scrub oak. Northward, low winter temperatures and a shorter growing season place a physiological limit on the distribution of the hardwood species. Southward, an absence of a period of low temperature dormancy that is necessary for after-ripening of seeds and to renew growth of buds restricts this vegetation

(B)

FIGURE 11–17 Coastal maritime live oak forest located along the east coast of the United States. Photograph *A* is a young live oak stand along the North Carolina coast. Photograph *B* shows the interior of a mature live oak stand with Spanish moss on Jekyll Island, Georgia. Photograph *B*, courtesy of the U.S. Forest Service.

type. In addition to covering much of the eastern half of the United States, this forest type is present throughout much of the British Isles, central Europe, northern Spain, Yugoslavia, Romania and through a portion of central Russia. In Asia, a temperate deciduous forest biome type is found in northern Japan, Manchuria, Mongolia, Korea, and south central China (Chungking-Hangchow area). An extensive list of faunal representative is given in Table 10–2 (Chapter X, "Ecological Succession") for the hardwood forest biome.

SOUTHEASTERN EVERGREEN FOREST BIOME

This biome includes the pine barrens of longleaf (*Pinus palustris*), shortleaf (*P. echinata*), loblolly (*P. taeda*), and slash pine (*P. virginiana*). The extensive stands extend along the coastal plain and piedmont areas of the southeastern part of the United States. In many areas, the longleaf pine has become the disclimax species as a result of recurrent fires in southeastern areas (see Chapter X). Loblolly pine is often the dominant tree near the northern portion of the biome, with longleaf and finally slash pine extending into the northern half of the Florida peninsula. Canebrakes dominated by the only native bamboo plant in North America (*Arundinaria*) are common in the southeast along the banks of streams and in coastal areas. Although this cane predominates in the lower marshy areas, along with cypress (*Taxodium distichum*) near the coast, live oak (*Quercus virginiana*) and a variety known as dwarf live oak (*Q. virginiana maritima*), with the epiphyte Spanish moss (*Tillandsia usneoides*) festooned from the boughs, form extensive maritime forest communities (Figure 11–17). Toward the subtropical portion of the biome, hammocks of tropical or subtropical vegetation such as the strangler fig (*Fiscus aurea*) and the sabal palm (*Sabal palmetto*), along with a number of epiphytes and vines of the orchid and pineapple family, are prominent features of the landscape. Many of the predominant faunistic representatives found in the southeastern evergreen biome are listed in Table 10–2, Chapter X.

GRASSLAND BIOME TYPE

In the past, an area extending from the Mississippi Valley westward to the Rocky Mountains and western deserts was occupied by a **grassland** or **prairie** type community (Figure 11–18). This type of vegetation extends into southern Saskatchewan and Alberta, running southward through Texas and on into eastern Mexico to Yucatan and Nicaragua. Prairie "islands" are located in the drier parts of Indiana and Ohio, with each "island" surrounded by deciduous forest (beech-maple climax vegetation). Synonymous terms for this type of biome, such as **steppe, campo, llano,** and **pampas,** are an indication of its widespread distribution throughout the world. In South America a spacious prairie biome type extends throughout much of Brazil, Argentina, Venezuela, and Paraguay. In Eurasia, a grassland region spans an area from the western edge and northern border of the Black Sea and Caspian Sea, across southern Russia and China to the East China Sea. Scattered, but much smaller, prairie areas exist in India, western China, Thailand, Cambodia, and Viet Nam. In Africa, expansive areas of this vegetation type (either grassland or savanna) cover areas of French West Africa, the eastern Belgian Congo (following the Nile River Valley northward), South Africa, and western Madagascar. In the Pacific, the northern half of Australia and the southern edge of New Guinea are carpeted with a grassland and savanna type of floral cover.

A temperate climate and frequent periods of erratic and limited precipitation (often interspersed with extended periods of drought) insure a grassland biome type. The average rainfall throughout the grassland areas of North America varies from thirty-five to forty inches in the northeastern regions, thirty inches in Texas, some twenty to

FIGURE 11–18 A prairie biome type of the midwestern portion of the United States. This photograph shows a few members of the buffalo herd of nearly 25,000 individuals that now roam the prairie areas of the Midwest. Courtesy of the Soil Conservation Service, U.S. Department of Agriculture.

twenty-five inches in the northwest, and only ten to fifteen inches in the far western portion of the biome. Most of the precipitation occurs in the spring, but often extended droughts characterize the fall of the year. In the summer, dry winds and high temperatures have a desiccating effect on prairie and savanna areas in many parts of the world. North American prairies may be subdivided into tall, mixed, and short grass areas in belts running roughly north and south. The eastern tall grass prairies have grasses that often grow to a height of eight or ten feet. Tall bluestem (*Andropogon furcatus*), big bluestem (*A. gerardi*), Indian grass (*Sorghastrum nutans*), and slough grass (*Spartina michauxiana*) are the dominant species in the tall prairie zone. West of the tall prairie, a drier belt of grassland, the mixed grass prairie includes little bluestem (*Andropogon scoparius*), needle grass (*Stipa spartea*), wheat grass (*Agropyron spicatum*), and several species of grama grass (*Bouteloua* spp.).

Prairie stands of the Far West, called the short grass prairies, are dominated by grama grasses and buffalo grass (*Buchloe dactyloides*). There are the dry prairie areas, which grade into the desert shrublands, for rainfall is more restricted; in some areas the soil will possess a layer of hard pan (calcium carbonate) only a few feet from the surface. Only the surface layers contain water, and during dry years there are only meager amounts available to the overlying vegetation. The faunistic composition of prairie and desert areas is presented in Table 11–6.

TABLE 11–6. *Faunal Composition of Prairie and Desert Areas of the United States*

NAME	PRAIRIE	DESERT
Class Mammalia:		
Black-footed ferret (*Mustela nigripes*)	X	
Coyote (*Canis latrans*)	X	
Thirteen-lined ground squirrel (*Citellus tridecemlineatus*)	X	
Black-tailed prairie dog (*Cynomys ludovicianus*)	X	
Plains pocket gopher (*Geomys bursarius*)	X	
Northern grasshopper mice (*Onychomys leucogaster*)	X	
Prairie vole (*Microtus ochrogaster*)	X	
White-tailed jackrabbit (*Lepus townsendii*)	X	
Black-tailed jackrabbit (*Lepus californicus*)	X	
Bison (*Bison bison*)	X	
Pronghorn (*Antilocapra americana*)	X	
Desert shrew (*Notiosorex crawfordi*)		X
Ringtail (*Bassariscus astutus*)		X
Hog-nosed skunks (*Conepatus leconotus*)		X
Kit fox (*Vulpes macrotis*)		X
Jaguar (*Felis onca*)		X
Townsend ground squirrel (*Citellus townsendii*)		X
Pallid kangaroo mouse (*Microdipodops pallidus*)		X
Dark kangaroo mouse (*Microdipodops megacephalus*)		X
Western pocket gopher (*Thomomys bottae*)		X
Apache pocket mouse (*Perognathus apache*)		X
Great Basin pocket mouse (*Perognathus parvus*)		X
Desert kangaroo rat (*Dipodomys deserti*)		X
Cactus mouse (*Peromyscus eremicus*)		X
Desert wood rat (*Neotoma lepida*)		X
White-throated wood rat (*Neotoma albigula*)		X
Sagebrush vole (*Lagurus curtatus*)		X
Antelope jackrabbit (*Lepus alleni*)		X
Desert cottontail (*Sylvilagus audobonii*)		X
Pigmy rabbit (*Sylvilagus idahoensis*)		X
Collared peccaries (*Pecari tajacu*)		X
Armadillo (*Dasypus novemcinctus*)		X
Class Aves:		
Ferruginous hawk (*Buteo regalis*)	X	
Lark sparrow (*Chonestes grammacus*)	X	
Short-eared owl (*Asio flammeus*)	X	
Greater prairie chicken (*Tympanuchus cupido*)	X	
Lesser prairie chicken (*Tympanuchus pallidicinctus*)	X	
Prairie warbler (*Dendroica discolor*)	X	
Bobolink (*Dolichonyx oryzivorus*)	X	
Sharp-tailed grouse (*Pedioecetes phasianellus*)	X	

T A B L E 1 1 – 6 *(continued)*

NAME	PRAIRIE	DESERT
Class Aves: *(continued)*		
Roadrunner *(Geococcyx californianus)*		X
Gila woodpecker *(Centurus uropygialis)*		X
Cactus wren *(Campylorhynchus brunneicapillum)*		X
Lucy's warbler *(Vermivora luciae)*		X
LeConte's thrasher *(Taxostoma lecontei)*		X
Class Reptilia:		
Bull snake *(Pituophis melanoleucus)*	X	
Prairie rattler *(Crotalus viridis)*	X	X
Ground gecko *(Coleonyx variegatus)*		X
Chuckwalla *(Sauromalus obesus)*		X
Desert iguana *(Dipsosaurus dorsalis)*		X
Leopard lizard *(Gambelia wislizeni)*		X
Zebra-tailed sand lizard *(Callisaurus draconoides)*		X
Desert horned lizard *(Phrynosoma platyrhinos)*		X
Gila monster *(Heloderma suspectum)*		X
Shovel-nosed snake *(Chionactis occipitalis)*		X
Whip snake *(Nasticophis taeniatus)*		X
Leaf-nosed snake *(Phyllorhynchus browni)*		X
Patch-nosed snake *(Salvadora lineata)*		X
Western coral snake *(Micruroides euryxanthus)*		X
Sidewinder *(Crotalus cerastes)*		X
Western diamondback rattler *(Crotalus atrox)*		X
Red rattler *(Crotalus ruber)*		X
Class Amphibia:		
Great Plains toad *(Bufo cognatus)*	X	

DESERT BIOME TYPE

As one leaves the prairie areas, a gradual transition from the short grass prairies through regions containing "winter fat" *(Eurotia lanata)*, a shallow-rooted plant common on dry, mildly alkaline soils of the South or on sagebrush *(Artemisia)* regions of the North takes place before reaching true **desert** country. From Colorado to California and from southern Idaho to southern Mexico, arid conditions, with only one or two rainy periods a year, results in a sparse distribution of perennials such as creosote bush *(Covillea glutinosa)*, mesquite *(Prosopis joliflora)*, organ-pipe cactus *(Lemaireocereus thurberi)*, and barrel cactus *(Ferrocactus cylindraceus)*. These plants are variously adapted to the arid climate where rainfall may vary from zero to ten inches. A photograph of typical desert vegetation taken in Nevada is shown in Figure 11–19. Most desert plants have a low transpiration rate owing to thick layers of cortical tissue, fewer stomata, or fewer leaves (or small leaves—that is, spines of cactus). An extensive, shallow root system and water storage areas in stems or roots that will store thirty or more tons of water in some of the larger cacti are adaptive aids in an environment where water is at a premium and evaporation rates are high.

In many areas of the desert, annuals must germinate, bloom, and reproduce during a rainy season of short duration that may occur twice a year (summer and winter) in some parts of the desert. Salt deposits of sulfates, borax carbonates, and chlorides will often accumulate in shallow basins where the evaporation rate is high. Greasewood (*Sarcobatus vermiculatus*), seepwood (*Suaeda intermedia*), and salt grass (*Distichlis spicata*) are common floristic representatives in these salty depressions of the desert. One of the most extensive deserts in the world is the Sahara Desert of North Africa. This area, in general, falls well within the criteria established for desert communities by Professor Wladimir Koppen of the University of Graz (Austria) in 1918. The Koppen deserts that occupy 14 per cent (8 million square miles) of the world's 56 million square miles of terrestrial environment are characterized by an average

FIGURE 11–19 A desert biome type typical of the more arid regions of the western United States. Joshua cacti are the predominant flora in this view of the Desert Game Range, Las Vegas, Nevada. Antelope and deer are found in this area, with mountain sheep in the surrounding mountains. Courtesy of Fish and Wildlife Service, U.S. Department of the Interior.

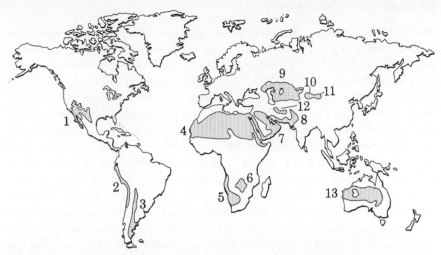

FIGURE 11–20 The location and extent of the world's major deserts: (1) North American deserts; (2) Atacamba-Peruvian Desert; (3) Patagonian Desert; (4) Sahara Desert; (5) Namib Desert; (6) Kalahari Desert; (7) Arabian Desert; (8) Thar Desert; (9) Turkestan Desert; (10) Takla-Makan Desert; (11) Gobi Desert; (12) Iranian Desert; (13) Australian Desert.

annual rainfall of less than ten inches and high temperatures. The Sahara Desert (Figure 11–20)—the world's largest desert, extending 3½ million square miles (almost as large as all fifty of the United States)—has mountains with elevations of 11,500 feet that will receive snow during the year; but most of the area receives less than an inch of rainfall during a twelve-month period.

Other major desert communities throughout the world, aside from the North American deserts, include the Australian Desert (covering nearly 44 per cent of the land area) in central and western Australia, the Arabian Desert, the Turkestan Desert of southwest Russia, the Atacamba-Peruvian Desert in Chile and Peru, the Patagonian Desert of Argentina, the Thar Desert of western India and Pakistan, the Iranian Desert of old Persia, the Takla Makan Desert of western China, the Gobi of Mongolia, and two deserts of South Africa, the Kalahari and Namib. The Arabian desert has nearly a third of its area covered with sand and a complete absence of rivers, and the Atacamba-Peruvian Desert of South America is the world's driest, with an average of less than half an inch of rainfall per year.

The world's deserts are located in areas where the prevailing winds have lost most of their moisture to the north or south of the locality. Where deserts lie along the western edge of continental areas, in many instances the onshore winds have been cooled by cold ocean currents and therefore lose little water as they move inland because they can carry little water owing to their cooler temperatures. In other areas, deserts have become established along the leeward sides of mountains, and prevailing air currents have lost most of their moisture before they have reached these regions (see Chapter V, "Climatology"). Along with the low precipitation values prevalent in desert areas, thermal values fluctuate with considerable amplitude over a short interval of time. The low humidity of the desert atmosphere allows for more intense penetration by the sun's rays. The blanket of humid air that tends to insulate moister environments throughout the world (decreasing daytime temperatures) will also prevent the rapid loss of heat from the earth's surface after dark. But in desert areas, where this protective blanket of moist air is lacking, nighttime temperatures may drop from a daytime high of 120° F. or more to a low of 50° F. or lower after the daylight period. Altitude and latitude will also alter the desert climate: the greater the altitude or the greater the distance from the equator, the cooler the desert. In this regard, the Sahara Desert of northern Africa is the hottest, and the Gobi Desert of Mongolia is the coldest.

TROPICAL RAIN FOREST BIOME TYPE

Although the **tropical rain forest** biome type is not found in North America, it is common in many other parts of the world located close to or within the limits of the Tropic of Cancer and Tropic of Capricorn. The most extensive stands of the tropical rain forest are located in southern India, southeastern Asia, the East Indies, Central America, northern South America, and central Africa (Congo and southern part of French Equatorial Africa). Usually, one's first impression of a tropical rain forest is an area containing such a maze of vines, giant ferns, trees, and shrubs that it requires a man with a strong back and a sharp jungle knife to blaze a path through this profuse mass of vegetation. Actually such an idea, though popularized in some films and novels, could not be further from the truth. This stereotyped concept of a jungle is found only where clearings have been made by man or where one encounters the forest margin (such as along streams or the ecological limit of the biome type). It is in these limited areas (Figure 11–21) that sunlight is able to penetrate and produce a tangled maze of vegetation. Within the forest the tree trunks are huge in comparison with those in temperate forest communities. The forest interior has a cathedral-like aspect, with tall unbranched tree trunks extending up toward a thick canopy comprised of many layers of vegetation that permit very little light to reach the forest floor. This drastic reduction in sunlight accounts for the open appearance of the forest interior, with few shrubs and herbs that can tolerate this reduced amount of light. Lianas or vines as thick as a man's body hang from trees in considerable numbers, and blooming epiphytes appear in profusion as one traverses a rain forest. Rain forests, as is true of many tropical areas, have a large

FIGURE 11–21 The forest edge of a tropical rain forest biome in Puerto Rico. Courtesy of the U.S. Forest Service.

number of species, but the total number of any one species is relatively low. The forest canopy, which is thick, consists of a number of distinct strata, or as Alexander von Humboldt described it, "a forest above a forest." A few trees such as ironwood (*Dialium guianense*) may extend above the canopy, extending up some 130 feet or more above the forest floor. The main canopy located between 75 to 100 feet from the forest floor may contain banak (*Virola brachycarpa*) and matalpo (*Ficus*), a somewhat lower stratum (40 to 60 feet) may contain negrito (*Simaruba glauca*), mountain trumpet (*Cecropia mexicana*), and cohune (*Orbignya cohune*). A third distinct layer, 20 to 30 feet above the soil level includes white copal (*Protium sessiliflorum*), waika plum (*Rheedia edulis*), timber sweet (*Nectandra*), and cacho venado (*Eugenia capuli*). A shrub layer of wild coffee (*Rinorea guatemalensis*) rises 10 feet or so above the jungle floor and receives very little light through the thick overlying canopy. The stranglers that are so common in tropical rain forests usually germinate in the fork of a tree, becoming epiphytes for some time. Usually two roots appear. One acts as a holdfast for the plant, maintaining its position in the tree; the other grows down toward the soil of the forest floor. After it reaches the soil, the plant grows rapidly, producing more roots that descend to the forest floor. These roots that wrap themselves around the trunk of the host tree gradually strangle the tree. The host tree finally dies, leaving a strangler with a hollow trunk (actually a number of fused roots).

As is true of tropical rain forest vegetation, the number of species of invertebrates and vertebrates in these areas is very high. In fact, Griscom (1945) has estimated that about 85 per cent of the bird species are of tropical origin. This figure may be a little high, but it is probably a fairly close estimate. Old World birds of the tropics include the guinea fowls, touracos, honey guides, pittas, and bulbuls of Africa. In the rain forests of the Oriental area, wood swallows, flower peckers, sunbirds, and drongos are common. In the Western Hemisphere potoos, puffbirds, jacamars, toucans, ant birds, honey creepers, and tanagers are numerous (see Table 11–7).

The warm, humid air of tropical rain forests throughout the world is an ideal environment for frogs and toads. Many of these amphibians are totally arboreal and never leave the trees even to lay eggs. *Rhacophorus* and *Phyllomedusa* lay their eggs in clusters on the branches of trees that overhang water. Upon hatching, the larvae drop into the water to complete their development. The tropical American female frog *Cerathyla bubalus* carries her eggs on her back until time of hatching. Among reptilian forms, chameleons with grasping feet and prehensile tails are common on Madagascar and in the rain forest of Africa. The agamid lizards of the Eastern Hemisphere and iguanid reptiles of the American tropical forests have representatives that are ground dwellers and arboreal. Most of the snakes, such as the pythons and boas, are large but not numerous, although many are very well adapted to arboreal life.

Mammals appear to be sparse, if one is concerned with a daylight census of active forms, but this is only because most of the mammals, with the exception of monkeys, are active only after nightfall. Opossums, sloths, bats, jaguars, leopards, and some rodents are nocturnal in habit. Many of the ground-dwelling mammals are small, stealthy forms. The small musk deer (*Tragulus*) and the forest goat antelope (*Nemorhoedus*) of the Malay area and the dwarf forest antelope (*Cephalophus*) of Africa are examples. In South American rain forests, the agoutis and peccaries are the ecological equivalents of forms cited. Even some of the larger mammals such as the swamp antelope (*Tragelaphus*) and the striped antelope (*Booceros*) of Africa tend to have secretive habits.

The tropical rain forest is devoid of a thick litter. The clay soil has little herbaceous growth because of the decreased light that finally reaches this stratum. Leaves and other debris that reach the forest floor undergo a rather rapid decomposition. The tremendous populations of insects, bacteria, and fungi quickly dispose of the falling detritus, so that in a matter of a few weeks entire trees or branches that have fallen disappear.

TABLE 11–7. *Distribution of the Avifæuna of Tropical Rain Forests Throughout the World*

NAME	DISTRIBUTION
Toco toucan *(Ramphastos toco)*	The Guianas, Brazil
Keel-billed toucan *(Ramphastos sulfuratus)*	Mexico to Venezuela
Emerald toucanet *(Aulacorhynchus prasinus)*	Mexico to Peru
Green aracari *(Pteroglossus viridis)*	Colombia through Brazil
Collared puffbird *(Bucco capensis)*	Colombia to Peru and Brazil
Large-billed puffbird *(Notharcus macrorhynchos)*	Mexico to Argentina
Paradise jacamar *(Galbula dea)*	Venezuela to Bolivia
Great jacamar *(Jacamerops aurea)*	Costa Rica to the Guianas and Ecuador
Great potoo *(Nyctibius grandis)*	Panama to Brazil
Chestnut-backed antbird *(Myrmeciza exsul)*	Nicaragua to Ecuador
Spotted antbird *(Hylophylax naevioides)*	Nicaragua to Ecuador
Paradise tanager *(Tangara chilensis)*	Colombia to Brazil and Bolivia
Scarlet-rumped tanager *(Ramphocelus passerinii)*	Mexico to Panama
Blue-gray tanager *(Thraupis episcopies)*	Mexico to Brazil
Swallow tanager *(Tersina viridis)*	Panama to Argentina
Plush-capped tanager *(Catamblyrhynchus diadema)*	Colombia, Venezuela to Peru, Bolivia
Ocellated turkey *(Agriocharis ocellata)*	Yucatan, British Honduras, Guatemala
Hoatzin *(Opisthocomus hoatzin)*	Amazon forest
Hawaiian honeycreeper *(Vestiaria coccinea)*	Hawaii
Jungle fowl *(Gallus gallus)*	Southeastern Asia
Garnet pitta *(Pitta granatina)*	Malaya, Sumatra, Borneo
Steere's pitta *(Pitta steerii)*	Philippines
Red-whiskered bulbul *(Pycnonotus jocosus)*	Indochina, Java, Sumatra
Purple sunbird *(Nectarinia asiatica)*	India to Indochina
Scarlet-backed flower pecker *(Dicaeum cruentatum)*	India to southern China, East Indies
Black drongo *(Dicrurus macrocercus)*	India to Formosa, Indochina, and Java
Vulturine guineafowl (Acryllium vulturinum)	Tropical east Africa
Greater honey guide *(Indicator indicator)*	Central and South Africa
Kuysna touraco *(Tauraco corythiax)*	South Africa
Scarlet-chested sunbird *(Cinnyris senegalensis)*	Central Africa
Variable sunbird *(Cinnyris venustus)*	East Africa

The frequent rains (eighty or more inches per year) leach much of the mineral material from the surface soils, leaving an impoverished mantle within the rain forest.

Selected References

Allee, W. C., and K. Schmidt. *Ecological Animal Geography* (New York: John Wiley, 1951), pp. i–xiii, 1–715.

Bornebusch, C. H. *The Fauna of Forest Soil* (Copenhagen: Nielsen & Lydiche, 1930), pp. 1–224.

Buxton, P. A. *Animal Life in Deserts* (London: Arnold, 1923), pp. i–xv, 1–176.

Carpenter, J. R. 1940. The grassland biome. Ecol. Monogr., **10**:617–684.

Chapman, R. N., C. E. Mickel, J. R. Parker, G. E. Miller, and E. G. Kelley. 1926. Studies in the ecology of sand dune insects. Ecology, **7**:416–426.

Cloudsley-Thompson, J. L. *Biology of Deserts* (New York: Hafner, 1954), pp. 1–224.

Darlington, P. J., Jr. *Zoogeography: The Geographic Distribution of Animals* (New York: John Wiley, 1957), pp. i–xi, 1–675.

Du Toit, A. L. *Our Wandering Continents: An Hypothesis of Continental Drifting* (London: Oliver & Boyd, 1937), pp. i–xiii, 1–366.

Griscom, L. 1942. Origin and relationships of the faunal areas of Central America. Proc. Eighth Amer. Sci. Congr., **3**:425–430.

Guppy, H. B. *Plants, Seeds and Currents in the West Indies and Azores* (London: Williams & Norgate, 1917).

Klopfer, P. H. *Behavioral Aspects of Ecology* (Englewood Cliffs, N. J.: Prentice-Hall, 1962), pp. 1–166.

Mayr, E. 1944. Wallace's Line in the light of recent zoogeographical studies. Quart. Rev. Biol., **19**:1–14.

Mayr, E. (ed.) 1952. The problem of land connections across the South Atlantic, with special reference to the Mesozoic. Bull. Amer. Mus. Nat. Hist., **99**:79–258.

Powers, S. 1911. "Floating islands," *Popular Sci. Monthly,* **79**:303–307.

Runcorn, S. K. (ed.) *Continental Drift* (New York: Academic Press, 1962), pp. 1–338.

Sclater, P. L. 1858. On the general geographical distribution of the members of the Class Aves. Jour. Proc. Linn. Soc., **2**:130–145.

Shelford, V. E., and A. C. Twomey. 1941. Tundra animal communities in the vicinity of Churchill, Manitoba. Ecology, **22**:47–69.

Simpson, G. G. 1940. Mammals and land bridges. Jour. Wash. Acad. Sci, **30**:137–163.

———. 1947. Holarctic mammalian faunas and continental relationships during the Cenozoic. Bull. Geol. Soc. Amer., **58**:613–688.

———. 1947a. Evolution, interchange and resemblance of the North American and Eurasian Cenozoic mammalian fauna. Evol., **1**:218–220.

Wallace, A. R. 1860. On the zoological geography of the Malay Archipelago. Proc. Linn. Soc. London 4:172–184.

Wegener, A. *The Origin of Continents and Oceans* (London: Methuen, 1924), pp. i–xx, 1–212.

Wilson, J. T. 1963. Continental drift. Sci. American, 208:86–100.

XII. The Basic
Environments –
Aquatic Areas

FRESHWATER AREAS

The ecology of freshwater areas may be referred to as **limnology.** This term usually implies a complete knowledge of a freshwater area including its physical, chemical, meteorological, and biological aspects. Freshwater communities throughout the world may be arbitrarily divided into two types: (1) The **lentic** type, or standing water habitats (Figure 12–1), exemplified by ponds, lakes, bogs, and swamps. In these areas, the circulation of water is slow and usually of a vertical type (spring and fall overturn) rather than horizontal. (2) The **lotic** type or running water habitat (Figure 12–2), such as a river, a brook, or a creek. In this type of community there is a greater horizontal movement of water. Very often along the length of these lotic habitats there are areas that approach the lentic type because slow or sluggish streams may have, along their course, a number of pool-type communities where conditions may approach the lentic type in terms of water movement, thermal stratification, and biotic composition.

The mass movement of water over any type of substrate will cause an erosion, or wearing away, of the parent material, whether it is a fine soil or solid rock. This activity, which is a result of the dynamic energy expended by lotic communities, is referred to as **degradation** by the

FIGURE 12–1 A typical lentic environment (pond community).

ecologist. The finer particles are carried as suspended materials, but the larger or coarser objects may be moved along gradually as a **traction, or bed load.** If the current along a stream loses some of its initial velocity, the larger particles of suspended material settle out first, along with a large portion of the bed load. The settling of such materials that have been eroded from areas upstream tends to build up the base level of the stream, as shown in Figure 12–3. This reduction in current velocity may, over a period of time, lead to extensive **aggradation,** or accumulation of bottom material. If the lotic type of community enters a lentic

FIGURE 12–2 A lotic environment represented by a small rock-strewn brook flow-ing through a woodland area.

environment, this aggradation of the finer particles of suspended matter is termed "silting in." A long-term accumulation of material will gradu-ally raise the bottom level of any lentic area and accelerate the invasion of hydrophytes into the deeper parts of the pond and lake. The accumu-lation of bottom material and the addition of organic debris hasten the progress of succession in aquatic areas, converting the pond or lake into a marsh and finally into a terrestrial community (see Chapter X). An increased amount of precipitation in any geographic area will often cause

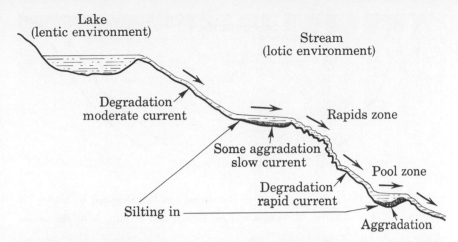

Lake
(lentic environment)

Stream
(lotic environment)

Degradation
moderate current

Rapids zone

Some aggradation
slow current

Pool zone

Degradation
rapid current

Silting in

Aggradation

**FIGURE 12–3 A transect of a lake and stream system showing regions of degrada-
tion and aggradation that lead to a continual, though often slow, change in the base
level of a stream system.**

flooding and increased erosion, which will increase the quantity of water,
which, in turn, will cause an increase in current and turbidity. This
change in the character of the lotic environment may have disastrous
effects on the stream biota because the increased velocity of the current
may carry the plankton normally associated with one particular area
many miles from its normal environment and loosen other organisms
from the stream bottom (vegetation) or rock surfaces (snails, insect larvae,
and so on). Thus climatological conditions may alter the entire biotic
character of a drainage system, including the lentic as well as lotic areas.
Increased turbidity will reduce light penetration and affect the photosynthetic activity of vegetation as well as clog gill systems of lamelli-
branch mollusks, thereby increasing the risk of mortality.

The current velocity of any stream will be governed by the steepness
of the basic gradient or the ratio of vertical drop to length of the stream
and the **hydraulic radius.** The hydraulic radius is a figure derived by
dividing the area of the cross section of a stream by the wetted perimeter
(Figure 12–4). The hydraulic radius will be proportional to stream
velocity. Streams with a more rapid current will have a much lower
temperature range from the stream surface to the stream bed; in other
words, the temperature will be more uniform at all depths. A more rapid
current will also result in a higher oxygen concentration of the water
because the chances of water mixing with atmospheric air are most certainly increased.

Current meters used to measure the velocity of any part of a stream
system may be placed at any depth to record the rate of movement. The
Haskell type of current meter, which employs a screw propeller, or the
Price type of meter with cups revolving around a vertical axis will give
accurate readings in any body of water. It has been found that the speed

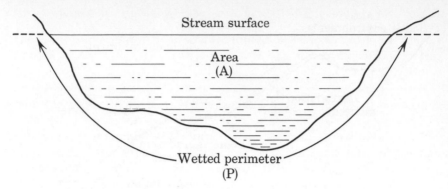

FIGURE 12–4 The hydraulic radius of the stream can be calculated by taking the area (A) which is equal to $\frac{r^2}{2}$ (where r is the radius) and dividing it by the wetted perimeter ($\frac{A}{P}$ = hydraulic radius).

of the current is most rapid anywhere from one tenth to four tenths of the total depth from the water surface. Atmospheric friction at the surface and substrate friction along the bottom and lateral margins of a stream (Figure 4–7, Chapter IV) tend to reduce the rate of flow. The velocity of the current in any stream system will determine the type of vegetation and faunal compositions of the area. In slow, sluggish streams, caused in part by a shallow vertical gradient, the oxygen concentration will be lower and the variations in temperature from source to mouth will be reduced. There are few if any rapids and a greater number of pool communities than are found along rapidly flowing streams. The number of planktonic organisms, rooted vegetation, and pool-type communities will be comparatively higher. In rapidly flowing streams the oxygen concentration will be higher owing to the increased number of riffle zones or rapids that cause a mixing of atmospheric gases with water. The erosion and carrying capacity are much greater than they would be in slower streams. During certain seasons normally sluggish streams become swift torrents often overflowing their banks and periodically flooding adjacent lowland areas. Sudden, but often brief, changes of this type are owing to an increased volume of water brought about by sudden thaws or abnormal amounts of precipitation.

The type of substrate or bottom material found in a particular lentic or lotic area will often determine the type and number of organisms that may exist in a particular region. Clay, silt, sand, pebble, boulder, or a combination of several types of substrate may characterize one segment of a pond or stream. The smaller the particle size (clays and silts) the fewer the organisms, but a boulder substrate may be heavily populated because it provides the sessile or sedentary communities of organisms the firm surface they require. In streams the various surfaces of a boulder will exhibit differences in current velocity. The upstream side and upper surface are areas where the current will be most rapid, while the lower surface and downstream side of a rock will be least affected by current velocity.

Wave action predominates in lentic areas (this has been discussed in the section titled "Waves" in Chapter IV). The larger the body of water, the larger the waves because wind (velocity and direction) is the most effective causative agent in wave formation. The surrounding terrestrial topography and the prevailing winds will of course modify any wave action, but, in general, the larger the body of water, the greater the amount of fetch (distance) over which the wind can react with the water surface. Usually wave action is more severe along one particular shore of a lake or a pond because of the prevailing wind direction. If waves are of sufficient size, they may very well limit the distribution of the biota in a particular area because continual waves may increase the turbidity of the water as well as shift the substrate, which brings about an abrasive effect that is injurious to many aquatic organisms, particularly sessile forms.

DAMS

Physical obstacles in the form of dams will cause radical changes in any lotic environment above and below the barrier. Dams of course will vary in size and lateral extent as well as origin. The natural dams produced by accumulation of debris, such as logs and other material carried to a certain point along the length of the stream or built by beavers, may result in a partial or complete damming of the streams (Figure 12–5). In partial damming, which materializes as a result of debris accumulation in an area where the stream's carrying capacity has decreased, a rapids zone may occur if the obstacles extend close to or above the water surface. Eddy currents as well as a mixing of atmospheric gases and increased oxygen concentration will often lead to a change in the floral and faunal populations that become established and replace the former aggregations that existed in these same areas. The dam itself will also serve as a suitable substrate for algae, bacteria, protozoa, coelenterates, and insect larvae that commonly inhabit such areas.

A complete dam will change a lotic environment on the upstream side into a lentic type area that may be quite extensive, depending on the general topography of the terrain as well as the height and lateral extent of the dam. The reduction of a current near the bottom of an established pond or pool allows for the appearance of lentic-type animal and plant communities. Adjacent terrestrial communities are often flooded and destroyed in the area, producing bog or swamp areas having the appearance of typical semiaquatic communities. On the downstream side of any sizable dam, there is often a "falls zone." The presence of a dam will

FIGURE 12–5   A beaver dam and pond on the Montezuma National Wildlife Refuge, Seneca Falls, New York. Courtesy of the Fish and Wildlife Service, U.S. Department of the Interior. Photograph by H. L. Dozier.

bring about periodic and radical changes in stream volume and current velocity, dictated by seasonal changes in climate. The sudden rupture or destruction of a dam may bring about extensive temporary flooding of downstream areas that causes erosion, dramatic changes in stream volume and carrying capacity, as well as wholesale destruction of terrestrial life.

MINERAL CONTENT OF WATERS

Nitrogen and phosphorus are present in relatively small concentrations in most freshwater areas. Phosphorus compounds may exist in concentrations of 0.05 milligram per liter, nitrites, of about 0.1 milligram per liter, and nitrates, of approximately 0.5 milligram per liter. The above figures are approximations at best and are cited only to give the student some rough idea of their concentrations; there are seasonal changes in quantity as well as distribution. Usually, there is a seasonal maximum, in early spring, in most layers of a pond as a result of the vernal overturn in deep water ponds and lakes. These substances become stratified in lentic environments during the summer, decreasing in the epilimnion as they are used up by planktonic populations, but maintaining a relatively high level of concentration in the hypolimnion. Both nitrogen and phosphorus compounds may become limiting factors in freshwater areas because the growth of phytoplanktonic organisms, particularly the blue green algae, depends directly on the nitrogen content of the water. Fish populations studied in ponds throughout the world are also directly affected by the nitrogen and phosphorus content of the water. A redistribution of these materials occurs during the fall overturn, followed by a buildup in concentration as the death of many organisms in winter replenishes the nitrogen and phosphorus content.

The calcium content of freshwater regions may vary from 9 milligrams (or less) per liter in soft water areas to 26 milligrams (or more) in hard waters. Soft water regions, due to the low calcium content, will have a low amount of bound carbonates, with only slight increases noted in the hypolimnion during the summer and winter stagnation periods. Hard water communities are more productive areas because of the high amount of bound carbonates. Mollusks, for example, usually are far more numerous in waters with 12 parts per million or more of bound carbonates. The physiological importance of calcium content cannot be underestimated for several reasons: it regulates shell formation; it is essential for plant and animal metabolism; it regulates the permeability of cell membranes; and it controls the hydrogen ion concentration (pH) of aquatic areas by formation of carbonates. Other minerals of variable importance are silicon, required by freshwater diatoms and sponges, and such minerals as iron, manganese, and copper that are often present in trace amounts but are very important in proper promotion of certain vital physiological activities of many organisms.

BIOTA OF LOTIC ENVIRONMENTS

Many of the freshwater plants and animals inhabiting streams must maintain their position within this body of moving water, often against a strong current. The greatest number of organisms are sedentary forms attached in some fashion to the substrate. A number of insect larvae such as stonefly nymphs (Pteronarcidae), blackfly larvae (Simuliidae), dobsonfly larvae (Corydalidae), and fish flies (Sialidae) are found only in running water. A number of organisms have accessory structures or appendages that enable them to maintain their attachment to the substrate. Blackflies, which are often found under waterfalls or in the rapids zone of streams, have a suckerlike protuberance on the ventral aspect of the thorax, armed with tiny hooklets. On the anal segment of the abdomen, there is a second sucker that has concentric rings of stout hooks. Mayflies of the Genus *Iron* have body and gill plates provided with suction pads, as well as gripping claws at the tips of the legs. Plant life in the form of clinging strands of the filamentous alga *Cladophora*, the red alga *Lemanea*, the mosses *Fontinalis* and *Hypnum*, the stonewart

Chara, and the gelatinous stalks of a number of genera of diatoms—all have holdfast devices of various sorts as well as a basic morphology that enables the species to cling to the surfaces of objects.

Many of the plants and animals that normally exist in communities where the current is rapid customarily live on the downstream surface or lower surface, where the full force of the current is reduced considerably. Some of the mayflies escape the full force of the current by burrowing

FIGURE 12–6   A deep pool zone located along a forest stream.

into the substrate, particularly into the loose gravel of swift mountain brooks in the numerous riffle zones that exist in these areas. Rounded, flattened, and streamlined bodies are commonly encountered among the aquatic fauna because the resistance presented by rounded contours is minimal. The river weed (*Podostemum*) will often harbor large numbers of invertebrates that seek protection provided by the leaves and stem of the plant.

Swimming organisms are very often transients in rapidly flowing streams—that is, they swim in areas of maximum current velocity for only brief periods. Organisms of this type include frogs, toads, turtles, mink, snakes, otters, and muskrats. Fish are very often positively **rheotaxic** —that is, they become oriented with the current and swim with or against it, depending upon their particular destination. A **catadromous** movement is the action of swimming downstream, as is true of the female eel that moves seaward to spawn. An **anadromous** movement is the action of swimming upstream or against the current, as is true of so many fish that move up into spawning areas (salmon, shad, striped bass).

Pool communities (Figure 12–6) of usually limited extent located along the length of streams are often populated by such plants as submerged hornwort (*Ceratophyllum*), tape grass (*Valisneria*), river bulrush (*Scirpus*), watershield (*Brasenia*), and others. These areas usually have deeper water than do other portions of the stream, with a much reduced current, and a substrate of fine sand, silt, or clay that has been dropped thereon as the carrying capacity of the stream has decreased. Pool communities serve as ideal environments for the drifting river plankton (usually called **potamoplankton,** in streams) including bacteria, blue-green algae, green algae, diatoms, protozoa, and rotifers. Mayfly larvae (Ephemeridae) are the principal burrowers and may provide nearly 20 per cent of the fish food during certain periods of the year. Dragonflies (Suborder: Anisoptera), horse fly larvae (Tabanidae), and bivalves are common bottom inhabitants. Water striders (Gerridae) and whirligig beetles (Gyrinidae) are common inhabitants of the quiet surface waters.

MARINE AREAS

The vastness of the oceanic environment can be more readily appreciated when it is considered in terms of per cent. Land and freshwater areas cover only a scant 29 per cent of the earth's surface; the remaining area—71 per cent—is covered with salt water. Throughout the world, the mean elevation for terrestrial areas is approximately 700 meters; the average depth of the marine environment is approximately 3,800 meters, or 2⅓ miles. All of the major salt water areas throughout the world are interconnected. Oceanic barriers, rather than being geographic, as is true of terrestrial and freshwater communities, are in the form of temperature, depth, pressure, and substrate zones. The distribution of oceanic areas is not uniform within our planet: the Western Hemisphere contains more ocean water than does the Eastern Hemisphere, and the Southern Hemisphere is far more aquatic than is the Northern Hemisphere.

Oceanography, a specialized branch of ecology dealing with all of the varied aspects of the marine environment, physical as well as biological, stems from humble beginnings in the mid-seventeenth century when two Italians, Marsili and Donati, collected samples with fishermen's oyster dredges. A Danish zoologist, O. F. Muller, used the same type of dredge in examining the sea bottom of northern waters. Sir John Ross, in a voyage to Baffin Bay in 1817–1818, used a bottom sampler of his own design and found marine worms at a depth of 6,000 feet. Victor Hensen of Kiel (Germany) was the first individual to propose the term *plankton*. He improved the Muller dredge and published information on the systematic and quantitative aspects of oceanic plankton. Edward Forbes, whose untimely death at the age of thirty-nine ended a scholarly career, stimulated dredging research in the mid-nineteenth century. Forbes noted that the number of marine species gradually decreased with increasing depth and that plants disappeared at a point not far below this depth, which he designated as the zero point. Forbes' zero point drew sharp and severe criticism from a number of scientific groups and was later rejected as further scientific exploration of the ocean bottom revealed life at depths much below Forbes' zero point. M. F. Maury, another oceanographic pioneer, published the first bathymetrical map of the North Atlantic in 1854, with contour lines at 1,000, 2,000, 3,000, and 4,000 fathoms.

Louis Agassiz, a man of many interests, stimulated oceanographic research in this country by founding the first marine laboratory, on Penekese Island in Massachusetts. Agassiz's interest in research and students, along with his desire to observe nature at first hand, contributed to the success of this undertaking. Other research laboratories were gradually established along the Atlantic, Gulf, and Pacific coasts and in other parts of the world (see Table 12–1). Many marine stations are affiliated in some way with various colleges and universities throughout the world. The establishment of a marine station (Naples, Italy) for zoological research along the Mediterranean coast by Anton Dohrn in 1872 was the first such institute of this type.

Alexander Agassiz, a son of Louis Agassiz, gained more fame than did his father in the field of oceanographic research. He was intimately concerned with such work for a period of nearly thirty years (1877–1905). In addition to his interest in the origin and composition of coral reefs, the younger Agassiz believed (as did his predecessor, Edward Forbes) that a deep azoic zone existed below a depth of two hundred fathoms. His idea was disproven by an Italian, Polumbo, who had designed a sampler that was operative at any depth in the ocean. This sampler was first used

TABLE 12-1. *Some of the Earlier and Larger Marine Biological Stations Located Throughout the World*

NAME OF STATION	LOCATION
Stazioni Zoologica di Napoli	Naples, Italy
Marine Biological Association of the United Kingdom	Plymouth, England
Royal Prussian Biological Station	Helgoland
University Biological Station	Drobak, Norway
Scripps Institution of Oceanography	La Jolla, California
Wood's Hole Oceanographic Institution	Wood's Hole, Massachusetts
Duke University Marine Laboratory	Beaufort, North Carolina

in the Pacific Ocean in 1884, between the Galápagos Islands and Hawaii. Later improvements in this sampling device were made by Eugen von Peterson, Carl Chun, and Victor Hensen.

MASS MOVEMENT OF WATER

Currents. Currents that are established in any body of water may originate from any one of a number of single factors, though usually there are several contributing causes. There are also a number of types of currents that may become operative in any body of water (marine or freshwater). Coastal, tidal, bottom, submerged, and Coriolis currents are a few that have been detected and described. With the improvement of electronic devices in oceanographic and limnological research, it is probable that other currents may be discovered in the future. Our discussion of currents, their causes and ecological effects, will be brief. (A detailed discussion of the subject may be found in any limnology or oceanography text.)

One of the causative factors for the establishment of a current is the thermal relationships that exist in any body of water. According to the theorem of Bjerknes, if the heat within any type of thermal section is to be transformed into mechanical energy, the heating must take place at a greater depth than the cooling. This is essentially what occurs in the circulation of oceanic water in either hemisphere. Cool dense water moves toward the equator from polar areas, becoming warmer, as it gradually moves southward, by conduction (contact with warmer layers of water). As it reaches the equator, it moves toward the surface because it is warmer and hence lighter than some of the surface water. It then begins to move poleward, cooling and becoming more dense in the polar areas (Figure 12–7). This circulatory pattern, which involves a warming of water at a greater depth, generates mechanical energy. However, the heating of vast quantities of water by conduction is a slow and very inefficient process, so that the thermal factor is not a prime force in the production of currents.

Another contributing factor in the production of oceanic currents are the salinity changes that result in density differences. In the drier, warmer parts of the ocean, as water evaporates, it increases the salinity and density of the surface water and causes it to sink. This series of events is counteracted in the more tropical areas by increased and frequent precipitation that dilutes the surface waters, thus reducing their density and maintaining them relatively close to the surface. As the water reaches polar areas, the salinity is reduced because of the conversion of ice to water. This reduction in density will tend to retard the thermal circulation that normally ensues at the poles and thus slows down the entire cycle.

FIGURE 12–7 A vertical transect of ocean waters with a simplified diagram of the vertical movement of water in the polar and equatorial areas owing to density changes brought about by thermal variation.

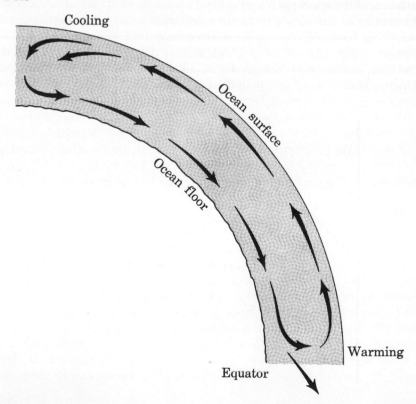

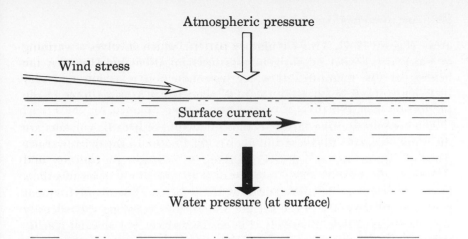

Atmospheric pressure

Wind stress

Surface current

Water pressure (at surface)

FIGURE 12–8 Forces responsible for, or preventing, the establishment of wind-induced currents in freshwater or marine environments. Once the wind speed establishes enough stress (long arrow) to counteract the atmospheric and water pressure (shorter arrows), surface currents can be established in any body of water.

Of all the causative agents, wind is probably the most important single driving force with respect to the origin of oceanic and lentic surface currents. The frictional contact that is established between the water surface and the atmosphere can initiate a movement of the surface waters. Wind-induced surface currents are established when wind speed is great enough in terms of stress value to overcome the perpendicular force of pressure, which of course varies with density (Figure 12–8). The speed of a surface current will usually be about 2 to 5 per cent of the wind velocity; thus a wind speed of twenty miles per hour may establish a

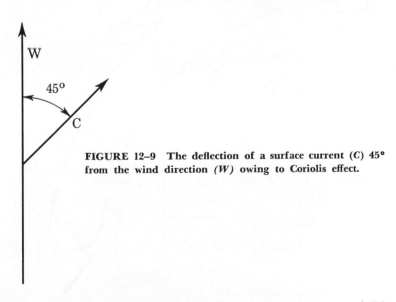

FIGURE 12–9 The deflection of a surface current (*C*) 45° from the wind direction *(W)* owing to Coriolis effect.

surface current of one mile per hour. In bodies of freshwater (large lakes) or in oceanic areas, it has been observed that the current established by wind does not follow a course parallel to wind direction, but is often as much as 45° to the right of the wind direction (Figure 12–9). The reason for this divergence is **Corioli's force,** named for the French physicist, Corioli, who expressed this factor in mathematical form. The deflectional force, which is caused by the rotational movement of the earth, deflects bodies of water (or air) to the right in the Northern Hemisphere, provided one faces the downstream (or downwind) direction and to the left in the Southern Hemisphere. In a shallow body of water, if we measure the angle of deflection of a surface current with respect to the wind, we would find it is somewhat less than 45° to the right of the wind direction. In water of infinite depth, where a wind has been blowing across the surface at a constant velocity for an infinite period of time, we establish an **Ekman spiral** if we measure the direction of submerged currents at variable depths (Figure 12–10). Thus, according

FIGURE 12–10 The Ekman spiral caused by wind-produced currents. Wind direction is represented by the *W* and arrow. Note that with an increase in depth, velocity (represented graphically by the length of arrows) decreases and direction continues to shift in a clockwise direction. From H. V. Sverdrup, M. W. Johnson, R. H. Fleming, *The Oceans: Their Physics, Chemistry and General Biology* by permission of Prentice-Hall, Inc., © 1942.

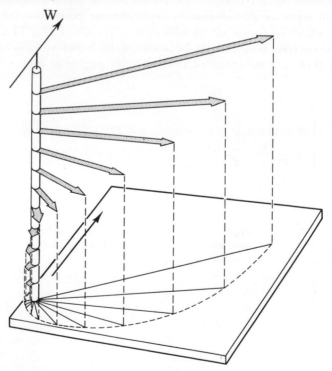

to the diagram, the current at depth D_1 is not only of reduced velocity (as indicated by the shorter arrow), but is also somewhat to the right of the surface current. The current at depth D_2 is reduced in velocity to a greater degree than at D_1 and is also positioned farther to the right so that as we follow the effect of surface currents at lower and lower levels, we find that the currents are reduced in velocity and displaced to the right, tending to form a spiral arrangement.

In small bodies of water the Coriolis force will not be as effective in the production of currents, but in large bodies of water this force will tend to incline the water surface, as shown in Figure 12–11. An opposing force, the acceleration pressure, results in a current that moves at right angles to these antagonistic forces. Although the configuration of major ocean currents is not caused solely by the Coriolis force, it does have an effect on their movement. If the Coriolis force were the only governing factor of surface currents, ocean currents would form a much smaller circle, about twenty kilometers in diameter.

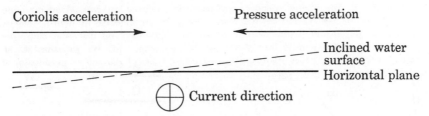

FIGURE 12–11 Pressure acceleration and Coriolis acceleration are opposing forces that establish currents which would be moving into or out of the page. The Coriolis acceleration is a somewhat greater force (longer arrow) that causes a slight inclination of the water surface on the right in the Northern Hemisphere.

Seiches. Winds blowing over lakes tend to pile water up along the lee shore (Figure 12–12). This accumulation of water on one side of the lake is called **wind set-up.** The amount of wind set-up is a direct function of the wind speed, length of the lake, and in inverse proportion to water depth. In Lake Erie, a sixty-mile-an-hour wind will cause a wind set-up of about fifteen feet. If the wind stops blowing, or decreases noticeably in velocity, the wind-set water begins to move toward the opposite shore; following this, there is a reversal of current back toward the wind-set shore. This oscillating current, which occurs in lakes and landlocked seas, is called a **seiche.** Although the level of the water will change along opposing shores (at each end of the seiche current), there is one area, roughly midway between, where the level of the water does not change; this is called the **node.** Seiche currents tend to be uniform in velocity throughout the body of water, except near the bottom, where the speed of water movement will be inhibited by the substrate. In this respect a

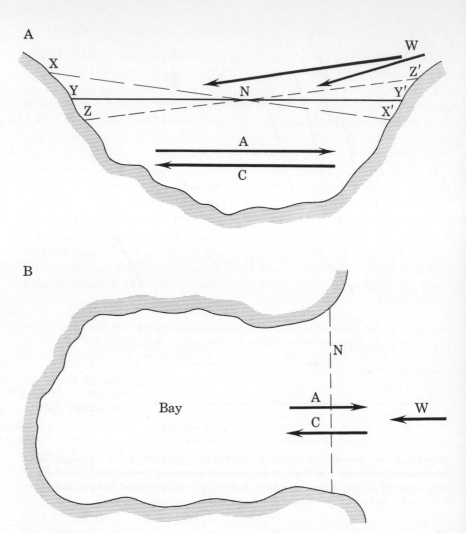

FIGURE 12–12 Diagram *A* illustrates the establishment of a seiche current (*A* and *C*) established as a result of variable winds (*W*) disturbing the water surface and causing a wind setup (*X*) along one shore, moving the water above the undisturbed water level (*Y* − *Y′*). The oscillating seiche current results in the changing water level along the opposite shore (from *Z′* to *X′*). The node (*N*) is located roughly midway between the two shores. Diagram *B* is a bay, as seen from aerial view, where wind-driven water establishes an oscillating (seiche) current (*A* and *C*), with the node located at point *N*, near the mouth of the bay.

seiche current in a landlocked body of water is quite similar to a tidal current that oscillates within a bay or estuary. In fact, if a wind of great enough velocity blows from the right direction, it is possible to produce a seiche within a bay or estuary.

Countercurrent. In the Northern Hemisphere, if there is a current flowing poleward, with a landmass to the left of its direction of flow,

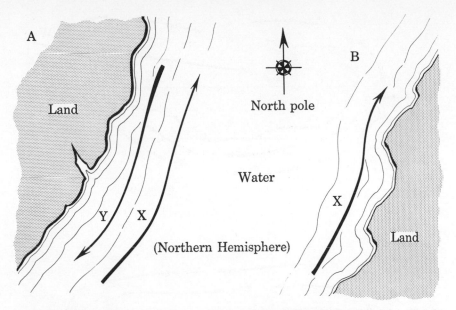

FIGURE 12–13 Diagram *A* illustrates the countercurrent (*Y*) established to the left of a poleward current (*X*) in the Northern Hemisphere. In Diagram *B*, if the landmass is to the right of the poleward current (*X*), no countercurrent is established in the Northern Hemisphere.

there is always a countercurrent on the landward side (Figure 12–13). An example is the Gulf Stream that moves poleward to the right of the North American continent. The Labrador Current flows in the opposite direction (countercurrent) along the landward side of this mass of water. On the other hand, if the landmass lies to the right of the current, there is no countercurrent because the current is usually closer to the shore (Diagram B, Figure 12–13). Countercurrents occur in bodies of freshwater, provided that a noticeable current is established, particularly around the periphery of islands, as is shown in Figure 12–14. The diagram represents the same principle cited for oceanic currents and the position of continental landmasses. The side of the island that lies to the left of the current will have a countercurrent. It might be mentioned that when a seiche current is established, the countercurrent will alternate in keeping with the movement of the oscillation, as is represented in Diagrams A and B of Figure 12–14. In the Southern Hemisphere countercurrents are established in the opposite way—that is, countercurrents will flow counterclockwise around an island, and they are established to the right of the direction of flow of the current with regard to a landmass, rather than to the left.

Major Ocean Currents. Figure 12–15 illustrates the major ocean currents, indicating the direction of flow and whether the current is a cold

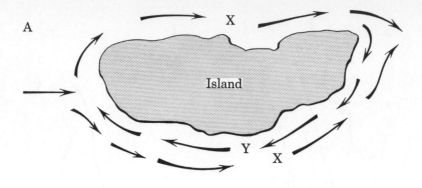

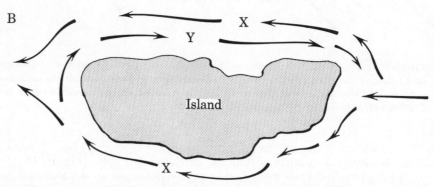

FIGURE 12–14 A current (X) from the left in Diagram *A* moves close to the upper shore of the island, but encircles the island along the lower shore, establishing a countercurrent (Y), moving in the opposite direction of the offshore current (X). In Diagram *B*, with a reversal of current direction, the countercurrent (Y) appears along the opposite shore in keeping with the general principle illustrated in Figure 12–13.

or warm water current. Broad currents of water flow in the equatorial region of all of the major oceans. The North Equatorial Current and South Equatorial Current flow from east to west. Both of these currents are deflected by the rotation of the earth (Coriolis force) and the continental landmasses they approach. The North Equatorial Current is deflected to the right (northward), and the South Equatorial Current to the left (southward), as we would expect if we keep the Coriolis effect in mind. The Equatorial Countercurrent flows in the opposite direction, from west to east, and is a narrow current as compared to the equatorial currents. Approximately 100 meters below the surface of the Equatorial Countercurrent in the Atlantic Ocean is the Cromwell Current, which flows in the opposite direction.

The general circulatory pattern of currents in the Atlantic and Pacific oceans is quite similar, as is indicated by Figure 12–15 and Table 12–2.

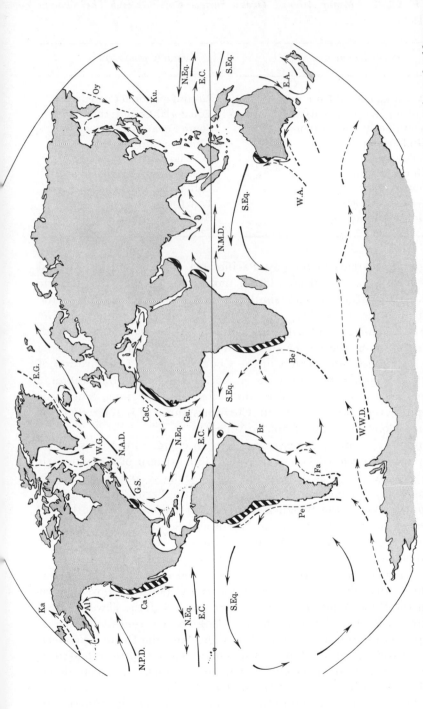

FIGURE 12–15 Major surface currents of oceanic waters throughout the world. Black-and-white barred areas represent regions of cold water upwellings. Current and drift abbreviations are Al, Alaskan Current; Ca, California Current; N.Eq., North Equatorial Current; E.C., Equatorial Countercurrent; Pe, Peru Current; W.W.D., West Wind Drift; N.P.D., North Pacific Drift; La, Labrador Current; W.G., West Greenland Current; E.G., East Greenland Current; G.S., Gulf Stream; CaC, Canary Current; Gu, Guinea Current; Br, Brazil Current; Fa, Falkland Current; Ka, Kamchatka Current; Ku, Kuroshio Current; Oy, Oyashio Current; N.M.D., Northeast Monsoon Drift; W.A., West Australian Current; E.A., East Australian Current; S.Eq., South Equatorial Current; Be, Benguala Current; N.A.D., North Atlantic Drift. Dashed arrows represent cold water currents, solid arrows represent warm water currents.

TABLE 12-2. *Major Atlantic Ocean Surface Currents and Their Pacific Counterparts*

ATLANTIC CURRENTS	PACIFIC CURRENTS
North Equatorial Current	North Equatorial Current
Equatorial Countercurrent	Equatorial Countercurrent
South Equatorial Current	South Equatorial Current
Gulf Stream	Kuroshio Current
Labrador Current	Oyashio Current
North Atlantic Current	North Pacific Current
Canary Current	California Current
Benguela Current	Peru Current
Brazil Current	Australia Current

Although the currents of the vast Pacific area are less well known and perhaps have a pattern of circulation more complex than the Atlantic pattern of circulation, a basic similarity exists. Very often, during the northern winter (December) or southern summer, a branch of the Equatorial Countercurrent will turn south off the western coast of South America, replacing the colder surface waters of the Peru (Humboldt) Current with the warmer waters of the Countercurrent. This invasion of normally cold water by warm water kills many fish and planktonic organisms and causes a fouling of the water for some time. Since this catastrophic event occurs at about Christmas time, it is referred to as "El Nino" along the coast of South America.

In a number of areas, currents may flow in circular form; this is particularly true of enclosed bodies of water. This pattern of circulation is called a **gyre.** A gyre is evident in the Sea of Okhatsk and in the Arctic Ocean as well as in the South Pacific, west of the Peru Current, and in the Atlantic, west of the Benguela Current. In a broader sense, the circular movement of currents in the North and South Atlantic (and the North and South Pacific) represent gigantic gyres of oceanic waters. A poorly defined or weak current is often referred to as a **drift.** In such a body of water, the net movement of water from one area to another is much slower than that encountered in a current. Thus the movement of water in the West Wind Drift (the largest single drift) is slower than it is in currents located to the north. The Falkland Current of the southeastern part of the South American shores, the Australia Current (eastern coast of Australia), and the Canary Current, along the northwest African coast, are weak and rather poorly defined currents that can be considered drifts. The Arctic Ocean is surrounded by landmasses, because of the limited amount of contact with other oceanic areas and the reduction of salinity by the continual melting of polar ice; the saline content of this water is approximately 30 parts per thousand (3 per cent) compared to the 35 parts per thousand (3½ per cent) of open ocean water in other areas. This body of water contributes frigid water to the Labrador and Oyashio Currents in the Atlantic and Pacific areas, respectively.

Ecological Effects of Currents. The continuous movement of vast quantities of warm and cold bodies of water over immense distances has a very definite effect on the climatic conditions of surrounding terrestrial areas, particularly along coastal areas. These bodies of water will alter the temperatures of the overlying air masses that are carried by atmospheric winds over coastal communities. One of the most effective currents in the world, with respect to modification of environmental conditions, is the Gulf Stream of the western Atlantic. This warm body of water of tropical origin not only modifies (warms) the climate of the southern and mid-Atlantic coasts of the United States, but continues across the North Atlantic (as the North Atlantic Drift) and warms the British Isles and western Europe. In fact, a derivative of the Gulf Stream extends into the Arctic Circle, rendering the Russian port of Murmansk ice-free throughout the year.

The Labrador Current is not as clearly defined nor as strong as the Oyashio Current, its Pacific counterpart off the northeastern coast of Japan. For this reason the Labrador Current and the Oyashio Current, being colder and more dense bodies of water, sink below the warmer currents that are flowing northward. The equatorial currents of the Indian Ocean are warm water currents that produce the tropical or subtropical climate of the surrounding areas, the East Indies, southeastern Asia, India, and the east African coast. Similarly, the tropical and subtropical climatic conditions that prevail along the Gulf states, Mexico, the West Indies, and northern South America are due to water invading the Gulf from the South Equatorial Current and to a lesser degree from the North Equatorial Current.

Thus we find that the movement of currents with respect to terrestrial areas has a definite effect on the distribution of plant and animal communities throughout the world. The type of biome that exists at any particular latitude may be quite different only a short distance away because of the passage of a different current. For example, the southern tip of Greenland and the entire island of Iceland, which lie at the same latitude (between 63 and 67 degrees north latitude), or just below the Arctic Circle, exhibit quite different environmental conditions. Only the coastal fringe of Greenland possesses tundra type climate, with the warmest month below 10° C. (50° F.), but above 0° C. (32° F.). The interior of Greenland has a perpetual frost zone where temperatures fall below 0° C. every month of the year. The northeastern part of Iceland will have a climate similar to that along the coastal areas of Greenland, but on the southwestern corner of Iceland a mesothermal forest climate

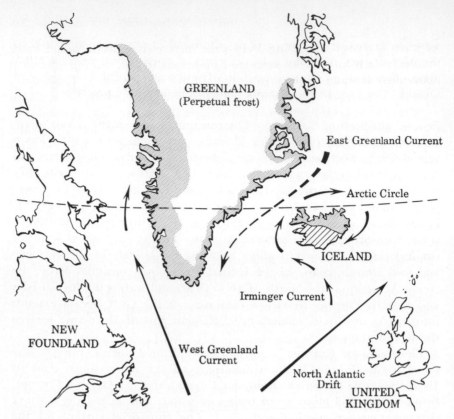

GREENLAND
(Perpetual frost)

East Greenland Current

Arctic Circle

ICELAND

Irminger Current

NEW
FOUNDLAND

West Greenland
Current

North Atlantic
Drift

UNITED
KINGDOM

FIGURE 12–16 Solid arrows represent warm water currents; dashed arrows cold water currents. Shaded terrestrial regions support tundra vegetation; diagonal striping in southern Iceland supports mesothermal vegetation.

prevails. On this part of the island, the coldest months will have average temperatures above 0° C., but below 18° C. (64.4° F.). The warmest months (usually less than four) will have temperatures above 10° C. (50° F.). So that nowhere in Iceland are temperatures as low as those that exist in the interior of Greenland at the same latitude (Figure 12–16). The reason for this climatic disparity is that the coastal waters surrounding Iceland are warm current derivatives from the North Atlantic Drift. Even more indicative of the variable effect of currents are the differences that prevail between the east and west coasts of Greenland. The east coast is considerably cooler because a cold current, the East Greenland Current, a derivative of frigid arctic waters, flows along this side of the landmass. But the West Greenland Current, a warm water mass from the North Atlantic Drift, warms the coastal area of the opposite shore, which produces a much deeper or thicker fringe of tundra type climate.

Upwellings. In certain oceanic regions, conditions produced by the movement of current and other factors cause or bring about a movement of some of the deeper water toward the surface. This vertical movement of water is termed **upwelling.** Very often surface currents of coastal water suddenly turn away from shore and move out to sea, causing a vertical movement of water in the area to replace this surface water. The sudden seaward movement of water is often caused by the Coriolis force, which is operative in both hemispheres, moving water to the right of the downstream flow in the Northern Hemisphere and to the left below the equator. In certain areas this active force may be supplemented by wind currents that facilitate the movement of surface waters (Figure 12–17). The most extensive upwellings occur along the California coast, off the west coast of South America, and off the west African coast. An upwelling is of ecological importance because it often brings deeper waters that are rich in nutrients to the surface where they may be used to enrich the planktonic populations. This increase in the phytoplankton and zooplankton will in turn lead to a larger fish population as well as marine invertebrates, which in turn will increase the coastal bird populations that prey on different species of fish. Although many of the deeper marine waters are rich in nutrients, it is only in the areas of an upwelling that these substances may be utilized because they are carried up into an area where the light penetration is great enough to produce photosynthetic activity necessary for the phytoplanktonic organisms. Around the periphery of Antarctica, the waters are rich in marine populations of plankton, larger invertebrates, and fish because of the extensive upwelling that occurs there. The cause for the upwelling is somewhat different in this region. As the surface waters become colder and are exposed to some evaporation, they increase in density, which causes them to sink and be replaced by the deeper, more nutritious waters.

We have been concerned primarily with surface currents because more

FIGURE 12–17 An oceanic upwelling, with arrows representing the vertical movement of these offshore waters carrying nutrients from the depths to the surface along the western shores of many continental landmasses.

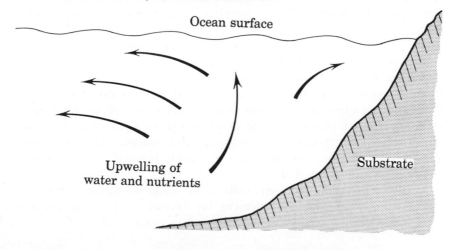

Ocean surface

Upwelling of
water and nutrients

Substrate

is known about these superficial bodies of water than is known about submerged currents. Oceanographers are aware of submerged currents that exist in many parts of the world, but their measurement, velocity, extent, and direction are far more difficult to chart. Where surface and submerged currents, or several submerged currents come into contact, there is a considerable amount of turbulence, particularly if the currents are moving in different directions. In fact, underwater storms of considerable violence are known to exist in certain areas and at certain times of the year. The violence of these storms undoubtedly far surpasses the effect of atmospheric storms, with which we are more familiar, because the weight and consequent force of water is many times that of an equal volume of air. The unfortunate *Thrasher* incident that occurred in the North Atlantic is believed by some oceanographers to have been caused at least in part by the unwitting entry of the nuclear-powered submarine into a turbulent mass of water from which it could not escape.

Various ingenious devices have been used to measure current velocity and to trace the movement of oceanic currents for several centuries. One of the simplest current meters is a small device in the shape of a cross that is used to measure the velocity of surface currents (Figure 12–18). There are two protruding nails near the tips of the cross arm that produce surface ripples. On the central axis there is a scale graduated to read velocities. The point at which the ripples cross the central axis indicates the current velocity. Different velocities will cause the ripples to cross at different points along the central axis.

The general direction of oceanic currents can be plotted by drift bottles that can be released at any point along the shore or at some point on the ocean surface. If a drift bottle, which is numbered, is placed within a current at a specific position (that is, by use of map coordinates), the general direction of current flow can be determined. There are a number of disadvantages, however, despite the ease with which bottles can be introduced into any surface current and their relative inexpense. Bottles may sink or may be ingested or destroyed by various marine vertebrates, particularly sharks, which are notorious for sampling anything that moves despite its nutritional value. Some individual may intercept the current bottle before it reaches its destination; or if it reaches its destination without running aground or being intercepted, it may be picked up and kept as souvenir and never reported. In addition to these hazards, drift bottles may be carried into several different currents and therefore not only be delayed but deflected far off course, thereby giving an erroneous impression of a particular current flow pattern. In short, drift bottles are far more useful in tracing current direction and speed over rather short distances or within confined bays or estuaries and freshwater environments.

A current pole that floats vertically in the water because it is weighted at one end is a valuable instrument for measuring the direction and

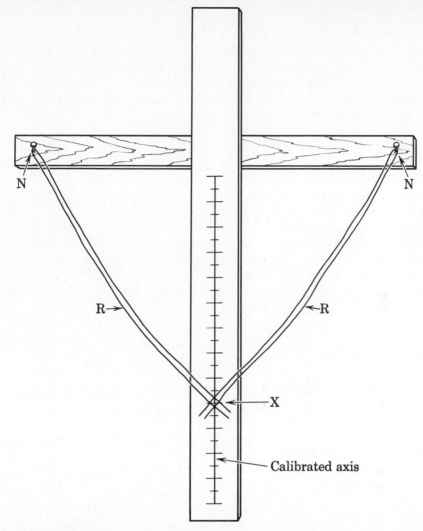

FIGURE 12–18 Simple current meter gives an estimate of surface current velocity. Ripples (*R*) formed at points of protruding nails (*N*) at tips of crosspiece cross the calibrated axis of the cross, giving a velocity reading at (*X*).

speed of currents within channels or for short distances at sea. The pole is 15 feet long; 6 inches of it emerges above the water surface. A more sophisticated device and one that is considerably more expensive is the Swallow neutral buoyancy float. It is a cylinder 15 feet in length and 5 inches in diameter that can be set to float at any depth. The float has a sonar pinger installed at one end, so that a vessel equipped with proper sonar gear can trace the direction and speed of the float by following the sonar ping. The value of this device is that it will render information on submerged currents, which is not possible with any of the other devices mentioned.

Tides. The periodic oscillation of vast quantities of water has an immense impact on the living organisms of the marine environment and connecting bodies of freshwater. Tidal flow of water will not only vary in terms of time and magnitude in one particular area, but there will be considerable differences from one area to another. The tides are caused by the gravitational force of the moon and sun. Until Newton's time and the formulation of the Law of Gravitation, there was no adequate explanation of tidal action. This law states that any two objects will exert a mutual attractive force *(F)* which is proportional to their respective masses *(M_1 and M_2)* and inversely proportional to the square of the distance *(D^2)* between their centers of gravity. If we were to calculate the tidal force of the moon with respect to the tides, we would use the following equation:

$$F = G \frac{M_1 \, M_2}{D^2},$$

where *G* is the gravitational constant. Since the tidal force is inversely proportional to the distance, the moon in spite of its smaller mass will exert a force of approximately twice the magnitude of that exerted by the sun. Or to be more precise, the tide-producing forces of the moon and sun are in the proportion of 59 to 26, respectively. Thus the influence of the moon is about $2\frac{1}{4}$ times that of the sun.

When the moon and sun are in alignment, as represented in Diagrams *A* and *B* of Figure 12–19, the tides are highest, because the gravitational attraction of both moon and sun are additive. These tides are called **spring tides.** It will be noted also that high tides will occur at the same time on opposite sides of the planet. The tidal bulge on one side is due to the gravitational attraction on that side. On the other side, because the gravitational force is less than it is at the center of the earth, there is also a tidal bulge. The **tidal range,** or distance between the high-tide mark and the low-tide mark, will be greatest during the spring tide. During the first and third quarter of the moon (Diagram *C,* Figure 12–19), the tidal range exhibits its lowest magnitude. The reason for this is that the sun and moon have become positioned so that they are in maximum disalignment, or diametrically opposite. This results in a **neap tide.** The spring and neap tides for any one area have a quantitative relationship of 13 to 5. Actually there are lags in time; the spring and neap tides will occur shortly after the earth, sun, and moon are so positioned as to produce the particular tidal action. There is also a daily tidal lag; the tides will materialize sometime after the tide-producing forces of the sun and moon are in the correct position.

If the moon were at rest, the tides would occur every 12 hours, because the earth makes one rotation every 24 hours. However, the moon is also rotating about the earth, making a complete rotation every $29\frac{1}{2}$ days; thus we find that the average interval between tides is about 12 hours

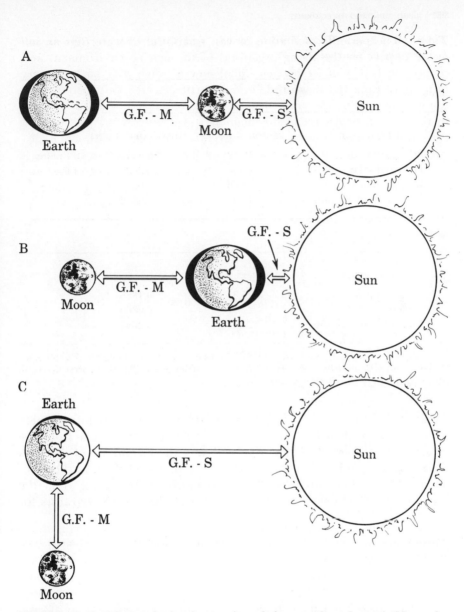

FIGURE 12–19 The gravitational attraction of the sun (S) and moon (M) on the earth's (E) tides. Diagrams A and B represent resultant spring tides; C yields a neap tide. Shaded areas on earth represent tidal bulges. G.F.-S. and G.F.-M refer to the gravitational forces exerted by the sun and moon respectively. Sizes of celestial bodies, distances, and tidal bulges are not drawn to scale.

and 25 minutes; the tides caused by the sun occur every 12 hours, as is represented in Table 12–3. Tides display an irregularity at any one point and from place to place because of many factors. The elliptical orbits of the moon and sun around the earth will vary the distance

T A B L E 1 2 – 3 . *Tidal Forces, Periods, and Coefficients in Regions with Semidiurnal or Diurnal Tides**

SEMIDURNAL TIDES

TIDAL FORCE	PERIOD IN HOURS	TIDAL COEFFICIENT
Principal lunar	12.42	0.4543 (45% of the force)
Principal solar	12.00	0.2120 (21% of the force)
Larger lunar elliptic	12.66	0.0880
Lunisolar interaction	11.97	0.0576

DIURNAL TIDES

TIDAL FORCE	PERIOD IN HOURS	TIDAL COEFFICIENT
Principal lunar	25.82	0.1886
Principal solar	24.07	0.0880
Lunisolar interaction	23.93	0.2655

* Adapted from H. U. Sverdrup, M. W. Johnson, and R. H. Fleming, *The Oceans: Their Physics, Chemistry, and General Biology* (Englewood Cliffs, N. J.: Prentice-Hall, 1942), pp. i–x, 1–1087. Used by permission.

between these objects, leading to a variation in the tidal force. There will also be a change in declination of the sun and moon from the equator over a period of time that will vary the magnitude of the tides from one geographic area to another over a period of time, as shown in Figure 12–20. The sun may deviate as much as 23 degrees from the equator; the total deviation of the moon is 28 degrees. Other causes for

FIGURE 12–20 Comparison of the maximum deviation of the sun and moon from the earth's equatorial plane.

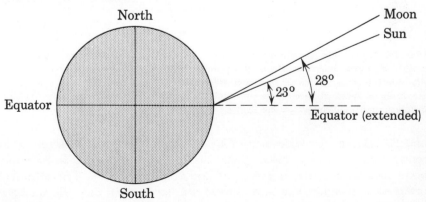

tidal irregularities are onshore or offshore winds, barometric pressure, and the contour of the shoreline. Differences in tidal amplitude are evident in the region of the Panama Canal, where shore contours effect a tidal amplitude of some 16 feet on the Pacific side of the Canal, with semidiurnal regularity. On the Gulf side of the Canal, there is a tidal amplitude of 1 or 2 feet and only one high tide (diurnal) per day.

TABLE 12–4. *Tidal Amplitude and Tidal Type in Various Parts of the Northern Hemisphere*

LOCATION	TIDAL AMPLITUDE (IN FEET)	TIDAL TYPE
Bay of Fundy	50 to 60	Semidiurnal
Alaska	40	Semidiurnal
Alaska (different area)	8 to 10	Diurnal
Sea of Okhatsk	40	Diurnal
Gulf of Mexico	3	Diurnal

Although most areas will have two high tides (flood tides) and two low tides (ebb tides) approximately every 24 hours, known as a **semidiurnal tide,** there are areas where only one high tide and one low tide will occur every day (**diurnal tide**). Table 12–4 gives an idea of tidal variation and its amplitude in different areas. Along most Atlantic coasts there are diurnal tides, with flood tide and ebb tide falling at about the same point; in the Pacific there is usually a mixed tide. In other words, though

FIGURE 12–21 The Coriolis force causes the elevation of high (*H*) and low (*L*) tide waters on the French side of the English Channel. H.P.R. represents the horizontal plane of reference or the location of the water surface if no Coriolis force were active. Topographical differences in many areas cause a greater tidal amplitude (*A*) on the French side of the Channel as opposed to the English side (*A'*).

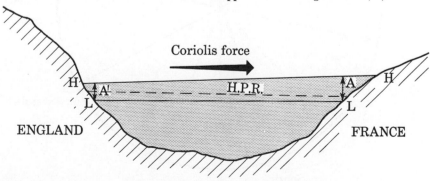

the flood tide mark may fall at about the same point, ebb tides are very unequal. In Honolulu, the low tides are equal for any one interval, but the flood tide is very low. Along the French coast there are broad sand flats that expose miles of flat shore during ebb tide. In the English Channel, the tidal range or amplitude varies because of the Coriolis force, as shown in Figure 12–21. The Coriolis force, supplemented by shore contour irregularities, produces a greater tidal amplitude on the French side of the Channel. On the English side, the tidal amplitude varies from 5 to 6 feet; on the French side, it is about 10 to 12 feet in range. The same thing occurs in bays or estuaries of the Northern Hemisphere; the Coriolis force produces a greater tidal range along the east shore.

Tidal Currents. The movement of any quantity of water from one place to another under natural conditions results in the establishment of a current. The movement of tidal water creates a **tidal current,** which is an oscillating type, along the coast. The current moves shoreward during

FIGURE 12–22 Rotary currents in offshore oceanic areas continually change direction in keeping with the time of day. Arrows in the diagram represent the direction of water movement at various times; numerals indicate the time of day, provided the area experiences semidiurnal tides.

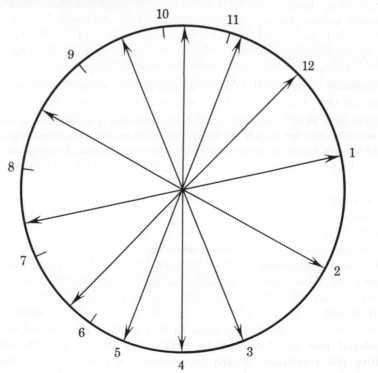

flood tide and seaward during ebb tide. For a short time there is a **slack current**—that is, the velocity is slowed and stops for a brief interval after reaching the high-water mark; this is called the **high-water slack.** The same series of events is repeated when the tide reaches the low-water mark; this is called a **low-water slack.** Approximately 5 to 20 miles off the coast there is a **rotary tidal current,** associated with tidal movement. Under these conditions there is never any slack; the current merely changes direction at a certain time of the day (Figure 12–22). One of the most rapid tidal currents has been recorded near the lower Amazon River in South America, at Para, where the tidal current sweeps in and rises 20 feet within a few minutes.

The tidal current velocity will vary in any inlet depending on the type of substrate, the conformity of the bottom, the amount of freshwater entering such an estuary, its rate of speed, and so on. If a tidal current is confined to a narrow inlet, it may enter as a powerful wave, known as a **tidal bore.** When the tide begins to ebb, water will leave this area with equal force, setting up a powerful tidal current that sweeps seaward. Many organisms living in the intertidal zone are washed by the flooding and ebbing of tidal currents which will introduce oxygen and food into these areas as well as carry wastes away. These intertidal organisms, in order to survive in such areas, have had to adapt to varying periods of emergence and submergence, particularly if they are sessile forms. In general, their position within the intertidal areas correlates with their tolerance to the varying conditions imposed by the tidal currents.

ESTUARIES

An **estuary**, according to the dictionary definition, is a passage or inlet where the tidal water comes in contact with a river current. Thus it is a confined arm of the sea, situated at the lower end or mouth of a river. It does not require much imagination to envision the turbulence one would expect to encounter in an area where a river current containing freshwater comes into contact with a tidal current of salt water. In a tidal estuary, there is an influx of freshwater at the upper end and a flooding of sea water at the lower end, as well as an outflow of dilute sea water. The amount of freshwater entering the estuary at its upper end will vary with the season, according to the amount of precipitation and flooding that occurs upstream. The flood tide volume of water entering a particular estuary may also be great, bringing about an increased amount of longitudinal movement of water. In a vertical section of a salt water estuary (Figure 12–23), it will be noted that the freshwater flowing from the river will be less dense than is the sea water; thus it flows out over the surface of the underlying mass of salt water. Parr's principle, first introduced into the literature in 1936, states that with high vertical stability (the conditions usually encountered in a tidal estuary) there is

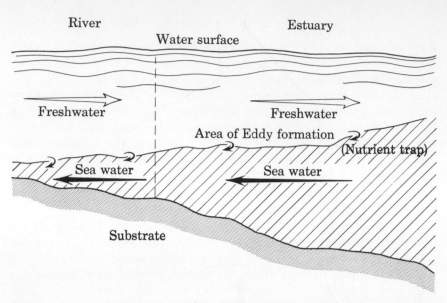

FIGURE 12–23 Horizontal turbulence established by the continual flow of freshwater from a river drainage system into an estuary above the salt water "wedge" flowing inward. The horizontal turbulence forms nutrient traps in the interface zone between the layers of fresh and salt water.

low vertical turbulence, but high horizontal turbulence. That is, at the boundary formed by the mass of freshwater coming into contact with the underlying mass of salt water, there is a great shearing force that creates a considerable amount of horizontal turbulence, which results in eddy formation. The eddies that form will contain nutrients that have been carried into the estuary and are circulated around in the boundary region. Such a zone is referred to as a **nutrient trap** by the ecologist. The eddies will promote a rapid diffusion of oxygen and food because eddy diffusion is many times more rapid than molecular diffusion. In fact, eddy diffusion may be as much as 10^{11} times greater than molecular diffusion (usually ranging from a million to several billion times the speed of molecular diffusion).

In shallow, temperate water estuaries, the salinity conditions will vary vertically (as has been discussed) and horizontally or across the estuary from one shore to the other. Figure 12–24 illustrates an estuary as seen from above. Diagram *A* shows the isohaline line (a line indicating equal salinity value) across the estuary as the tidal current is moving into it. Diagram *B* shows the isohaline delineation of the same estuary as the tidal current ebbs. The reason for the curvature in the salinity line across the estuary is that the tidal current is moving more rapidly along the center of the channel and therefore altering the salinity more rapidly in these areas. Usually we find that there is a greater salinity range in the center of the estuary in contrast to the river or seaward ends. The

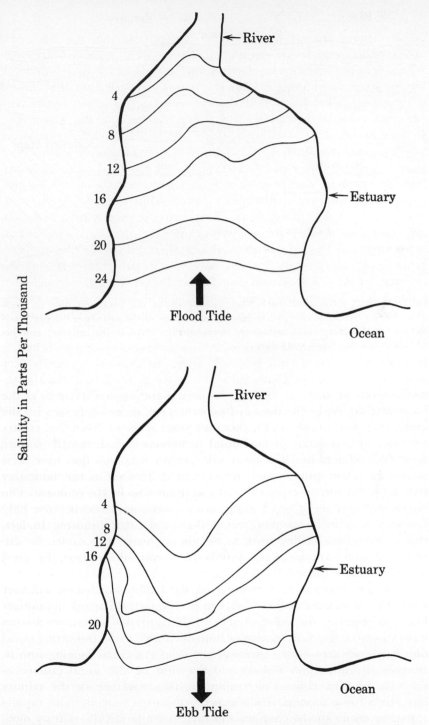

FIGURE 12–24 Isohaline lines across an estuary at flood tide (Diagram *A*) and ebb tide (Diagram *B*), with the figures indicating parts of salt per thousand along the water surface.

salinity values are taken at a constant depth, so that the horizontal measurements represent a salinity value at a given depth. Salinity measurements at the surface are relatively low, but values increase with depth for any given point along the estuary. In some estuaries the tidal current is so strong (tidal bore) that vertical stratification is practically nonexistent because of the extreme turbulence (according to Parr's principle: If there is low vertical stability, there will be high vertical turbulence and low horizontal turbulence). Salinity values will change diurnally or semidiurnally in the estuary in keeping with the tidal currents. Superimposed on these short-term changes in salinity values are the seasonal changes that will occur. In temperate areas, salinity values are characteristically low in the spring, when precipitation is usually high and melting snow has flooded streams throughout the drainage system. Low temperatures at this time of the year will often reduce the rate of evaporation and consequently keep salinity values rather low. During the summer, salinity values will usually be higher because droughts or reduced precipitation limits the amount of freshwater entering the estuary, and increased evaporation at higher temperatures reinforces the salinity changes.

Northern and tropical estuaries exhibit differences worth mentioning. In the fjord (estuaries) of northern areas, the channel is usually deep with a rocky substrate. This solid substrate serves as an excellent area for sessile forms of animals that can tolerate saline variability and for the algae that are normally absent or very sparse in many of the silt bottom estuaries of the temperate region. The water is very cold in these areas, for much of it is derived from mountain streams that carry water formed from melting snow and glacial ice. The surface waters of fjords will have a very low salinity. Because of the very low salinity and somewhat higher freezing point (in contrast to neighboring marine areas) ice often forms on the surfaces of these channels. Ice formation will reduce the light penetration as well as the thermal values of the estuary, causing a migration or repetitive killing of some of the organisms during the hiemal period. Tropical estuaries have very dilute salinities during the rainy season because flood waters churn into the estuary, reducing the salinity values to a very low level. Accompanying the flood waters is a considerable amount of suspended organic and mineral material that will reduce the light penetration and increase the turbidity of the water. As the dry season follows, the rate of evaporation increases, and sea water invades the deeper reaches of the estuary, causing an increase in the salinity. Permanent residents of tropical estuaries must be able to tolerate a considerable fluctuation in salinity values as well as variations in the amount of turbidity (silt content) of the water.

Extensions of the estuary into low-lying flat or deltalike areas often create what is commonly known as a **salt marsh.** Although salt marshes (Figure 12–25) may be considered separate habitats, there is often a con-

FIGURE 12–25 A coastal salt marsh community with a sand bar in forground, which is submerged at flood tide. In the background is a common salt marsh grass (*Spartina alterniflora*).

nection with an estuary; for this reason they may be considered as an extension or part of an estuary. Salt marsh grasses, particularly species of *Spartina,* are usually the predominant vegetation replacing the algae, which predominate as the floral component of the estuary proper. The substrate is usually a soft mud that has been carried in by the swifter currents of the estuary. Flooding of salt marshes by spring tides and the more frequent flood tides alter the salinity, often suddenly, in these areas. Water is often much shallower than in adjacent estuaries, so that water temperatures may rise far above values in estuaries during the summer months, followed by a reversal of these thermal trends during the cooler parts of the year.

Biota of Estuarine Waters.   Organisms of estuarine waters must be able to tolerate continually changing salinity conditions, which are of tidal and seasonal nature. In other words, euryhaline species are far more likely to inhabit estuarine areas on a permanent or semipermanent basis. The silt content and turbidity of the water will often be high and a factor of some importance with regard to colonization. Increased silt content of many such areas is adverse to the flora because it drastically reduces the light penetration. Bivalve mollusks are unlikely residents; spat (immature bivalves) will not settle and survive on silt surfaces, and gills of adult lamellibranchs are quickly clogged by silty water.

Fisher-Piette found that many estuarine species were definitely influenced by salinity changes with regard to their position in the La Rance Estuary in France. After several years of normal climatological conditions there was a year in which precipitation was abnormally high, causing floods and reduced saline conditions in the estuary. This brought about a seaward movement of many of the estuarine species, according to a published account (1931). Later (1933), the same investigator published the results of an investigation after a period of abnormally low rainfall, which of course resulted in an increase in salinity. Many of the same species that had moved seaward under the more dilute conditions reversed their position and moved up the estuary in keeping with the elevated salinity of the water.

Estuarine species may be grouped into three categories (see Table 12–5): (1) There are a number of marine species that will exhibit only a

TABLE 12–5. *Zonation of Various Marine and Estuarine Invertebrates in the Tamar Estuary Adapted in Part from Data by Spooner and Moore (1940)* *

CLASS	SCIENTIFIC NAME	MARINE	ESSENTIALLY ESTUARINE	STRICTLY ESTUARINE
Polychaeta	*Amparete grubei*	X		
Polychaeta	*Phyllodoce maculata*	X		
Polychaeta	*Lanice conchilega*	X		
Pelecypoda	*Abra prismatica*	X		
Polychaeta	*Nephthys hombergi*		X	
Gastropoda	*Nerita fulgurans*		X	
Gastropoda	*Littorina littorea*		X	
Crustacea	*Carcinus maenas*		X	
Polychaeta	*Nereis diversicolor*			X
Gastropoda	*Hydrobia ulvae*			X
Gastropoda	*Neritina piratica*			X
Crustacea	*Cyathura carinata*			X

* G. M. Spooner and H. B. Moore. 1940. The ecology of the Tamar estuary VI. An account of the macrofauna of the intertidal muds. Jour. Mar. Biol. Assoc. United Kingdom, **24**:283–330.

limited amount of penetration into an estuary. They are usually far more common along the outer limits of the estuary, where the salinity conditions more nearly approach those of the open ocean. (2) There are groups of animals that are found primarily in estuaries (column 2 of Table 12–5), but they may also be found in certain marine areas if conditions relate to their ecological and physiological requirements. (3) There is a group of organisms that are restricted to the estuarine environment and are not found in marine areas. This latter group is most numerous in the upper reaches of an estuary where the salinity conditions are much reduced. Some animals, such as the crab, *Carcinus,* can tolerate reduced salinities, provided temperatures are high. In this case a limiting factor (salinity) will often be altered in terms of tolerance if other ecological conditions are altered. This is not only true of adults but, it has been reported, for immature stages (including the development of eggs) as well.

Various estuarine genera and species and even subspecies often demonstrate a graded sequence in estuaries, dictated by a varying tolerance to salinity conditions. The amphipod *Gammarus locusta* that inhabits estuarine areas along the Baltic coast has an inhibited growth rate (becomes more stunted), with deeper penetrations of these brackish water areas. Three subspecies of *Gammarus zaddachi* are located at different positions within an estuary. In addition to the permanent residents of the estuarine areas, there are temporary inhabitants that invade these areas primarily in search of food. Shrimp and fish move in and out of many coastal inlets; they follow the tidal rhythm, moving in with flood tide and leaving the area as the tide ebbs. In this way, they are not exposed to severe salinity changes, yet are able to take advantage of the increased amount of food often found in these areas. In fact it has been noted in the Tamar Estuary of England that a species of flounder (*Pleuronectes flesus*) follows the shrimp into the estuary to feed on this plentiful supply of food. A related species, *Pleuronectes limanda,* when it is a young fish, feeds on crustaceans (primarily shrimp), but later changes its diet and feeds on the polychaet *Sabella.* The gray mullet (*Mugil*), moving in and out with the tidal rhythm, feeds on vegetation in estuaries.

Birds that utilize the rich food supply of estuaries include the American oystercatcher (*Haematopus palliatus*), found commonly along the coastal estuaries from California to Chile and from New Jersey to Argentina. With their long, blunt, powerful bills they chisel limpets off alga-encrusted rocks and open oysters and clams with considerable ease. Plovers (*Charadrius*) feed on a number of small invertebrates, particularly the crustaceans. Another group, the curlews (*Numenius*), may be found inland, feeding on berries, seeds, and insects during the summer, but inhabiting estuaries, salt marshes, and mud flats during the winter, feeding on worms and other small invertebrates by probing into the mud with their long bills. The long-billed curlew (*Numenius americanus*) spends its summers on the North American prairies, but winters along the Gulf Coast and Guatemala. The crab plover (*Dromas ardeola*), a noisy bird frequenting the coasts of East Africa and southwest Asia, pounds crabs and other crustaceans as well as mollusks to pieces with its heavy sharp bill.

404 | BASIC CONCEPTS OF ECOLOGY

Selected References

Baker, F. C. 1918. The productivity of invertebrate fish food on the bottom of Oneida Lake, with special reference to mollusks. N.Y. State Coll. For., Tech. Publ., 9:1–264.

Ball, R. C. 1948. Relationship between available fish food, feeding habits of fish and total fish production in a Michigan lake. Mich. State Coll. Agric. Exp. Sta., Tech. Bull., 206:1–59.

Ball, R. C., and D. W. Hayne. 1952. Effects of the removal of the fish population on the fish food organisms of a lake. Ecology, 33:41–48.

Beaufort, L. F. de. *Zoogeography of the Land and Inland Waters* (London: Sedgwick & Jackson, 1951), pp. i-viii, 1–208.

Burkenroad, M. D. 1946. Fluctuations in abundance of marine animals. Science, 103:684–686.

Carpenter, Kathleen E. *Life in Inland Waters with Special Reference to Animals* (London: Sedgwick & Jackson, 1928), pp. i-xv, 1–267.

Chandler, D. C. 1944. Relation of limnological and climatic factors to the phytoplankton of 1941. Trans. Amer. Micros. Soc., 63:203–236.

Clarke, G. L. 1946. Dynamics of production in a marine area. Ecol. Monogr., 16:321–335.

Coker, R. E. *Streams, Lakes, Ponds* (Chapel Hill, N.C.: Univ. of North Carolina Press, 1954), pp. i-xviii, 1–327.

Dansereau, P., and F. Segadas-Vianna. 1952. Ecological study of the peat bogs of eastern North America. Can. Jour. Bot., 30:490–520.

Day, J. H. 1951. The ecology of South African estuaries. Part I. A review of estuarine conditions in general. Trans. Roy. Soc. So. Africa, 33:53–91.

Dexter, R. W. 1947. The marine communities of a tidal inlet at Cape Ann, Massachusetts: a study in bio-ecology. Ecol. Monogr., 17:261–294.

Faure-Fremiet, E. 1951. The tidal rhythm of the diatom *Hantzschia amphioxys*. Biol. Bull., 100:173–177.

Fisher-Piette, E. 1931. Sur la penetration des diverses especes marines sessiles dans les estuaires et sa limitation par l'eau douce. Ann. Inst. Oceanogr. Monaco., 10:213–243.

———. 1933. Nouvelles observations sur l'ordre d'euryhalinite des especes litorales. Bull. Inst. Oceanogr., 619:1–16.

Forbes, S. A. 1887. The lake as a microcosm. Bull. Ill. Nat. Hist. Surv., 15:537–550.

Greenbank, J. 1945. Limnological conditions in ice-covered lakes, especially as related to winter-kill of fish. Ecol. Monogr., 15:343–392.

Hardy, A. C. *The Open Sea* (Boston: Houghton Mifflin, 1956), pp. i-xv, 1–335.

Hedgpeth, J. W. 1957. Treatise on marine ecology and paleoecology. Mem. Geol. Soc. Amer., 67:1–1296.

Jewell, Minna E., and H. W. Brown. 1929. Studies on northern Michigan bog lakes. Ecology, 10:427–475.

Jones, N. S. 1950. Marine bottom communities. Biol. Rev., 25:283–313.

Korringa, P. 1947. Relation between the moon and periodicity in the breeding of marine animals. Ecol. Monogr., 17:347–381.

Moore, H. B. *Marine Ecology* (New York: John Wiley, 1958), pp. i-xi, 1–493.

Murray, J., and J. Hjort. *The Depths of the Ocean* (New York: Macmillan, 1912), pp. i-xx, 1–82.

Nicol, E. 1935. The ecology of a salt marsh. Jour. Mar. Biol. Assoc. United Kingdom, 20:203–261.

Odum, H. T. 1956. Primary production of flowing waters. Limn. and Oceanogr., 1:102–117.

Pearse, A. S., H. J. Humm, and G. W. Wharton. 1942. Ecology of sand beaches at Beaufort, North Carolina. Ecol. Monogr., 12:135–190.

Riley, G. A. 1940. Limnological studies in Connecticut. Part III. The plankton of Linsley Pond. Ecol. Monogr., 10:279–306.

Sanders, H. L. 1956. The biology of marine bottom communities. Bull. Bingham Ocean. Coll., 15:345–414.

Sparck, R. 1935. On the importance of quantitative investigation of the bottom fauna in marine biology. Jour. Conseil., 10:3–19.

Stephenson, T. A., and Anne Stephenson. 1950. Life between tide-marks in North America. I. The Florida Keys. Jour. Ecol., 38:354–402.

———. 1952. Life between tide-marks in North America. II. Northern Florida and the Carolinas. Jour. Ecol., 40:1–49.

———. 1954. Life between the tide-marks in North America. III. Nova Scotia and Prince Edward Island. Jour. Ecol., 42:14–70.

Sverdrup, H. U., M. W. Johnson, and R. H. Fleming. *The Oceans: Their Physics, Chemistry and General Biology* (Englewood Cliffs, N. J.: Prentice-Hall, 1942), pp. i-x, 1–1087.

Walford, L. A. *Living Resources of the Sea* (New York: Ronald Press, 1958), pp. i-xv, 1–321.

Welch, P. S. *Limnological Methods* (New York: McGraw-Hill, 1948), pp. i-xviii, 1–381.

———. *Limnology* (New York: McGraw-Hill, 1952), pp. i-xi, 1–538.

Wright, J. C. 1958. The limnology of Canyon Ferry Reservoir. I. Phytoplankton-zooplankton relationships in the euphotic zone during September and October, 1956. Limn. and Oceanogr., 3:150–159.

ZoBell, C. E. *Marine Microbiology* (Waltham, Mass.: Chronica Botanica, 1946), pp. 1–240.

XIII. Statistical Procedures in Ecology

This chapter will deal with some of the elementary statistical procedures of interest to the ecologist or student of ecology. It is intended as a brief introduction to some of the more common statistical procedures that are being used with increased frequency by ecologists in the analysis of data included in research articles. The particular problem and the data that are forthcoming will determine the statistical techniques required for the critical analysis from which may be drawn pertinent conclusions of interest to students of ecology throughout the world. It is extremely important that any scientific investigator appreciate the value and methods of statistical techniques available to him so that he may be aware of the validity or nonvalidity of his particular data. However, it is also important that a statistical procedure is not or should not be considered an end in itself. A quotation from Hedgpeth (1957, p. 48) may emphasize and clarify this point: "The old saw that statistics are the ultimate degree of prevarication is too often true in ecology because a sample, however obtained, is treated as sacred, and data are subjected to statistical procedures which add their own bias. A naive faith in standard deviation or correlation *per se* as proving something, and a failure to realize that many of the data of ecology are nonparametric and hence not amenable to parametric tests, have made many of the statistical analyses in ecological literature of uncertain value."

PRESENTATION OF DATA

The inclusion of graphs, tables, diagrams, and photographs in reports, research papers and texts can often clarify details or reduce the amount of verbal explanation of results, equipment, and other materials. The oft-quoted phrase, "a picture is worth a thousand words," also applies to graphs, tables, charts, and diagrams in many scientific reports. On the other hand, there is at times a tendency to include various graphic or photographic material in a paper or text merely to make the particular work appear more impressive. Fortunately, this is seldom done, but such temptation should be curbed early in an individual's scientific career.

Any table, whether it is a reference table giving detailed information or facts or a simple table clarifying the material in context, should be properly titled and contain proper headings, so that the body of the

FIGURE 13–1 A bar graph with three different conditions indicated and using a different graphic symbol for each condition. From *Graphic Charts Handbook* by Anna C. Rogers. Copyright 1961. Public Affairs Press. Used by permission.

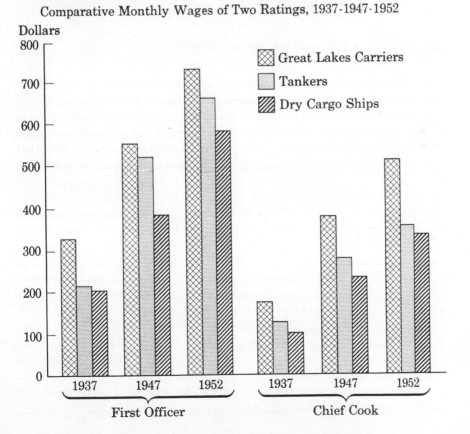

Comparative Monthly Wages of Two Ratings, 1937-1947-1952

table is clearly understood. Usually a table will enable the reader to make a comparison of a number of different statistics or facts that will clarify introductory information, results, or conclusions. Graphs, which are of necessity less detailed than are tables, enable the reader to grasp facts and relationships more quickly than is generally possible from other types of presentation. Like tables, graphs, to be meaningful, must be properly prepared. They must be titled. Numerical graphs are drawn to scale; the numerical values must be clearly presented along the left axis and the base. Line graphs, bar graphs, and pictographs are the most commonly utilized types in scientific papers. Preferably, line graphs should not contain more than three or four lines of comparative data. If more than three lines are shown, the usefulness of the graph may be sacrificed because the graph becomes increasingly more difficult to interpret. Values centered around a rather confined range of values may cause such an entangled group of lines as to discourage the reader even before he begins to analyze the data presented. Regardless of the number of lines used, all of them should be symbolically different—that is, each line (solid, dotted, broken, and so on) should differ from the others. If bar graphs are used, bars representing different factors should be represented by different symbols (Figure 13–1).

FREQUENCY DISTRIBUTION

In an analysis of statistical data it is often possible to establish a number of classes or categories. For example: Suppose that we have collected a number of mammals in the field and in the course of identifying them in the laboratory, they are measured. The measurements of all specimens may be subdivided into a number of size classes, as shown in Table 13–1 and Figure 13–2. In establishing classes, we may deal with either **discrete**,

TABLE 13–1. *Crown-Rump Measurements of Small Mammals, Separating the Fauna into Size Classes and Indicating the Total Number (Frequency) of Animals in Each Size Class*

CROWN-RUMP LENGTH IN CENTIMETERS	FREQUENCY
3.5 to 5.4	12
5.5 to 7.4	10
7.5 to 9.4	18
9.5 to 11.4	19
11.5 to 13.4	14
13.5 to 15.4	8

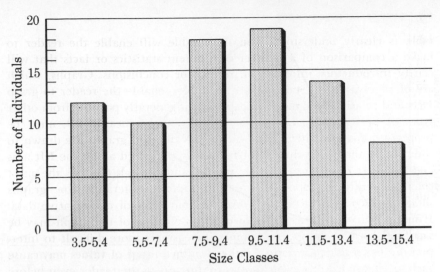

FIGURE 13-2 Graphic representation of data presented in Table 13-1, indicating a higher frequency for the two central size classes of the range.

or **continuous, variables.** A discrete variable is one that involves units that differ from one another by finite amounts; in other words, the units cannot be separated into smaller subdivisions. If we were counting the number of individual plants or animals in different quadrats of a sample area, the frequency totals would be in whole numbers because these represent a discrete variable. A continuous variable is one that involves units that may be subdivided into fractional amounts, so that an infinite number of subdivisions may be interspersed between the larger values by means of instruments capable of making such measurements. Thus we might subdivide a number of animals into size classes on the basis of crown-rump length and measure these animals to the nearest tenth of a centimeter. Let us assume we have a population of small mammals that have been measured; the smallest individual is 4.2 centimeters long (crown-rump measurement) and the largest is 14.8 centimeters. If we divide these individuals into size classes running, let us say, from 3.5 to 5.4 cm., 5.5 to 7.4 cm., 7.5 to 9.4 cm. . . . and 13.5 to 15.4 cm., we are dealing with continuous variables, as these measurements have an infinite number of units existing between the major subdivisions. It is possible to interval an infinite number of units, for example, between 13.2 and 13.3; thus there would be values of 13.21, 13.22, 13.23, and so on.

As is indicated in Figure 13-2, whether we are using a line graph or bar graph, there will be some classes that display a greater frequency than others. In many instances, it is possible that one class will have a higher frequency than do others within the population. And it is possible, and usually probable, that one must deal with skewed or asymmetrical curves in ecological problems, as is represented in Figure 13-3

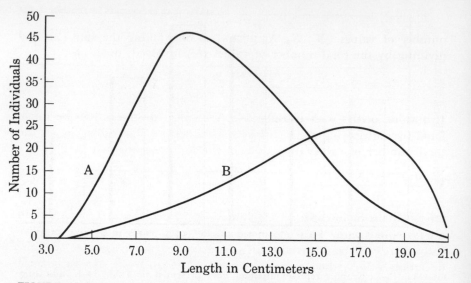

FIGURE 13–3 Skewed curves of size distribution in two populations of mammals. Curve *A*, skewed to the right, indicates a young population with a large proportion of individuals of small size. Curve *B*, skewed to the left, indicates a greater number of mature individuals existing within the population with little reproductive activity or success, as is evidenced by the small number of immature size classes.

by curves *A* and *B*. Careful measurements and proper graph construction can often be of considerable value in ecological work. For example, curve *A* in Figure 13–3 indicates a relatively young population, as the size classes are skewed in such a fashion that we can deduce there are a greater number of smaller size classes (proportionately higher juvenile population). Ecologically this may mean that either a population has just recently invaded and colonized the area and taken advantage of the more desirable ecological conditions that are extant in the region, or that the population has recovered from severe climatic or catastrophic factors and has entered a period of reproductive activity that eventually will reestablish the aggregation in that particular area. Curve *B* indicates a population that contains a greater number of mature or senescent individuals with a lag or actual deficit in reproductive activity. Some ecological factor or factors have impeded the reproductive process, and if this factor is not alleviated or modified to a certain degree, it is possible that the population may become extinct in that locality.

CENTRAL TENDENCY

The manner in which certain values tend to center, or cluster, around a particular range of measurements or values is referred to as **central tendency.** The **arithmetic mean,** or so-called average value, is one way of measuring central tendency. ($\overline{X}$) is easily computed by taking a number of values $(X_1, X_2, X_3 \ldots$ and so on), taking the sum (Σ), and dividing by the total number of values (N) involved; thus,

$$\overline{X} = \frac{X_1 + X_2 + X_3 \ldots X_n}{N}, \quad \text{or} \quad \overline{X} = \frac{\Sigma X}{N}.$$

If a value occurs with considerable frequency, the mean can be calculated by multiplying the factor by its frequency (f) and dividing by the total number of values presented, in the following manner:

$$\overline{X} = \frac{f_1 X_1 + f_2 X_2 + f_3 X_3}{f_1 + f_2 + f_3}, \quad \text{or} \quad \overline{X} = \frac{3 \times 3.3 + 6 \times 3.6 + 2 \times 3.8}{3 + 6 + 2} = 3.55+.$$

One point is of interest: an algebraic sum of deviations from the mean always equals zero. This becomes evident when we realize that numerically there will be as many units above the mean as below, so that the deviation values when calculated from the mean quite obviously must equal zero.

The **median** may vary from the mean because it is a value that divides a series of units so that one half or more of the values are equal to or less than the median, and one half or more of the items are greater than the median. Thus, if we have a series of measurements as follows: 3.3, 3.8, 3.9, 4.2, and 4.8, the median would be 3.9 (the mean would be 4.0). However, if we have a series totaling an even number of values rather than an odd number, the median is calculated by taking the average of the two central values. Consequently, in a series with values listed as follows: 3.2, 3.4, 3.5, 3.7, 4.2, and 5.8, the median would be 3.6, or the average between the two central values of the series, 3.5 and 3.7. The arithmetic mean would be

$$\frac{3.2 + 3.4 + 3.5 + 3.7 + 4.2 + 5.8}{6}, \text{ or } 3.96+.$$

A **mode** is a value within a series around which many of the values tend to be concentrated. Thus, in a normal curve as shown in Figure 13–4, the mode would be located somewhere within the peak of the curve. The equation for determining the mode is

$$M_0 = L_1 + \frac{\Delta_1}{\Delta_1 + \Delta_2} i,$$

where L_1 is the lower limit of the frequency class, Δ_1 is the difference between the frequency of the modal class and the class to the left in a graph, Δ_2 is the difference between the frequency of the modal class and the class to the right of the modal class, and i is equal to the class interval used. In some instances, there is no mode, since values may show no concentration; in others, there may be bimodal curves, or frequencies (a concentration around two values in a series), as is shown in Figure 13–5.

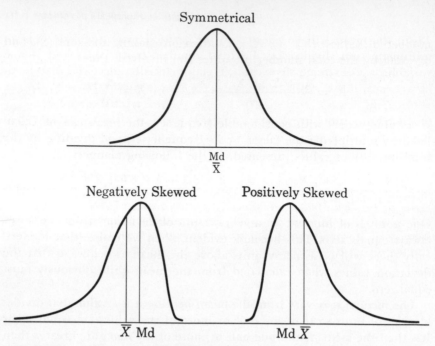

Symmetrical

Md
$\overline{X}$

Negatively Skewed   Positively Skewed

$\overline{X}$ Md   Md $\overline{X}$

FIGURE 13–4 Three curves of distribution. The upper curve is a normal (symmetrical) curve indicating the identical location of the mode and mean. The two lower curves are skewed, with a consequent displacement of the mode and mean. From *Social Statistics* **by Hubert M. Blalock. Copyright 1960. McGraw-Hill Book Company. Used by permission.**

The three different indicators of central tendency—the mean, the median, and the mode—are used in varying degrees for statistical work. This is as it should be because it depends upon the data and investigation as to how useful one or the other of these measurements may be. At times, a mean value may be useless or of very limited value. In cases where we are dealing with extreme values or skewed curves (Figure

FIGURE 13–5 A bimodal curve with the modes represented by lines under each peak of the curve. From *Social Statistics* **by Hubert M. Blalock. Copyright 1960. McGraw-Hill Book Company. Used by permission.**

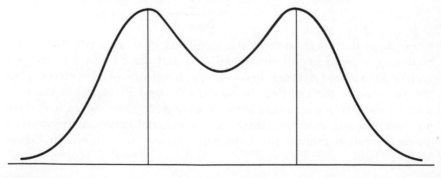

13–6), the mean will be affected to the greatest extent because it is an arithmetic sum divided by the total number of variables and if one variable is so extreme in nature, it may markedly affect the placement of the mean along a distribution curve. The median and mode will be affected to a much lesser extent by the skewed nature of the curve. A median value from any group of statistics is often easier to calculate than the mean value. We also find that the median is not as sensitive to extreme values at either end of the range of statistics as is the mean. At

FIGURE 13–6 The location of the mean, median, and mode coincide in unimodal curves (*a*, *b*, and *c*). Mean and median coincide in bimodal and trimodal curves (*d* and *e*), but in skewed curves the mode is closest to the peak, the median is some distance away, and the mean is situated farther out in the tail of the curve. From *Measurement and Statistics* by Virginia Senders, Copyright 1958. Oxford University Press. Used by permission.

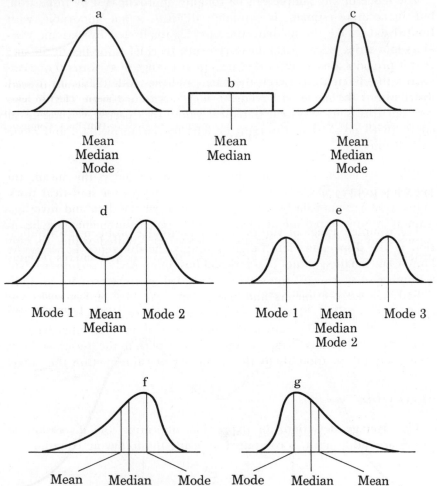

times, the median is a more logical statistic than the mean. For example, in estimating the average number of offspring produced by a particular species of invertebrate or the total number of seed released by a certain species of plant, it is sometimes more logical to employ the median rather than the mean. A few abnormally prolific organisms may tend to distort the picture if one relies on the mean because in this case the mean would be well above the median. The median would be the point below which half of the population sample falls or the point above which half the population sample lies. There are certain disadvantages inherent in the calculation of a median. Medians cannot enter many algebraic calculations; it is not possible to compare medians as accurately as arithmetic means; the standard error of a median is larger than the standard error of a mean; and, furthermore, it is impossible to base a median on other medians.

The mode of any sample can be roughly approximated by inspection, but an accurate estimate is extremely difficult, if not impossible, with limited data. Like the median, the mode is unaffected by extreme variables in a series of statistical measurements. Its chief value lies in the fact that it provides a measure of skewness in any range of statistics if one calculates the difference between the mean and the mode. Thus, in skewed distributions the mode will render a more accurate picture of the average, but this is its only real statistical value. In a perfectly symmetrical curve (with no skew to the right or left) the mean, median, and mode will all coincide.

DISPERSION

The complete range of values for any particular problem is an indication of the **dispersion**. The range is simply the difference between the largest and smallest values of a series. Thus, in an earlier section, we had a number of specimens; the smallest recorded measurement for an individual was 4.2 centimeters and the largest was 14.8 centimeters from crown to rump. This gives us a total range of 10.6 centimeters ($14.8 - 4.2 = 10.6$). Of course the range, like the mean, is unduly influenced by either an exceedingly large or small value within the series without giving any information about the frequency of values within the range.

DEVIATIONS

The **average deviation**, an expression indicating the dispersion of values around a mean, is computed by using the following equation:

$$a = \frac{\Sigma d}{N},$$

where a = average deviation, d = deviations from the mean, regardless of sign and N = the total number of variables. In a normal distribution, about 57.5 per cent of the values will fall within the plus or minus average deviation from the mean. The standard deviation, a far more valuable statistical tool than the average deviation, can be utilized to compute or determine the skewness of a population curve, in tests of statistical significance and the calculation of the correlation coefficient. The average or mean deviation, is the average distance of all the deviations of a particular sample from some measure of central tendency. Usually this measure of central tendency is the arithmetic mean, but it is possible to calculate the mean deviation by using the median. If the median is used, then it should be so indicated, because it is usually understood that the mean is being used as the basis for calculations. Some observations will be located above the mean (positive deviation), and some values will be below the mean (negative deviation). If we used negative and positive signs to designate the position of the deviation relative to the mean, then we would have a mean deviation that would always be zero. For this reason, the signs of the deviations are always ignored when calculating the mean deviation. To calculate the mean deviation, the following formula can be used:

$$\text{Mean deviation} = \frac{\Sigma(d)}{N},$$

where $\Sigma(d)$ refers to the sum of the deviations with the signs ignored and N is the total number of variables in the sample. Suppose we are counting the numbers of organisms of a particular species that have been removed from ten sample plots and we have the following values: 10, 12, 5, 15, 13, 15, 8, 10, 10, and 12. There are a total of ten calculations (N) representing ten sample plots, and they yield a mean of eleven. If we total the deviations from the mean ($\Sigma|d|$) it gives a value of 24; dividing this value by N gives us a mean deviation of 2.4. This means that the average deviation from the mean in this case is 2.4. The mean deviation is not altered in value to the degree that a standard deviation would be altered by large deviations from the central tendency of the sample. The mean deviation is seldom used in statistical work because it is an inconvenient term to use in algebraic calculations; we find that relationships regarding the theory of errors, the normal curve, and comparison of other statistical constants becomes increasingly difficult if we rely on this statistic. These difficulties can be avoided by using the standard deviation.

The standard deviation may be calculated by using the following equation:

$$s = \sqrt{\frac{\Sigma d^2}{N}},$$

where s = standard deviation, d = deviations from the mean, and N = the number of values involved. In other words, by taking the deviations from the sample mean, squaring each one, and totaling these squared deviations, dividing by the total number of individual values, and taking the square root of this last figure, we have the standard deviation of any sample. The standard deviation is a very useful measure of dispersion; therefore, it is imperative that anyone contemplating statistical procedures in population ecology become familiar with this procedure. Table 13–2 shows the computation involved in establishing the standard deviation for a particular population.

TABLE 13–2. *Computation of the Standard Deviation by Calculating the Deviations from the Arithmetic Mean*

WEIGHT IN GRAMS	DEVIATION	DEVIATION SQUARED
X	d	d^2
59.0	− 3.27	10.692
66.3	+ 4.03	16.240
64.2	+ 1.93	3.724
89.3	+27.03	730.620
47.2	−15.07	227.104
52.3	− 9.97	99.400
59.1	− 3.17	10.048
60.8	− 1.47	2.160
498.2		1,099.988

$$\bar{X} = \frac{\Sigma X}{N} = \frac{498.2}{8} \qquad \bar{X} = 62.27 \qquad s = \sqrt{\frac{\Sigma d^2}{N}} = \sqrt{\frac{1,099.988}{8}}$$

$$= \sqrt{137.498} = 11.7$$

In calculating the standard deviation (*s*) it is not necessary to determine the deviation from the mean in each individual case; we may substitute $X - \bar{X}$ (where X is the recorded value and $\bar{X}$ is the arithmetic mean) instead of using d (the deviation). It is then possible to use an alternate formula,

$$s = \sqrt{\frac{\Sigma X^2}{N} - \left(\frac{\Sigma X}{N}\right)^2},$$

so that all that is needed in each case is the individual values (X) and their squares (X^2); from these we can calculate the standard deviation. Thus, if we take the data used in Table 13–2 and calculate the standard deviation by using the formula for individual values, we can derive the standard deviation according to the procedure presented in Table 13–3.

TABLE 13–3. *Computation of the Standard Deviation by an Alternate Method, Using the Squared Values of Raw Data*

WEIGHT IN GRAMS (X)	SQUARED VALUE (X^2)
59.0	3,481.00
66.3	4,395.69
64.2	4,121.64
89.3	7,974.49
47.2	2,227.84
52.3	2,735.29
59.1	3,496.81
60.8	3,696.64

Total	498.2	32,129.40

$$s = \sqrt{\frac{\Sigma X^2}{N} - \left(\frac{\Sigma X}{N}\right)^2} = \sqrt{\frac{32,129.4}{8} - \left(\frac{498.2}{8}\right)^2} =$$

$$\sqrt{4,016.17 - 3,877.55} = \sqrt{138.62} = 11.7$$

The standard deviation in both instances is 11.7+. Thus both methods will give us comparable results. Therefore, circumstances will dictate the most convenient means of computation. Finally, it is possible to compute the standard deviation by grouping values, the number of cases within a particular group or frequency (f), and calculating the mid-values of each group. If we should use the previously cited example dealing with the crown-rump measurements of small mammals, it is possible to use the equation

$$s = \sqrt{\frac{\Sigma fd^2}{N}}$$

to determine the standard deviation. This equation is most useful where we deal with grouped data and have computed the frequency distribution within the various groups, as is illustrated in Table 13–4.

In any normal curve of distribution, one standard deviation above and below the arithmetic mean will include 68.27 per cent of the values, or over two thirds of all the values listed for that particular case. Two standard deviations above and below the mean includes 95.45 per cent of all the individuals or values; three standard deviations above and below the mean will include 99.73 per cent of the values, as indicated in Figure 13–7. In many instances, even though we are not dealing with a curve of normal distribution, the values will still lie approximately as indicated within the various standard deviations or their multiples. In a curve of normal distribution, a plus and a minus standard deviation of

TABLE 13–4. *Computation of the Standard Deviation from Grouped Data by Calculating Mid-Values of Each Group and Their Deviations from the Arithmetic Mean*

CROWN-RUMP MEASURED IN CM.	NUMBER OF MAMMALS (f)	MID-VALUES	DEVIATION (d)	DEVIATION SQUARED	PRODUCT (fd²)
3.5–5.4	12	4.45	−5.0	25.0	300.0
5.5–7.4	10	6.45	−3.0	9.0	90.0
7.5–9.4	18	8.45	−1.0	1.0	18.0
9.5–11.4	19	10.45	+1.0	1.0	19.0
11.5–13.4	14	12.45	+3.0	9.0	126.0
13.5–15.4	8	14.45	+5.0	25.0	200.0
	81 (N)				753.0 (Σfd²)

$$\bar{X} = 9.45 \qquad s = \sqrt{\frac{\Sigma fd^2}{N}} = \sqrt{\frac{753}{81}} = \sqrt{9.29} = 3.05$$

1.96 from the arithmetic mean includes 95 per cent of all the values within the curve; a plus and minus standard deviation of 2.58 includes 99 per cent of all the individuals or items within a normal curve of distribution.

FIGURE 13–7 A normal curve of distribution including the location of standard deviations from the mean and the per cent of the curve affected by each deviation above and below the mean. From Frederick E. Croxton and Dudley J. Cowden, *Practical Business Statistics.* © 1934, by permission of Prentice-Hall, Inc., Englewood Cliffs, N. J.

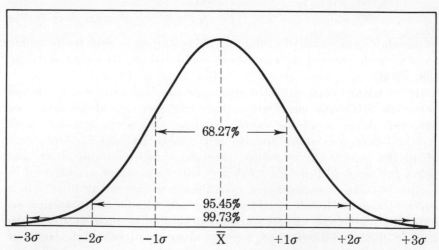

SKEWNESS

In plotting any distributional curves in natural populations, it is possible, and generally probable, that we usually encounter some degree of skewness. A skewed curve will vary to some degree from the hypothetical curve of normal distribution represented in Figure 13–7. It is seldom (if ever) that we may expect to encounter a perfect curve of normal distribution in plotting populations in terms of size, age groups, or the other countless environmental factors that exhibit some measure of dispersion. There are a number of ways to calculate the degree of skewness. Perhaps one of the most readily calculated measures of skewness, as well as one of the most reliable in an ecological sense, is the Pearsonian measure of skewness devised by Karl Pearson. According to the Pearsonian formula, skewness (S_k) is equal to the arithmetic mean minus the median multiplied by 3 and divided by the standard deviation, or

$$S_k = \frac{3\,(\bar{X} - \text{Med.})}{s}$$

Relative skewness determined by the forementioned formula will yield results in pure numbers. These values will vary from zero (no skewness) to a plus or minus 3 (maximum skewness). Skewness to the right is always represented as a positive number; skewness to the left is always negative. Thus according to Figure 13–3, curve *A* is skewed to the right and represents positive skewness; curve *B*, which is skewed to the left, is a negative skew value. If we take the weights in grams listed in the distributional series of Table 13–3, the arithmetic mean is 62.2 ($\bar{X}$); the median is the arithmetic mean of 59.1 grams and 60.8 grams because they are the two central values of the array. Since we are dealing with an even number of values, the median is calculated by taking the mean of the two central values, which would be 59.9+. The standard deviation (*s*) is 11.7. The formula

$$S_k = \frac{3\,(62.2 - 59.9)}{11.7}$$

gives us a skew value of 0.58, a positive value indicating that the distributional curve based on these values would give us a skewed curve to the right.

LINEAR CORRELATION

Statistical correlation involves positive or negative relationships between two factors or conditions. Positive correlation involves a relationship between small values of one series and small values of the other series. Figure 13–8 demonstrates a linear correlation between the length of certain animals and their respective weights. A total of 23 individuals were measured and weighed (each individual is represented by a dark spot on the chart). Most of the organisms (11) lie within a rather narrow range of values, weighing from 21 to 28 grams and measuring from 38 to 50 centimeters in length. In this case, the longer the organism the more it weighed. Perfect positive correlation would be indicated by a straight sloping line running from the lower left-hand corner of a graph (Figure 13–8) to the upper right-hand corner. Perfect negative correlation would be indicated by a straight line running downward from the upper left-hand corner to the lower right-hand corner. Of course, in order to demonstrate correlation (negative or positive), an investigator must always pair conditions or factors because there must be a condition X to compare with condition Y. One of the initial steps followed in determining the degree of correlation is the construction of a scatter plot, as represented in Figure 13–8, where the position of each organism is determined by the intersection of lines drawn from the abscissa and ordinate. Each spot represents one and only one organism. Scatter plotting is a valuable process because it tells the investigator whether there is any linear (straight-line) correlation or nonlinear correlation and whether it is negative or positive correlation.

One important point to bear in mind is that a high degree of correla-

FIGURE 13–8 Scatter diagram representing linear correlation of weight with crown-rump length in mammals. Greatest number of organisms are confined to the area enclosed by a square.

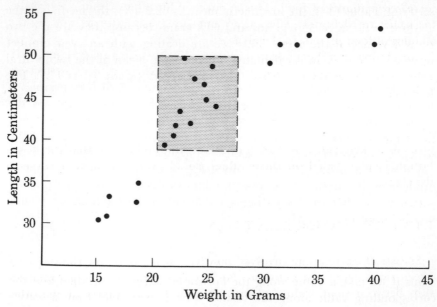

tion in some instances may not be determined by the two variables dealt with in the problem—that is, a high or low value for one variable may not be caused by a high or low value for another variable. The presumed high degree of positive or negative correlation may be due to an entirely different cause and not dependent on the variables. For example, the amount of precipitation in Arizona has nothing to do with the rate of transpiration from plants in Michigan, though climatic conditions in the northern state may yield values that would appear to demonstrate either a positive or negative correlation when they are compared with precipitation values in the southern area. In other instances, two variables may be affected by a third factor, though the two variables do not cause any direct affect on each other. However, any change in the third factor will cause changes in the two variables. Without some knowledge of the factors involved, an investigator may assume, as a result of a superficial examination of statistical values of the two variables, that they are directly correlated. An example of this assumed correlation is evident from some of the present writer's research on the ecology of several species of springtails. In the past the amount of moisture in an area has been correlated with population size. The greater the humidity or moisture in the immediate area, the greater the population size, indicating, it was presumed, a high positive correlation. But recently it has become obvious that the correlation is actually due to increased quantities of food in the form of fungi and spores. A greater amount of fungus will be present if the moisture is high, and the increased quantity of food means higher population values. Therefore, although high population numbers appear to be correlated with large quantities of moisture, they are actually the result of increased amounts of food. This is not true for all species of springtails, for some are definitely affected by moisture variability as well as the amount of food present in the area.

Correlation can be measured statistically by using several methods. These methods are based on the fact that the correlation is perfect or, as has been previously stated, that the increase of one of the variables is accompanied by a proportionate increase (positive correlation) or decrease (negative correlation) of the other variable. One way in which the degree of correlation may be checked numerically is by means of the coefficient of correlation, represented symbolically by the letter r. Pearson devised a procedure which involves taking the ratio of the mean product of deviations of the two variables to the geometric mean of the variances, so that in calculating a coefficient of correlation, we would use the following formula:

$$r = \frac{\Sigma \, (X - \overline{X}) \, (Y - \overline{Y})}{\sqrt{\Sigma \, (X - \overline{X})^2 \, (Y - \overline{Y})^2}}.$$

Thus if we take a value along the horizontal axis (X variable) and the corresponding value along the vertical axis (Y variable) from a scatter plot graph, along with the mean for X and Y values, we can calculate the correlation coefficient. An alternate formula for determing the coefficient of correlation is

$$r = \frac{\Sigma (X - \overline{X})(Y - \overline{Y})}{(N-1) \, s_x \, s_y},$$

where N refers to the total number of paired observations and s_x and s_y are the standard deviations of X and Y variables. A correlation coefficient may vary from -1 (perfect negative correlation) to $+1$ (perfect positive correlation). Any value close to 0 would denote a lack of correlation or a relatively low correlation.

SAMPLING POPULATIONS

Some discussion about population estimates has been presented in Chapter VIII, "Population Ecology." Additional statistical information is presented in this section. In any sampling procedures used by an ecologist, the basic goal is to gain more information about a population (or several populations) so that logical and unbiased conclusions may be reached. It is impossible, and would certainly be impractical, to examine the entire population in the field. For this reason, the ecologist relies on information obtained from a number of samples. Sampling will result in a number of **parameters,** which are statistical constants of some particular population. Common parameters that are the result of sampling information include values such as the population mean, median, mode, variance, and so on. Sample parameters are represented by Latin symbols (letters), whereas population parameters are signified by Greek letters, as is shown in Table 13–5.

T A B L E   1 3 – 5 .   *Symbols Used for Some of the More Common Sample and Population Statistical Parameters*

PARAMETER	SAMPLE SYMBOL	POPULATION SYMBOL
Frequency of a single class	f	
Standard error of mean	$s_{\bar{x}}$	
Summation of quantities		Σ
Correlation coefficient	r	ρ
Deviation	d	
Variance	s^2	σ^2
Standard deviation	s	σ
Mean	$\overline{X}$	μ

In sampling a population it may be possible, though not feasible in terms of time expended, to enlarge the samples or increase the number of sample units until we are, in fact, sampling the entire population. As the sample increases in size, any estimate that is made relative to the population falls within smaller limits of the true value. In order for sampling to be most effective with respect to any population, an investigator must be sure that (1) all of the samples belong to a single population, (2) the samples include any variations that are distinctive of the population, and (3) any population characteristics appear in about the same proportion in the sample. Of course, it is not always possible to fulfill all of the above conditions with ideal precision, but the closer we can approach the cited conditions, the more valid our conclusions will be with respect to any particular population.

In any ecological sampling the investigator should attempt, whenever possible, to employ random sampling techniques. This is extremely important if he is to draw any statistical meaning from the data, because the theory of probability that is used to interpret population parameters relies on random observations. The only conscious selection involves the area and population chosen for study. But every sample unit within the population area should be considered a probable choice for observation. Any attempt to subject the choice of sample units to a particular system or to exclude the choice of certain samples is an unpardonable bias.

CHI SQUARE AND CONTINGENCY TABLES

In ecological work, as in other scientific problems, it is often necessary to determine the probability of a particular population distribution or event taking place completely by chance. In biological applications, the **chi square test** might consist of determining the effect of some treatment on a population. Let us take a hypothetical problem. We wish to test a new pesticide (insecticide) relative to some particular commercial crop. Past records indicate that insects killed 4,000 out of every 10,000 crop plants in certain geographic areas over periods of time. Thus in an untreated area the expected ratio of dead to surviving plants would be a ratio of 4,000 to 6,000. However, after treating a plot with the insecticide, we find that only 50 out of every 10,000 plants are killed by insects. To determine whether this difference in survival is due to mere chance or to the action of the pesticide, we perform a statistical test, a chi square test, on the data available. In order to analyze the data, we may tabulate the information as shown in Table 13–6. By using the classical formula for the computation of chi square,

$$X^2 = \Sigma \frac{(F_1 - F_2)^2}{F_2},$$

where F_1 represents the observed frequencies, and F_2 the expected frequencies, we can determine the chi square value. The numerical values presented would give us the following values in the equation:

$$X^2 = \frac{(9{,}950 - 6{,}000)^2}{6{,}000} + \frac{(50 - 4{,}000)^2}{4{,}000},$$

which would then yield

$$X^2 = \frac{15{,}602{,}500}{6{,}000} + \frac{15{,}602{,}500}{4{,}000} = 6{,}501.0.$$

Now, referring to the table of chi square (see any statistical text), we find that occurrence of such a figure solely by chance would be far less than a

TABLE 13-6. *Hypothetical Data with Statistics Necessary for the Computation of Chi Square Values by Means of the Classical Chi Square Equation*

	OBSERVED FREQUENCY	EXPECTED FREQUENCY
	(F_1)	(F_2)
Number survived	9,950	6,000
Number killed	50	4,000
Total	10,000	10,000

probability factor of .001. We check the above value in the table, using one degree of freedom, or $n = 1$. Thus, assuming that no other controlling factor is responsible for the extreme discrepancy in results, we may assume that treatment with the insecticide has produced truly significant results in our purely hypothetical problem.

In this instance, we have dealt with a case where we are reasonably sure of what to expect on the basis of past experience. Such statistics are often not available when a specific environment is being sampled. Even if we were in possession of a considerable number of population statistics about a particular type of organism in relation to a specific type of environment, such information would provide us with only a crude estimate as to the population size of a specific area, which might be influenced by climatic conditions that are entirely different from those described in any published accounts. It is necessary under these circumstances to construct a two by two contingency table and determine the chi square value from a modified formula that does not include any expected frequencies but only the observed frequencies of a particular population. Let us take an actual example from the literature (Knight,

1963) and attempt to determine whether the distribution of organisms is what we would expect on the basis of probability or whether there are environmental factors that alter the distribution. A deciduous stand was sampled for a particular subfamily of springtails (subfamily Tomocer-inae). In carrying out the distributional aspect of the problem, it was considered important to determine whether there was a significant micro-stratification of *Tomocerus* in the forest floor. Consequently, the soil was divided into several microstrata from the soil surface downward: litter layer, fermentation layer, humus layer, and mineral soil layer. Statistical data derived from an ecological analysis of stratification could be treated in several ways to determine the chi square values—by either comparing seasonal figures or annual totals. Table 13–7 includes several two by two contingency tables that resulted from the study.

TABLE 13–7. *Contingency Tables for Tomocerus flavescens separatus (Part A) and Tomocerus lamelliferus (Part B) Containing the Necessary Statistics to Compute the Chi Square Values Based on Random Sampling Data**

PART A
ANNUAL TOTAL FOR *Tomocerus flavescens separatus*

	QUADRATS WITH	QUADRATS WITHOUT	TOTAL	CHI SQUARE
Litter	5	43	48	
Fermentation	36	12	48	40.9
Total	41	55	96	

PART B
VARIATION IN SEASONAL DISTRIBUTION FOR *Tomocerus lamelliferus*

	VERNAL	ESTIVAL	TOTAL	CHI SQUARE
Fermentation	46	57	103	
Humus	121	87	208	4.54
Total	167	144	311	

* Clifford B. Knight. 1963. The microstratification of *Tomocerus* (Collembola) in a beech-maple forest of North Carolina. Amer. Midl. Nat., **70**:187–196.

In Part A, Table 13–7, the litter and fermentation layers of the forest soil were compared to determine the probability of the represented dis-tribution purely on the basis of chance. The number of quadrats with individuals of the springtail *Tomocerus flavescens separatus* are compared with the total number of these sample units that lacked the organism in these two microstrata. By using a different equation, the chi square value can be determined. The equation is as follows:

$$X^2 = \frac{N (ad - bc)^2}{(a + b) (c + d) (a + c) (b + d)},$$

where N represents the total number of quadrats sampled (96), and the other letters represent figures contained in various parts of the contingency table (Table 13–8). By substituting the values from the contingency table in Part A, Table 13–7, we have the equation

$$X^2 = \frac{96 (5 \cdot 12 - 43 \cdot 36)^2}{(48) (48) (41) (55)},$$

which gives us a chi square value of 40.9. In Part B, Table 13–7, two seasonal aspects of distribution between the fermentation and humus levels of the forest floor are compared for *Tomocerus lamelliferus*. Using the same equation and inserting the proper numerical equivalents, we have

$$X^2 = \frac{311 (46 \cdot 87 - 57 \cdot 121)^2}{(103) (208) (167) (144)},$$

which yields a chi square value of 4.5.

TABLE 13–8. *Two by Two Contingency Table with Letter Symbols Representing the Part of the Table to Be Used in the Modified Chi Square Equation*

	QUADRATS WITH	QUADRATS WITHOUT	TOTAL
Litter	a	b	$a + b$
Fermentation	c	d	$c + d$
Total	$a + c$	$b + d$	N

We now utilize the null hypothesis, a type of reasoning employed by statisticians to determine whether the hypothesis is to be accepted or rejected. A null hypothesis, according to *Webster's Third New International Dictionary,* is "the assumption that any observed difference between two samples of a statistical population is purely accidental and not due to a systematic cause." In the present situation, the null hypothesis might be stated as follows: There is, within reasonable limits of probability, no observable statistical difference between the populations located in different microstrata. The assumption according to the null hypothesis then is that the observed values could be recorded, with a reasonable degree of probability, as being the result of purely accidental arrangement. How small should this probability be in order to bring about a rejection of the null hypothesis? Is there any universal probability level recognized by statisticians? Both of these questions can be answered quite simply: The hypothesis is never proven or disproven by a student of statistics; it is either accepted or rejected on the basis of reasonable doubt. In other words, we find that the degree of confidence in the hypothesis is so low that we reject it or so high that we accept it. There is no universal probability level that we regard as the common cutoff point at which to reject or accept a mass of data on the premise that the particular event has occurred as a result of chance. However, in most biological work, it is common to use the 5 per cent probability value as the arbitrary limit to determine rejection or acceptance of the null hypothesis. If our results should yield a chi square value that falls at the 5 per cent level or less for a particular degree (s) of freedom relative to the probability level, it is usually sufficient grounds for rejecting the hypothesis.

If we refer to a table of values for chi square, the probability at the 5 per cent level would give us a value of 3.841. Thus any chi square value equal to or more than 3.841 indicates that the probability of this event occurring purely by accident would be about 5 per cent or less of the time. In the first example, the chi square value of 40.9 was derived by comparing populations in litter and fermentation layers and noting their presence or absence in quadrats throughout the year. This event would not occur by accident with a probability of even .001 (chi square value = 10.827)! This is calculated on the basis of one degree of freedom, a value adhered to for all two by two contingency tables. In the second example, populations of *Tomocerus lamelliferus* in the fermentation and humus levels are compared for two seasonal aspects (spring and early summer). A chi square value of 4.9 indicates that the probability of this event occurring would be less than 5 per cent, though it could occur 2½ per cent of the time (X^2 value = 5.024). Since the probability of its occurring is less than 5 per cent of the time, the value is considered statistically significant, implying that something other than pure chance is operating to bring about the distribution of populations indicated in Table 13–7.

When we are dealing with small samples, chi square values may tend to be misleading because the error introduced into the calculations is always in the same direction. Invariably we derive a smaller probability, meaning that the null hypothesis will be rejected more often than it should. In dealing with small samples where the total frequency or N is greater than 40 and the class with the lowest observed frequency is less than 10, it has been common practice to use the Yates' correction for continuity. This adjustment yields a somewhat modified equation for the determination of chi square values. The Yates' equation is as follows:

$$X_y^2 = \frac{(ad - bc - \frac{N}{2})^2\, N}{(a + b)\, (c + d)\, (a + c)\, (b + d)}$$

provided that $(ad - bc)$ is a positive number; if it is negative, the equation is modified as follows:

$$X_y^2 = \frac{(ad - bc + \frac{N}{2})^2\, N}{(a + b)\, (c + d)\, (a + c)\, (b + d)}.$$

In computing the annual total for *Tomocerus flavescens separatus* in Part A, Table 13–7, it will be noted that the total frequency of observations was 96 and the class with the lowest observed frequency was 5, which means that the Yates' correction should be used in this particular case. If we substitute the proper values in the equation cited above, we have

$$X_y^2 = \frac{(5 \cdot 12 - 43 \cdot 36 + \frac{96}{2})^2\, 96}{(48)\, (48)\, (41)\, (55)},$$

which yields a chi square value (Yates' correction) of 38.3, a somewhat lower value (but still highly significant) than the 40.9 obtained by using the uncorrected equation. In the second example (Part B, Table 13–7), though the total observed frequencies exceeds 40, the class with the lowest observed frequency was 46, well above the maximum of 10 required for using the Yates' correction equation. Another approach, which is more acceptable to a greater number of persons involved in statistical work, is not to use the calculation of chi square when one of the observed frequencies within a contingency table is less than 10, but to use a more exacting technique (and a very laborious one) for the derivation of probability that involves multinomial distribution. The latter method is discussed in Fisher (1950).

I have attempted to include some statistical techniques most frequently used by ecologists. The material presented in this chapter, however, is only an introduction to the many statistical procedures available to biologists at the present time. Space limitations do not allow a full or extensive treatment of all statistical techniques that could, and in some cases, should be used by ecologists in the analysis of field or laboratory data. The use of statistical procedures will tend to remove the temptations of personal bias or subjectiveness from ecological papers in the future. Although it is unlikely that ecology will ever become a discipline that uses statistics or mathematical techniques to the extent that they are used in genetics and biophysics, a greater number of ecologists are using simple statistical procedures to convey their message to fellow-workers in the field.

Selected References

Bailey, N. T. J. *Statistical Methods in Biology* (London: English Universities Press, 1959), pp. i–ix, 1–160.

Cochran, W. G. *Sampling Techniques* (New York: John Wiley, 1953), pp. 1–330.

——. 1954. Some methods for strengthening the common X^2 tests. Biometrics, **10**:417–451.

Cochran, W. G., and G. M. Cox. *Experimental Designs* (New York: John Wiley, 1957), pp. 1–611.

Croxton, F. E. *Elementary Statistics with Applications in Medicine and the Biological Sciences* (New York: Dover Publications, 1953), pp. i–vii, 1–376.

Fisher, R. A. *Statistical Methods for Research Workers* (Edinburgh: Oliver & Boyd, 1950), pp. i–xv, 1–354.

——. *The Design of Experiments* (Edinburgh: Oliver & Boyd, 1951), pp. i–xv, 1–244.

Fisher, R. A., and F. Yates. *Statistical Tables for Biological and Medical Research* (Edinburgh: Oliver & Boyd, 1948), pp. i–viii, 1–112.

Hedgpeth, J. W. (ed.) 1957. *Treatise on Marine Ecology and Paleoecology.* Geol. Soc. of America. Memoir 67, **1**:i–viii, 1–1296.

Kempthorne, O., T. A. Bancroft, J. W. Gowen, and J. L. Lush (eds.) *Statistics and Mathematics in Biology* (Ames, Iowa: Iowa State College Press, 1954), pp. i–ix, 1–632.

Kermack, K. A., and J. B. S. Haldane. 1950. Organic correlation and allometry. Biometrika, **37**:30–41.

Knight, C. B. 1963. The microstratification of Tomocerus (Collembola) in a beech-maple forest of North Carolina. Amer. Midl. Nat., **70**:187–196.

Simpson, G. G., Anne Roe, and R. C. Lewontin. *Quantitative Zoology* (New York: Harcourt, 1960), pp. i–vii, 1–440.

Snedecor, G. W. *Statistical Methods Applied to Experiments in Agriculture and Biology* (Ames, Iowa: Iowa State College Press, 1956), pp. 1–534.

Yates, F. *Sampling Methods for Censuses and Surveys* (London: Griffin, 1953), pp. 1–401.

XIV. The Ecological Outlook

In conclusion, it is perhaps fitting to investigate the possible applications and prospects for the future of this relatively young discipline called ecology. Several inconsistencies are quite obvious in even a superficial review of existing ecological progress. In spite of our vast array of ecological equipment or apparatus that can be put to ecological use, many relatively simple problems remain unsolved through neglect. In other instances, what appears to be a very simple problem proves to be a very complex one because of the interplay of a number of intangible or variable factors in nature. Another obvious paradox is the fact that at the present time the scientific world stands on the very threshold of an immense amount of ecological data compiled from satellites and exploratory rocket flights into outer space. Yet, on the other hand, some of the most powerful nations on our planet possess an awesome array of armament, the key to total destruction that could swiftly and irreversibly nullify scientific progress.

Ecology has been defined as a field of study concerned with the interrelations between organisms and their environment. The environment is a vast complex of factors that surround us and dictate our general state of health and many of our reactions. The fact that we are unable to divorce ourselves from this surrounding medium and that it is in intimate contact with every individual every minute of every day from birth to death, whether he is scuba diving or orbiting the earth, makes environment of vital importance to everyone regardless of whether or not he is cognizant of the fact.

We are entering an era of expanding populations, when certain environmental conditions will exert a degree of concern never before encountered by man in the course of human history. Here are a few of the problems that will face future generations of people throughout the world:

1. In view of increasing populations in nearly every social aggregation, how long will our present agricultural productivity effectively feed the world's population?

2. Are our present supplies of water sufficient to provide growing communities with adequate, pure, unrestricted amounts of water for future generations? If not, where and how can our present sources be augmented?

3. Can all nations continue to support needed building projects that infringe on many of the natural areas and still retain populations of wildlife, or must we contend with the extinction of one species after the other as a sacrifice that must be made for "progress"?

4. To what level can air pollution spiral before human life and wildlife are endangered to the point of causing mass epidemics of pollutant-causing sickness and death?

5. Will the present level of nuclear radiation tend to have an accumulative effect on future generations in terms of future food supplies and environmental contamination when natural background radiation and cosmic radiation are considered?

6. Have we at present produced conditions brought about by the uncontrolled use of pesticides and insecticides in certain areas that may become more dramatic and terrifying as future generations come in contact with organic and inorganic residues resulting from careless use and irresponsible marketing by commercial chemical cooperations?

These are problems that face every man, woman and child—not only now but in future generations—and every one of the few questions cited are of environmental concern. All of these problems must eventually be resolved in some way by either the ecologist, the economist, or sociologist (applied ecologists of a sort), and some help from a varied array of non-ecologists.

SPACE ECOLOGY

In this chapter some of the more important problems and promising areas for future research in ecology are presented. With man's initial conquest of space and the prospect of encountering new environmental situations on other planets, the future holds a promise of excitement and challenge, with many research possibilities for astroecologists. Little is known for certain about environmental conditions in outer space other than some of the data gathered from man's few, brief orbital flights and information (much of which is classified and hence unavailable to many ecologists) relayed to earth from satellites. Some of the satellites presently orbiting our earth have been feeding valuable information about weather conditions, existing storm centers, potential disturbances likely to develop into hurricanes, and other types of destructive storms. In order to make even initial, exploratory flights to the moon and some of the closer planets, it will require tremendous sums of money, a great deal of scientific and technical knowledge—and certainly some unavoidable failures. This possibility of failure in certain instances is a risk that must be accepted by the public. Whether or not the United States or some other nation is first to land on the moon or first on Mars is of little scientific consequence. Of far greater importance is the willingness of any nation to disclose scientific information so that the worldwide scientific community may process the data and draw logical, sound statements with regard to that particular extraterrestrial area.

Any team of investigators sent into space or to other satellites or planets to extract information should be aware of the fact that an understanding of ecology is of paramount importance. The temperatures, amount of radiation, type of substrate, chemical substances present, the amount of gravitational force, and many other factors—all of an ecological nature—will be of interest. If our scientific accomplishments in space progress in the future as they have in the past few years, it is not unreasonable to expect that texts and other published material on space ecology will become as commonplace as those covering any terrestrial subject. Engineers and scientists have many problems of an ecological nature that must be solved before any expedition from earth can hope to establish even a temporary station on another planet. Ecological data regarding conditions in outer space began with the first scientific balloon flights that recorded a quantity of data by means of instruments aboard the gondola. Although balloon flights still take place, a far more refined array of electronic instruments and recording apparatus within orbiting satellites forwards a far greater and continuing quantity of information to tracking and recording stations around the world.

Aside from the environmental conditions which exist in outer space, and most particularly on the planets and satellites of our solar system, ecologists of the future will be concerned with the forms of living matter that may exist in these extraterrestrial environments. Whether or not living organisms inhabit these areas—at least life as we know it— appears to be highly improbable. Life, as we know it, implies the presence of carbon (organic) compounds including the amino acids, fatty acids, purines, pyramidines, and other allied substances producing entities conceivably quite different from terrestrial life, but chemically similar. Research of an extraterrestrial nature will undoubtedly be confined to our solar system in the foreseeable future. Most scientists agree that only two planets—Venus and Mars—might possibly foster living entities. Recent data obtained from telemetric instruments involved in the Mariner II space probe indicates that the Venusian environment possesses temperatures far too high for organic life (Barath, et al., 1963). Mars appears to present an environment that is nearly as unfavorable to (organic) life. Temperatures, though not as unfavorable as those on Venus, are probably not ideal for any conceivable carbon-containing life. The fact that microorganisms have been cultured under conditions believed to simulate those on Mars (Hawrylewicz, Gowdy, and Ehrlich, 1962) does not weaken or contradict the supposition that the planet is probably lifeless. Even microorganisms would require some water and some carbon dioxide in the surrounding atmosphere. Both materials may be absent. It is believed that the so-called "ice caps" are, in fact, concentrations of nitrous oxide. The concentrations of nitrogen oxides that probably make up the atmosphere, according to some astronomers, would present a lethal environment that would effectively prevent the establishment of organic life as we know it.

Most recently, G. G. Simpson (1964) has cast considerable doubt on the possibility of extraterrestrial life. In fact the value of extraterrestrial biological studies has been challenged by Simpson. It is probable that many biologists are in sympathy with Simpson's view that our federal government is spending far too much on programs oriented toward the search for extraterrestrial life. There is a definite possibility that more than a vestige of truth lies in the following statement made by Simpson (p. 769), with reference to the development of exobiology (space biology): ". . . a curious development in view of the fact that this 'science' has yet to demonstrate that its subject matter exists!" However, it would seem that in this respect, negative information is as important in a scientific sense as is positive information. No one at the present time can say with certainty that no life exists within our solar system, excepting on our own planet. Certainly the odds seem to strongly favor a negative hypothesis, but without exploratory space expeditions it is not possible to deny the existence of life elsewhere.

The hypothesis that there may be life on other solar systems cannot be rejected, because it has been estimated by some very competent astronomers that the number of planets that might possess atmospheric and environmental conditions approximating those found on earth may be in the neighborhood of 100 million or more. With this figure in mind, it is conceivable that organic life could have arisen on these fantastically distant planets—distances which are best expressed in light years. A brief recapitulation of the most widely accepted origin of life on earth and the subsequent organization necessary to produce the species that have evolved since the beginning of life may allow a more rational evaluation of the probability of organic life existing or having existed on other planets. Oparin (1957), Calvin (1961), and Ehrensvard (1962) have explored the possible origin of life on our planet and agree unanimously that life has originated from nonliving chemical elements that have combined under favorable environmental conditions and have been transformed into living matter by energy. Harold Urey and Stanley Miller succeeded some years ago in forming amino acids and other organic molecules under conditions believed to be similar to those that existed on our planet at this period in the geological past. Miller (1955) has discussed the experiment in which the elements carbon, hydrogen, oxygen, and nitrogen were exposed to electrical discharges to produce amino acids, the important building blocks of organic matter. Given sufficient time these organic molecules may then combine to produce far more complex chemical entities with considerable diversity of arrangement. With the tremendous time span—over 3 billion years on our own planet— organic evolution has progressed from the simple heterotrophic molecules that arose in ancient seas to the most advanced forms of life that now inhabit our planet. It is highly probable that many planets in other solar systems with similar environmental conditions are as old as or older than earth, so that the time span undoubtedly necessary for organic evolution as we know it poses no problem. But the fantastic number of ways in which organic molecules can conceivably combine and the necessity for an organization that is capable of duplication (reproduction), of utilizing and transforming available energy, of forming new molecular combinations (evolution), and of reproducing these new variants impose conditions that are less likely of fulfillment on other planets. That is, it becomes apparent that life as we know it on our planet does not exist elsewhere. If we go a step further, the improbability of parallel organic evolution is even less likely. Once we have the organic macromolecules organized into functional systems, variability imposed by genetic systems necessary to allow adaptation to a fluctuating environment results in increasing diversification. That mutations, recombinations, and natural selection imposed on organic entities would be duplicated borders on the impossible.

We have assumed that life is, in terms of chemical structure, similar on all planets. However, it is possible that a different type of "life" based on a different chemical framework (that is, other than carbon) exists in other planetary environments. If this possibility develops as our space probes continue, it will necessarily require an entire revision of our concept of living matter. However, even if it is found that no demonstrable life is present in outer space, establishment of the fact that it does not exist and information regarding environmental conditions will be of value.

NUCLEAR RADIATION

Of particular interest to the ecologist are the effects of ionizing radiation on living systems and the after-effects, often subtle, they may have on a diverse number of species. **Ionizing radiation** is the term used for designating high energy protons or gamma rays emitted by certain radioactive materials during decay. This type of radiation is capable of extracting electrons from stable atoms, resulting in electrically charged particles called ions. Ionizing radiation has been an environmental factor since the beginning of life on our planet. Thus all living organisms have been exposed to low levels of ionizing radiation, very often referred to as background, or natural, radiation. However, in the past nineteen years, man has developed the technical ability to produce atomic piles and release tremendous amounts of energy in the form of thermonuclear blasts. These explosions caused by fissionable substances have loaded the atmosphere with radioactive material that raises the level of radiation far above that caused by background radiation. The fallout debris still aloft at the present time will continue to descend for the next decade, though barring any further extensive nuclear testing, the peak of radioactive fallout has probably passed. There are several ways in which the radiation level may increase in the coming years, despite the fact that the United States, Great Britain, and the Soviet Union honor a test ban treaty now in effect. France is a nonsigner of the test ban pact and may well carry on enough nuclear testing at any time and anywhere to add significant amounts of fallout debris to the atmosphere. Red China is an ever-present potential prospect in terms of nuclear testing, though at this writing she does not possess the capability, so far as is known, of producing thermonuclear devices. Another possible source of increase in the level of ionizing radiation is the release of radioactive substances from underground weapons tests still permitted according to the test ban treaty. There is a future prospect of experimentation on nuclear devices to be harnessed for peaceful uses such as the construction of canals and harbors; in this case, there is the ever-present danger of releasing unexpected quantities of fallout. Finally, there is the ever-present danger of accidents in the increased number of nuclear power plants that are beginning to appear throughout the world. Any accident, which federal agencies consider highly improbable because of safeguards installed at these plants, could load the immediate area with considerable quantities of ionizing radiation that will kill, cripple, and alter the animals and vegetation in the surrounding area.

At the present time, there are no protective guides to warn the citizenry about excessive quantities of fallout radiation in any area, though the Federal Radiation Council has promised the publication of guides within the near future. Guides used by atomic workers have been established on the basis of past experience with radium, X-radiation, and animal experiments employing radiation. The guides used by atomic workers are established with limits well below the level where detectable biological damage has ever been observed in humans. However, even these guides do not assure beyond a fragment of doubt that there may be some undetectable damage to some part of the body. Certainly we cannot expect the establishment of any magic number or formula above which there is predictable danger and below which we can be assured of perfect safety, because, as Paul Tompkins, executive director of the Federal Radiation Council, has stated: "We can't prove the presence of deleterious effects. We cannot prove the absence. The possibility of deleterious effects is assumed. The existence has not been demonstrated. It is only the possibility which has been assumed."

Many questions and problems harass the ecologist and other scientific groups interested in the effects of radiation on living plants and animals. One important problem is the potential danger to living organisms of future generations from fallout radiation, which, at the present time at least, is below the level of natural background radiation that has always been present. If there is a danger, how much fallout radiation would be required before we could definitely link plant and animal mortality, disease, and illness with fallout? Atomic explosions release most of the energy (about 85 per cent) in the form of airblast, subsurface shock, and thermal radiation. The remaining energy is released in the form of radiation. The radiation produced by an atomic blast will fall out at variable rates over a period of time. In a surface detonation, about 15 per cent of the radioactive particles will enter the stratosphere, from which most of the debris will continue to fall out over broad geographic areas for six months to several years. Five per cent of the debris enters the lower atmosphere (tropospheric fallout); the majority of this debris settles on land and oceanic surfaces within a few weeks after detonation. The remaining 85 per cent is deposited as local fallout, usually within a few hours. At the present time, no human deaths can be attributed to fallout anywhere in the world with the exception of 230 natives on the island of Rongelap and one Japanese fisherman exposed to heavy nuclear fallout from a nuclear test explosion on Bikini in 1954 (Figure 14–1). The Atomic Energy Commission claims that the terminal illness of the fisherman was not typical of radiation illness.

With the exception of radioactive carbon (C^{14}), three chemical elements that have gained more attention than the other several hundred known radioactive isotopes of thirty-six chemical elements are strontium-90, cesium-137 and iodine-131. Most radioactive substances are of little biological concern because they have a relatively short **half-life,** a matter of a few minutes, in a majority of instances. Radioactive iodine has a half-life of eight days: it takes eight days for half of the radioactivity

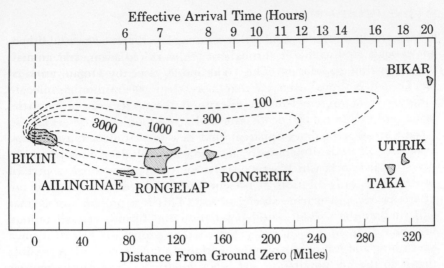

Effective Arrival Time (Hours)

BIKAR

100

300

3000   1000

BIKINI

AILINGINAE   RONGELAP   RONGERIK

UTIRIK

TAKA

0   40   80   120   160   200   240   280   320

Distance From Ground Zero (Miles)

FIGURE 14–1 Fallout pattern 96 hours after an atomic explosion at Bikini in 1954. Dotted lines represent dosage in roentgens per hour. Reprinted by permission from George M. Woodwell, "The Ecological Effects of Radiation," *Scientific American*, 208:40-49, June 1963. Used by permission.

to dissipate, another eight days for another half of the remaining radioactivity to dissipate, and so on. Radioactive iodine enters a number of substances that are ingested by different organisms in the course of passage through food series (called food chains by some authors) and is known to accumulate within the thyroid gland, where it plays an intimate role in the formation of thyroxine. There is a strong indication that it may cause thyroid cancer in higher vertebrates if present in high enough concentration. But here again the medical profession as well as biologists are beset with the nagging question, how much is too much? Radioactive strontium and cesium have half-lives of twenty-eight and thirty-six years, respectively. Thus the living biota will be exposed in many cases to radioactivity from these two elements for the rest of their lives, even if there is no further testing! Strontium poses a health hazard to the human population as well as to other advanced groups of life because it tends to concentrate in bone and, it is believed, is one of the causes of bone cancer and leukemia. Cesium enters muscle tissue in considerable amounts, and even though much of it is eventually eliminated from the organism in about six months, there is the possibility that it may cause irreversible genetic changes in different organisms during its brief residence within the body. Radioactive carbon (carbon-14) has been previously discussed in "Paleoecology," Chapter IX. Although not produced directly from a nuclear blast, neutron particles convert atmospheric nitrogen into carbon-14 which has a half-life of over five thousand years!

The world population is increasing at the rate of approximately

80,000 people per day, or 29 million humans per year. There is simply not enough food available throughout the world to adequately nourish this increasing population. The Food and Agriculture Organization of the United Nations estimates that more than 500 million people are suffering from protein-deficient diseases at the present time. From the birth rate exceeding the death rate and acute food shortages extant in certain areas, it becomes apparent that new food sources must become available. There is undoubtedly not enough arable land to support the necessary livestock, which serves as the most important single source of protein. The only solution, at present, is to resort to more intensive use of freshwater and marine species of fish. This is a protein supply that will support the present world population and furnish enough protein for some time in the future, provided that proper safeguards against overfishing and fish population decimation are not abandoned. A possible threat to the fish population and other aquatic wildlife are the nuclear reactors that are being established along seacoasts, rivers, and estuaries because of the large quantities of water needed for cooling the operative apparatus. Some of the radioactive by-products enter aquatic areas, exposing fish and other aquatic wildlife to these materials. At present, the Radiobiological Laboratory of the U. S. Fish and Wildlife Service, Bureau of Commercial Fisheries, located on Pivers Island at Beaufort, North Carolina, is concerned with the study of the action of these radio-active by-products that are released into sea water.

At present, ocean water receives radioactive waste material from several sources. Oceanic disposal sites for low level radiation waste from industrial and scientific installations have been established along the Atlantic and Pacific coasts. At present, only four major areas have been used in the Pacific, though it is anticipated that the total number may be expanded to twenty, extending from the Columbia River area to the Mexican border. Twelve disposal sites with a minimum of seventy-five miles between adjacent locations have been used along the Atlantic coast. Fifty-five gallon drums containing radioactive wastes mixed with concrete, it is assumed, will provide containment for a least ten years. By this time radioactive decay will have reduced most of the radioactive isotopes to nonhazardous levels, excepting for strontium-90, cesium-137 and cobalt-60. High and intermediate radiation wastes or those with a long half-life are entombed in large metal-cement tanks on land covering many acres, but safely removed from possible contamination of underground water supplies.

Radioactive materials and fallout from nuclear tests—underwater or above the surface—pollute this vast environment with ionizing radiation. The possible sinking of a nuclear-powered vessel as well as the leaching of radioactive materials from soils on land can conceivably add to the amount of radiation that accumulates in the marine environment. However, due to the immense volume of water, it is unlikely that oceanic

areas will in themselves become dangerously radioactive, despite the fact
that they have functioned and will continue to function as depositories
for radioactive materials from many sources. At present, the level of
radioactivity in oceanic areas is far below that encountered in many
terrestrial areas. One danger is the possibility that some forms of sea life
that are a possible food source may accumulate greater quantities of these
nuclear isotopes (just as some forms accumulate high concentrations of
trace chemicals, such as vanadium) and therefore become dangerously
radioactive.

It is a known fact that phytoplankton can concentrate radioactive
materials at a level that far exceeds that of the surrounding water. This
organism is then consumed by herring and oysters at the rate of several
million per few minutes. This naturally is going to lead to an accumulation of radionuclides within the tissues of these organisms. Fishes—
including the spot, flounder, sea mullet, and croaker—and mollusks—
including the clam, oyster, and scallop—have been exposed to radiation
in the form of radioactive food and radioactive water obtained from
water in the vicinity of nuclear reactors. The Radiobiological Laboratory
at Beaufort, North Carolina, has found, through controlled experiments,
that radioactive substances with a half-life long enough to reach man,
normally accumulate within the bones, scales, shells, and viscera of fish
and mollusks. In contrast to the greater quantities accumulating in these
organs and tissues is the much smaller amount found in muscle tissue.
With the exception of shellfish viscera, the more highly radioactive tissues
are not normally eaten in any quantity by man. The food series that
transpires in the sea can become easily contaminated with radioactive
material because herrings, oysters, clams, and scallops consume phytoplankton directly from sea water. Shrimp and crabs consume dead plankton and organic detritus that reaches the bottom—all of which could
conceivably be radioactive. Haddock and codfish do not feed on plankton
directly but ingest various species of mollusks that do. The menhaden,
a plankton feeder, is a commercially desirable product of the sea. In
1962, commercial fishermen had taken a record catch of over $2\frac{1}{2}$ billion
pounds of this fish as compared to slightly over 300 million pounds of
salmon, the runnerup. Menhaden enters the human food series indirectly
by being used as a meal in feed ingested by poultry and livestock. However, it is assumed that menhaden will be one of the main components of
a fish flour protein concentrate that will be used to supplement protein-
deficient diets of humans in different parts of the world. In a fish meal
of this type the scales, bone, and viscera are all ground up, and, as was
mentioned earlier, it is these parts of the organism that concentrate radioactive material in far greater quantity than is true of muscle.

Many important research programs will inevitably materialize in the
future as the dangers of radioactive contamination continue to plague
natural populations as well as human assemblages. There is the prospect

that certain groups of pest species such as oyster drills, the lamprey, starfish, and other organisms might be eradicated in certain areas by radiosterilization techniques. The effects of radiation as regards genetic changes in marine life and on fish populations that are exposed to acute doses of radioactive materials are of great interest. Since marine life has never been exposed to radiation levels equal to those on land, it is difficult to predict what would occur in the case of certain life cycles, food series, and populations of invertebrates and vertebrates that at present live in an exceedingly safe environment in terms of radiation level as compared to radioactivity in some terrestrial localities.

Radiation studies on terrestrial ecosystems have been in progress for some time to determine the effect of radiation on natural vegetation. At the Brookhaven National Laboratory on Long Island, experiments have been conducted on two types of ecosystems: a mixed deciduous forest and a young old field stand. These ecosystems were exposed to a source of gamma radiation. Cesium-137 was used in a stand containing white oak, scarlet oak, and pitch pine. The source could be lowered into a lead shield or raised by a remote-controlled winch to control the time of exposure. No tree survived exposures of 360 roentgens per day (Figure 14–2). A **roentgen** may be defined as a unit of radiation dosage, or the amount of energy released in a region exposed to ionizing radiation (a dental X ray releases a local dose of 1 to 5 roentgens). The term is named for Wilhelm Roentgen, a German physicist, known for his work in the field of X-radiation. Technically a roentgen is the amount of X-radiation produced, in 1 cc. of air at 0° C. and 76 mm. of mercury, a degree of conductivity great enough so that one electrostatic unit of charge is measured at saturation. Most trees were killed by a dosage in excess of 60 roentgens per day. Pine trees were most sensitive; they were killed with dosages of 20 to 30 roentgens per day. In the old field community which was exposed to gamma radiation from a source of cobalt-60 and populated by groundsel (*Senecio*) and pigweed (*Chenopodium*) radiation levels of 300 roentgens per day were required for fatal dosage, though values between 100 and 300 roentgens did alter growth and reproductive activity.

From present findings, it is apparent that the younger successional stages of terrestrial communities are more resistant to ionizing radiation than are the more advanced or climax aggregations. Mosses and lichens, pioneer species of bare rock succession, have survived total exposures of 200,000 roentgens at Brookhaven Laboratories. Robert B. Platt and J. T. McCormick have observed the effects of an unshielded nuclear reactor in a forested valley near Atlanta, Georgia. Early successional communities of rock outcrops suffered large changes in structure only at dosages in the range of 20,000 to 40,000 roentgens administered over a period of almost four months, with daily dosages ranging from 170 to 310 roentgens. As Woodwell (1963) has pointed out with regard to old field plants, the

FIGURE 14–2 Infrared film of irradiated forest at Brookhaven National Laboratory, Long Islnd. View is directed toward radiation source in the distance, with dosages in roentgens on signs in foreground. Notice the effects of extreme radiation in background where vegetation is in greater proximity to the source. Reprinted by permission from George M. Woodwell, "The Ecological Effects of Radiation," *Scientific American, 208*:40-49, June 1963. Used by permission.

early successional stages are annuals that survive the winter as "comparatively radiation-resistant seeds, and dividing cells producing new tissues are at the bases of leaves which may be at ground level or below resulting in some shielding from a radioactive source." Though pines exposed to 27 roentgens per day died before they had received a total exposure of 27,000 roentgens, cones removed from these trees contained seeds, 95 per cent of which were alive. In general, in terms of biomes and our present knowledge of the effects of ionizing radiation, it is assumed that forested areas are more drastically affected by radiation than are tundra, grassland, or desert biomes.

POLLUTION

Increasing amounts of air and aquatic pollution are destined to require greater attention on the part of ecologists and other scientific groups in the future. Air pollution has excited considerable attention, particularly in urban areas and highly industrialized sectors in a number of countries. **Smog** is a term that has entered our most recent editions of the dictionary; Webster's Third New International Dictionary defines smog as "a fog made heavier and darker by smoke and chemical fumes." The recent invasion of atmospheric regions by chemical by-products, fine particles of carbon, and a number of other contaminants has been blamed for a number of deaths in certain industrialized areas throughout the world. Carbon monoxide fumes generated by internal combustion engines, notably automobiles, buses, and trucks are increasing as the total number of operative means of transportation increase in keeping with population increases. There are indications that the incidence of lung cancer, sickness, fatigue, and even death may be in part due to increases in toxic gases—namely the insidious, odorless, invisible carbon monoxide spewing from exhaust systems in urban areas. Some initial attempts have been made to seek a solution to a problem that could eventually cause a toll much greater than the 4,000 human deaths attributed to a dense blanket of deadly smog that covered parts of London several years ago. In the future, large industrial plants as well as the automotive industry may be forced to install devices that would reduce or alter the amount and number of pollutants added to the atmosphere over a period of time.

Aquatic pollution that reaches lethal levels in terms of inhabitants of lotic and lentic environments has concerned the ecologist for a much longer period of time. Stream pollution and its effect on the indigenous flora and fauna has caused considerable concern in the more highly developed parts of the world. A number of investigators have found that there is a considerable difference in the biota found above a point in a drainage system where no sewage or commercial wastes are introduced into the stream and the living communities that subsist in polluted areas of the same stream. Even more dramatic, in an ecological sense, are the collection data available from a particular part of a river before pollution and after the introduction of pollutants. For, in this case, we have an opportunity to sample the very same areas where climatic conditions are comparable. The only variables of importance are the foreign materials introduced into the water and their subsequent effect on the environment. The terrific death toll of certain game fish and commercially important species of aquatic mollusks such as oysters and clams as a result of accidental entry of small quantities of industrial waste have excited such attention in local areas that more stringent restrictions have been enforced. It is unfortunate that the aquatic biologist and ecologist were ignored for nearly half a century and that we have lost so many of our invertebrate fauna and much of the endemic vegetation of our waterways before there was public interest strong enough to excite any local action.

In most areas where pollution is severe enough to cause problems, it is usually due to three contaminants: sewage, industrial wastes, and more recently, organic and inorganic pesticides. Solid materials entering drainage systems and estuaries may not be chemically toxic, but they can clog burrows as well as blanket respiratory surfaces (the gills of mollusks and annelids). Soluble materials and various insoluble organic materials may often bring about changes approaching anaerobic conditions, particularly where the current is sluggish and the displacement of water is slow. Such situations often arise as a result of the oxidation of organic debris, which will at times and under certain conditions extract considerable quantities of oxygen from the water, reducing the oxygen concentration below the critical level for certain groups of organisms. The bulk of paper mill waste oxidizes in water in about 5 days, though the lignin fraction will require from 90 to 140 days for complete oxidation. There are various soluble substances discharged into aquatic areas that, taken singly or considered as individual compounds, would not cause alarm. But upon entering the aquatic area and combining with other materials introduced at the same time or with substances present in the water, they may produce an exceedingly lethal broth. To be sure not all of the flora and not all of the fauna will be severely affected, but often the more resistant forms may multiply and completely upset the balance of nature or interrupt the vital food series in the area. In these respects, pollution may have a long-range effect because even after the pollutants have disappeared, the ecological communities have changed so radically as a result of contamination that it requires years or longer before the original aggregations are restored, if ever.

Silent Spring, the excellent popular book by the late Rachel Carson (1962), warns the populace about the dangers of uncontrolled and careless application of insecticides and pesticides by man. She presents a detailed and documented account of the effect on various forms of wildlife, including a detailed discussion of the toxic effect of aquatic pollution by these chemical substances. One case cited by Miss Carson was the extensive spraying of millions of acres of balsam fir with DDT by the Canadian Government in the area of the Miramichi drainage system in an attempt to control outbreaks of the spruce budworm. Results were disastrous, for within two days of the spraying there were, along the entire watershed, dead and dying salmon, brook trout, and a vast assortment of aquatic invertebrates including caddis fly, blackfly, and stone fly larvae. Perhaps the disastrous results would have been in order to some degree if the budworm populations had been permanently reduced in the area, but this was not the case. The spray program was merely a stopgap solution, as has been true in many so-called control programs. There are countless other cases of wholesale destruction of aquatic life by the application of insecticides. Parts of the southern states have been sprayed and dusted in an attempt to eradicate the fire ant. Heptachlor and dieldrin have been used most extensively in control programs, and their effect on aquatic life was pointed out by Miss Carson (pp. 140–141): "In Louisiana, farmers complained of loss in farm ponds. Along one canal more than 500 dead fish were seen floating or lying on the bank on a stretch of less than a quarter of a mile. In another parish 150 dead sunfish could be found for every 4 that remained alive. Five other species appeared to have been wiped out completely." These high rates of mortality are brought about by runoff water from terrestrial areas carrying these toxins in solution to freshwater environments. Effects other than wholesale mortality have also been noted in certain areas. For instance, Coho salmon that escaped lethal concentrations of DDT showed symptoms of blindness brought on by a definite opacity of the lens. The Canadian Department of Fisheries stated that DDT was present in a concentration of about three parts per million in these cases!

Salt marsh populations have been exposed to repeated spraying with DDT in attempts to control salt-marsh mosquitoes. Among those invertebrates that have experienced greatest losses according to Mills (1952) were the fiddler crabs, whose populations numbered 100,000 or more in some areas prior to mosquito control programs and were reduced to 100 or less sickly, stumbling organisms, following the application of insecticides. Young commercial shrimp are exceedingly sensitive to a wide variety of pesticides, so that lethal doses are reported in quantities of parts per billion rather than the more common parts per million. Phytoplankton are also exceedingly sensitive to small amounts of a wide assortment of pesticides on the order of a few parts per billion. A considerable array of invertebrates and some vertebrates depend on these populations of phytoplankton as a primary food supply. If organic or inorganic pesticides do not kill these organisms directly, they will kill them indirectly by depriving them of food, thus insuring a slow starvation among some of the more tolerant species.

PESTICIDES AND PROBLEMS OF CONTROL

The increase in usage of pesticides, particularly insecticides, has mounted considerably in recent years, according to published accounts. Production increased from 124,259,000 pounds in 1947 to 637,666,000 pounds in 1960. Modern pesticides are primarily of the organic type; they are either chlorinated hydrocarbons or organic phosphorus compounds. One of the chlorinated hydrocarbons, dichlorodiphenyltrichloroethane, more popularly known as DDT, was first synthesized in 1874 but did not become one of the most popular insecticides of all times until 1939. This compound, hailed as the solution to the problem of insect depredations, has fallen far short of the goal. As a matter of fact, a large number of insects have evolved insecticide-resistant strains, so that it has become necessary to utilize new (and often more potent) insecticides. As Rachel Carson states so succinctly in Silent Spring: "In the United States, DDT

resistance among flies had become widespread in the Tennessee Valley
by 1948.... Attempts to restore control with dieldrin met with little
success, for in some places the flies developed strong resistance to this
chemical within only two months. After running through all the available chlorinated hydrocarbons, control agencies turned to the organic
phosphates, but here again the story of resistance was repeated. The
present conclusion of experts is that 'housefly control has escaped insec-
ticidal techniques and once more must be based on general sanitation.' "
But the fly is only one example of the growing number of resistant insect
species; by 1960, there were 137 species known to be resistant to all
insecticides that had been developed up to that time.

Of course during the initial period in which ecologists and agricultural
scientists became aware of the resistance, it was believed that stronger
insecticides would be the ultimate solution. Such has not been the case.
In the frantic quest to develop stronger chemicals to combat pest species,
various chlorinated hydrocarbons made their appearance on the commercial market. Chlordane penetrates the skin and can be carried into
the respiratory system in vaporous form far more easily than DDT.
Dieldrin is roughly 5 times as toxic as DDT when ingested, but 40 times
as poisonous when absorbed through the body wall. Endrin is the ultimate in toxicity in terms of known chlorinated hydrocarbons. If we
realize that this compound is 15 times as toxic as DDT to mammals, 30
times as toxic to amphibians, and 300 times as toxic to fish, we can appreciate its relative power. One of the most widely used organic phosphorus
compounds is parathion; its toxicity and danger have been well documented in the literature (Brown, 1951; Quinby, 1958; Metcalf, 1959;
Toivonen, 1959; Hayes, 1960).

One possible solution to the deadly threat of insecticides and pesticides, and one which will tend to reduce the financial burden of pest
control, is **electrostatic particle charging.** The principle is not new in
application, for it has been used for a number of years to eliminate
smoke in industrial installations and consequently reduce air pollution.
But its application in agricultural work is a recent innovation. Initial
tests first began at Michigan State College, and now tests in progress at
North Carolina State College may prove to be a boon to farmers and
ecologists. If all turns out as expected, dusters and sprayers will be able
to do a more efficient job with far less material and with no drift of
harmful powders or sprays into adjacent field or woodland areas. In
principle, electrostatic charging involves a high DC voltage applied to an
ionizing chamber. As the particles pass through the chamber, they take
on an electrical charge and as the insecticide is blown out it becomes
attached to all parts of the plant surface and soil by electrical attraction.
About 80 per cent of the charged dust strikes the plant or soil, reducing
drift to a negligible degree in winds as strong as twenty-five miles per
hour. In tests on bean crops in Florida, twice as much dust clung to

plants with only half of the usual rate of application. It is calculated that on cotton alone, farmers can save nearly $180 million a year in quantities of insecticides used in controlling insects and do a more effective job of controlling them than is possible by using conventional methods. By using smaller quantities of insecticides, natural communities will no longer suffer the tremendous losses that have been experienced in some areas in the past.

A solution that holds more promise for the future than any known program of insecticide or pesticide control is the technique of natural control. Unlike the never-ending search for new chemical compounds and the spiraling costs, the techniques of natural control promise to be far more permanently effective without disrupting the natural communities, the balance of nature, or the normal food series. Sterilization of segments of an insect population may prove to be a most useful method of biological control without the residual effects of chemical poisons that endanger the rest of the plant and animal community. G. A. Runner realized in 1916 that insects could be sterilized by exposure to X-radiation. Dr. Edward Knipling, chief of the Entomology Research Branch of the United States Department of Agriculture, proposed in 1950 that if the male screw worm were sterilized by X-radiation treatment in a laboratory and then released in large enough quantity, they would compete so successfully with fertile males that the number of fertile eggs laid by the females of the wild population would gradually decrease. The female, having copulated with a sterilized male, would oviposit unfertilized (sterile) eggs that would never hatch. Furthermore, if sterilized males were released periodically in large numbers, the number of sterile egg clusters would increase until the species would become extinct in the area. In 1954 sterilized screw worms were flown to the Dutch island of Curaçao in the Caribbean to test the feasibility of sterilization control on this insect that had formerly cost the United States livestock industry more than 40 million dollars annually. Several months after the release of sterilized screw worms, this insect had been eradicatd on Curaçao. Similar tests are now being carried on with a number of other insects, tsetse flies, melon flies, mosquitoes, fruit flies, and others. The method promises to yield important results in years to come.

Other proposals are receiving serious considerations in testing laboratories in a number of countries as alternatives of pesticide spray programs. One such possibility is the use of **chemosterilants**—that is, chemicals that will effectively sterilize the insect if ingested. Actually chemosterilant in some cases is a misnomer, because some of the proposed chemicals do far more than sterilize the insect. One group of compounds might be termed **antimetabolites** because they are similar in chemical structure to substances required for certain metabolic processes to continue. However, the substituted compound actually interrupts the metabolic activity and causes eventual death. A second group of chemosterilants are alkylating agents capable of reacting with the chromosomes, causing their fragmentation or destruction. The latter group of chemical substances are highly reactive and it is suspected that they may cause cancer or mutations. Until safer substitutes can be found for some of the chemosterilants, it is best that we proceed with caution in this field until continued research produces substances which are less likely to cause dangerous aftereffects. Use of synthetic insect sex attractant substances to aid in trapping harmful species of insects has the advantage of selective attraction affecting only the target insect and not killing other organisms in the indiscriminate way common to pesticides.

Another time-tested remedy that works with satisfactory results is the importation of natural enemies of certain pest species. Several examples of this type of biological control that have been effective can be cited. In Australia, about 1925, prickly pear (*Opuntia*) was growing on 60 million acres of land. Half of this area was so densely populated that it was estimated that the biomass of this species alone exceeded five hundred tons per acre. The population of this useless vegetation was increasing so rapidly that 1 million acres per year were becoming agriculturally valueless. For the next five years, about 3 billion moths (*Cactoblastis cactorum*) were imported into the region in an attempt to control and destroy the plant (Dodd, 1936). The moth, being exposed to such vast expanses of a food source, multiplied and dispersed throughout the affected territory. The larval stages consumed and destroyed the prickly pear so that by 1934 the last large stand of prickly pear disappeared. Local populations of the plant occur in isolated areas growing from seed, but the moth disperses and locates these patches. Oviposition occurs and the larvae destroy these isolated stands.

In the latter part of the nineteenth century, the southern California citrus industry was threatened by a cottony-cushion scale (*Icerya purchasi*). An attempt at biological control—the importation of a small number of adult vedalia ladybird beetles (*Rodolia cardinalis*)—was initiated in 1888 and met with considerable success. Within five months this predaceous beetle that had been initially placed on one tree had controlled the cottony-cushion scale population in an entire orchard. Within a few years the scale insects were brought under control throughout southern California. Smith (1939), in a discussion of biological control by insects, has offered two explanations for the unqualified success of the predator: (1) The predator beetle has exhibited much greater powers of dispersal than has the prey, thus enabling it to control scale insects in a relatively large geographic area. (2) The reproductive potential of the predator has been high. This latter factor enables the beetle population to increase in numbers within a short period of time and thus prevent any sudden population explosion by the prey. Although biological control has probably resulted in failure more often than it has produced a successful solution, a more thorough knowledge of the ecology of the species (autecology) might have saved a considerable amount of disappointment.

A VITAL RESOURCE—WATER

A study of the world's water resources during a ten-year period, from 1965 to 1975, referred to as the International Hydrological Decade, will attempt to solve some of the world's most urgent water problems. Some of the processes that will receive attention from scientists of nearly one hundred nations are of general ecological interest; others are of a far more specialized (hydrological) nature. Such subjects as the following will be intensively studied: the earth's water cycle (the cyclic movement of water from the atmosphere as precipitation, the movement of water through the soil and drainage systems and its evaporation or transpiration back into the atmosphere), the manner in which snow and ice accumulate, and the effects of agriculture on present water supplies. One major problem, in addition to increasing water yield adequate to meet the proposed needs of future populations will be a thorough study of soil erosion that washes away more than 3 billion tons of topsoil in the continental United States every year. Erosion has brought about the ruination of nearly 25 per cent of the nation's croplands. Sections of the southwest are deeply gullied; yet in parts of Russia where climatic conditions are similar in every known respect there has been no wholesale removal of soil.

The International Association of Scientific Hydrology, during meetings in Berkeley, California, was responsible for establishing plans for the ten-year study. Initial plans for the long-range study were first proposed in Athens, Greece, in October 1961. The ambitious program is being guided by the United Nations Educational, Scientific and Cultural Organization, with advice and aid from a number of other international associations. Many authorities state that dwindling quantities of usable water poses a more serious problem than does the eventual disappearance of coal and iron deposits. Many critical situations must be faced and attempts made to solve such problems because large quantities of water are utilized by living organisms. For example, a plant requires about 1,000 pounds of water to produce 1 pound of food, a ratio of 1,000 to 1. The average per capita use of water totals nearly a ton per year in food and drink. Industries are using large quantities of water and it is predicted they will require twice as much water in 1980 in the United States as is being used at the present time. The quantities required for a few industries may give some idea of the amounts used. For example, it takes 365,000 gallons of water to produce a ton of rayon yarn, 500,000 gallons for 1,000 yards of wool cloth, and over 1 million gallons for 1,000 barrels of high octane gasoline. A considerable amount of water is bound in frozen form as ice, snow, and glacial reserves. Another problem, of course, is the unequal distribution of precipitation. In the United States about 60 per cent of the 7 trillion tons of annual rainfall covers a scant 35 per cent of the land area. Approximately 72 per cent of this annual rainfall is lost through runoff, evaporation, or transpiration. Consequently, only about 28 per cent is available to replenish the subterranean water supply. National water requirements within the continental United States was 41 billion gallons per day at the turn of the century compared to an estimated 300 billion gallons per day in 1960.

A number of possible solutions have been and are being considered by groups of hydrologists throughout the world. One such suggestion is the feasibility of towing huge chunks of antarctic ice into continental harbors and siphoning off the freshwater produced as the ice melts. Desalination of sea water is a practical but, thus far, a very expensive means of augmenting water supplies. In many instances, with proper equipment and techniques, used water can be purified and reused continuously, even to the point of reclaiming and decontaminating sewage water. One very dramatic technique of water conservation has proved successful in the San Dimas Basin between San Bernardino and Los Angeles, California. This area was a waterlogged swamp when the first white settlers entered the area, but with drainage the area became a fertile citrus-growing region. Irrigation had lowered the water table to a depth of 150 feet by 1915 and to 460 feet below the surface fourteen years later. Hydrological engineers diverted runoff water into deep wells and dry stream beds rather than allow this valuable supply of water to enter marine areas. Because of the recharging of underground storage reservoirs in this way, the water table is now only 85 feet below the surface. Certainly there are many areas throughout the world that could benefit from the lesson learned in the San Dimas Valley of California. Intelligent use of existing drainage systems must be made in many parts of the world if man is to maintain increasing populations. Proper placement of dams along a major drainage system, as is evident from the accomplishments of the Tennessee Valley Association, has produced sufficient supplies of water for irrigation, reserve supplies of water, proper areas for spawning of fish, available areas for maintenance of aquatic wildlife, and hydroelectric power at low cost to furnish the necessary electrical energy required by neighboring communities and industrial complexes.

One area in the northern Midwest is profiting from a series of dams placed across the northern portion of the Missouri River, and will gradually experience even greater benefits. The Missouri originates in part from a number of small anastomosing streams in Montana, Wyo-

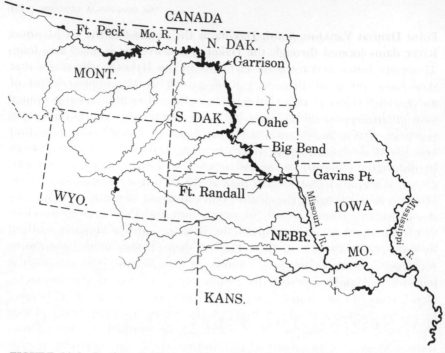

FIGURE 14–3 Portion of Missouri River System in the Dakotas, showing the location of dams and reservoirs.

ming, the Dakotas, and Colorado (Figure 14–3). Every spring, ice jams with huge cakes of ice tore away piers, damaged bridge supports, and caused considerable damage along its length. In June, an additional series of disasters endangered crops and wildlife in the lowlands bordering this stream, because it is during this month of the year that snow melt in the southeastern mountain ranges of Montana is at its peak. The inundation of fertile croplands and timbered lowlands often caused a second loss of wildlife within a few months, following the flooding caused by ice jams earlier in the spring. Frequent flooding caused extensive erosion and a tremendous loss of topsoil along the lengths of many tributaries and consequently a continuous turbidity that was so pronounced along certain parts of the mighty Missouri it required nearly an hour for the material (soil and organic debris) to settle in a container of water dipped from the river. Under these conditions of high turbidity, light penetration and hence photosynthetic activity was most certainly impeded. This had its effect on the food series transpiring within these waters.

In the dammed headwaters of the Missouri there is now a string of clear water reservoirs that furnish adequate habitats for game fish including pike, bass, and trout that have replaced the small catfish and bullheads that formerly inhabited the muddy reaches of the river. Gavins

Point Dam at Yankton, South Dakota, is the smallest of the six Missouri River dams located through the Dakotas, and even it is 8,700 feet long. There are bitter and resentful elements in the Dakotas who claim that they have lost more than they have gained by the impoundment of water and the loss of rich timberlands in the valley areas. A short-range view might support their claims, but from a long-range analysis of future potential, this most certainly is not so. Some of this valuable land that now lies at the bottom of massive reservoirs would have been swept away by the raging Missouri in the course of time. Long-range plans for irrigation of semiarid areas once a part of the former dust bowl area of the Midwest will strengthen agricultural reclamation of these areas as well as provide for future growth in population and in industrial development. Turbines set in motion by the large quantities of water spilling through power tunnels in these massive dams have provided the entire area with low-cost electricity, enough in fact to supply a city with a population of about 950,000 people.

HARNESSING THE TIDES

One of the most ambitious and promising projects proposed by the Department of the Interior within the past few years is the feasibility of utilizing the tides as a source of electric power. The area chosen for this experimental project is Passamaquoddy Bay (Figure 14–4), located on the United States-Canadian border between Maine and New Brunswick. The idea is not new; it was first proposed over forty years ago. But because of the nearly 7½ miles of dams that would be required at various points near the mouth of the bay, the project never received serious attention until a committee of the Department of the Interior considered it an economically feasible project. The tides that are predictable—cyclic and as dependable as the earth's rotation and gravitational force—represent a tremendous potential source of electric power in many parts of the world. A portion of the Bay of Fundy was chosen as the site of the initial project because tides of 40 to 50 feet, the world's highest, occur in this area. Passamaquoddy Bay is an expanse of water off the main Bay of Fundy, with tides that range from a maximum of 26 feet to a minimum of nearly 13 feet, an average tidal range of a little more than 18 feet. The bay, about 110 square miles in size, would act as a high storage pool for incoming tidal water. Water from this bay would drop into turbines in a lower pool that would be formed by adjacent Cobscook Bay. A million kilowatts of electrical power would be produced during the hour of tidal peak and carried over transmission lines to Boston, Massachusetts, and neighboring Canadian sites. It is proposed that construction be in three phases and much of the major work be performed by the United States Army Corps of Engineers under federal contracts.

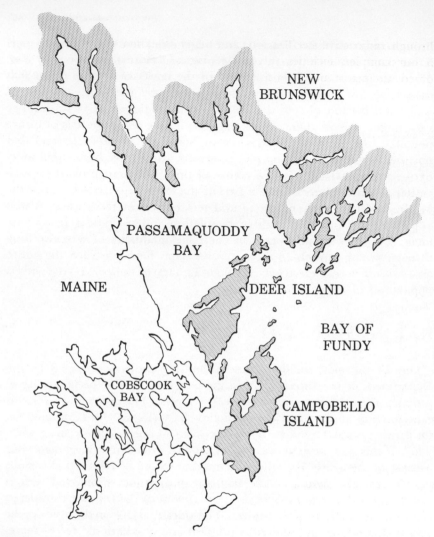

FIGURE 14–4 The lower end of the Bay of Fundy with connecting Passamaquoddy and Cobscook Bay, showing the area to be utilized for proposed tidal dams. New Brunswick shore and islands are shaded; those of Maine are unshaded.

To deny the importance of the ecologist in our present society is tantamount to intellectual myopia. Pure ecological research or research for its own sake with no thought of practical application continues at an accelerated pace throughout the world in every major university and college in every important nation. These pure scientists are concerned with wresting from nature some of its most subtle secrets. Many of the published papers contain material that can be utilized by the applied ecologists. Wildlife and forestry management, erosion control, crop rotation, proper management of drainage systems and watershed areas, proper carrying capacity for livestock ranges, future control of insect populations through radioactive sterilization, and many other matters of importance in our complex societies rely on ecological information. Ecology has forged an important niche for itself in the realm of pure and applied biology.

Selected References

Barath, F. T., A. H. Barrett, J. Copeland, D. E. Jones, and A. E. Lilley. 1963. Mariner II: Preliminary reports on measurements of Venus. Microwave radiometers. Science, 139:908–909.

Brown, A. W. A. *Insect Control by Chemicals* (New York: John Wiley, 1951), pp. i–vii, 1–817.

Butler, P. A. 1960. Effects of pesticides on commercial fisheries. Proc. Gulf and Caribbean Fish. Inst., 13:168–171.

Calvin, M. *Chemical Evolution* (Eugene, Ore.: Univ. of Oregon Press, 1961), pp. 1–41.

Carson, Rachel. *Silent Spring* (Boston: Houghton Mifflin, 1962), pp. i–x, 1–368.

De Ong, E. R. *Chemistry and Uses of Pesticides* (New York: Reinhold, 1956), pp. 1–334.

Dodd, A. P. 1936. The control and eradication of prickly pear in Australia. Bull. Ent. Research, 27:503–517.

Ehrensvard, G. *Life: Origin and Development* (Chicago: Univ. of Chicago Press, 1962), pp. 1–164.

Graham, E. H. *Water for America* (New York: Oxford Univ. Press, 1956), pp. 1–111.

Green, I. *Water, Our Most Valuable Resource* (New York: Coward-McCann, 1958), pp. 1–96.

Hart, H. C. *The Dark Missouri* (Madison, Wisc.: Univ. of Wisconsin Press, 1957), pp. 1–260.

Hawrylewicz, E., B. Gowdy, and R. Ehrlich. 1962. Micro-organisms under a simulated Martian environment. Nature, 193:497.

Hayes, W. J., Jr. 1960. Pesticides in relation to public health. Ann. Rev. Entomol. 5:379–404.

Knipling, E. F. 1957. Control of screw-worm flies by atomic radiation. Sci. Monthly, 85:195–202.

La Brecque, G. C. 1961. Studies with three alkylating agents as house fly sterilants. Jour. Econ. Entomol. 54:684–689.

Langbein, W. B., and W. G. Hoyt. *Water Facts for the Nation's Future* (New York: Ronald Press, 1959), pp. i–xiv, 1–288.

Lindquist, A. W. 1955. The use of gamma radiation for control or eradication of the screwworm. Jour. Econ. Entomol. 48:467–469.

Metcalf, R. L. 1959. The impact of the development of organophosphorus insecticides upon basic and applied science. Bull. Entomol. Soc. Amer., 5:3–15.

Miller, S. L. 1955. Production of some organic compounds under possible primitive earth conditions. Jour. Amer. Chem. Soc., 77:2351–2360.

Mills, H. R. "Death in the Florida Marshes," *Audubon Magazine* (1952).

Oparin, A. I. *The Origin of Life on the Earth* (Edinburgh: Oliver & Boyd, 1957), pp. i–xviii, 1–495.

Quinby, G. E., and A. B. Lemmon. 1958. Parathion residues as a cause of poisoning in crop workers. Jour. Am. Med. Assoc., 166:740–746.

Shepard, H. H. *The Chemistry and Toxicology of Insecticides* (Minneapolis: Burgess, 1939), pp. i–iii, 1–383.

Simpson, G. G. *This View of Life: The World of an Evolutionist* (New York: Harcourt, 1964), pp. i–ix, 1–308.

Smith, H. S. 1939. Insect populations in relation to biological control. Ecol. Monogr., 9:311–320.

Springer, P. F., and J. R. Webster. 1949. Effects of DDT on saltmarsh wildlife. U.S. Fish and Wildlife Serv., Spec. Sci. Rept. No. 10.

Toivonen, T. 1959. Parathion poisoning increasing in frequency in Finland. Lancet, 2:175–176.

Woodwell, G. M. 1962. Effects of ionizing radiation on terrestrial ecosystems. Science, 138:572–577.

———. 1963. The ecological effects of radiation. Sci. American, 208:40–49.

INDEX*

Abiotic, definition of, 50
Abiotic factors, **2, 26**
Absolute humidity, **107**
Abstract community, **229**
Abyssobenthic zone, **46**
Acceleration phase, negative, **213**
  positive, **212**
Acheta, 158
Adams, C., 16
Adaptability, seral, **304**
Adaptation, moisture of animals, 312
Additional considerations relative to succession, 307–309
Adhesion in soils, **69**
Adiabatic cooling, **107**
Aeration of soils, 65
Aerial community, **235**
Aerial pollution, 441
Aestival, **3**
Africa-Madagascar geological connection, 328
African rain forest, 35
Agassiz, A., 376
Agassiz, L., 5, 376
Age, computing by radioactive carbon, 266
Aggradation, definition of, 367
Air capacity of soils, **65**
Allee, W., 10, 142, 217, 251
Allen's rule, 21
Alopex lagopus, 193
Alpine tundra, **338**
Amplitude, wave, 83
Anadromous, **38, 375**

Anderson, D., 179
Andrewartha, H., 10, 218
Anemometer, **126**
Animal communities, aquatic, 276
Animals and moisture adaptation, 312
Ant, 140
Antarctica, 99
Anticyclonic movement, **128**
Antidorcas, 164
Antimetabolites, **446**
Antipriptic wind, **124**
Apis, 216
Aplodinotus, 185
Aptenoides, 165
Aquatic and terrestrial areas, temperatures in, 313
Aquatic animal communities, 276
Aquatic plant communities, 276
Aquatic pollution, 442
Arabian Desert, 359
Arboreal species, 23
Archibenthic zone, **46**
Arctic fox, 193
Arctic tern, migration of, 169
Arctic tundra, **338**
Arhythmic fluctuations, 247–249
Arithmetic mean, **410**
Arnon, D., 179
Asclepias, 195
Aspection, **306**
Association, **231**
Associational community, **231**
Asthenosphere, **323**

---

* Names set in italics indicate scientific names.
  Numbers set in bold face (dark numbers) indicate ecological terminology.